Non-Destructive Examination in Relation to Structural Integrity

Proceedings of the 1st International Seminar on 'Non-Destructive Examination in Relation to Structural Integrity' held at the International Congress Center Berlin, Berlin (West), Germany, 22nd August 1979, in conjunction with the 5th International Conference on Structural Mechanics in Reactor Technology. Organizational Support: Bundesanstalt für Materialprüfung (BAM), Berlin; ICC Department of Organization and Operation.

Seminar Technical Co-ordinator and Chairman, Dr R. W. Nichols, Head of Risley Nuclear Power Development Laboratories, UK Atomic Energy Authority, Risley, Warrington, Cheshire

Non-Destructive Examination in Relation to Structural Integrity

Edited by

R. W. NICHOLS

D. Met., F. Eng., Hon. F. Brit. Inst. NDT

Technical Co-ordinator and Chairman of the Seminar; Chairman, International Council of Pressure Vessel Technology; Editor, The International Journal of Pressure Vessels and Piping

APPLIED SCIENCE PUBLISHERS LTD
LONDON

APPLIED SCIENCE PUBLISHERS LTD
RIPPLE ROAD, BARKING, ESSEX, ENGLAND

British Library Cataloguing in Publication Data

International Seminar on Non-Destructive Examination
in Relation to Structural Integrity, *1st, West
Berlin, 1979*
Non-destructive examination in relation to structural
integrity.
1. Nuclear pressure vessels—Testing—Congresses
2. Non-destructive testing—Congresses
3. Fracture mechanics—Congresses
I. Title II. Nichols, Roy Woodward
III. International Conference on Structural
Mechanics in Reactor Technology, *5th, West Berlin,
1979*
621.48'35   TK9211.5
ISBN 0-85334-908-8 ✓

WITH 24 TABLES AND 142 ILLUSTRATIONS

The selection and presentation of material and the opinions expressed in
this publication are the sole responsibility of the authors concerned.

Printed in Great Britain by Galliard (Printers) Ltd, Great Yarmouth

Dedication

The meeting of which this volume is the proceedings was one of several specialist meetings held in Berlin immediately after the 5th International Conference on Structural Mechanics in Reactor Technology, colloquially and affectionately known as SMIRT5. The very concept of these SMIRT Conferences and the effective realisation of them into the successful technical contributions that they undoubtedly are arises essentially from the vision, vigour and enthusiasm of Professor Tom Jaeger. He and his wife Brunhilde have the ability to make busy experts the world over find time to work for him, to gather around him and to enjoy the friendship, social goodwill and technical interchange that they so much catalyse. It is to Professor and Mrs Jaeger that I dedicate this volume, for without their efforts it would not have existed.

R. W. NICHOLS

Preface

An important aspect of the assessment of structural integrity, particularly of such high integrity structures as are associated with nuclear reactor pressure circuits, is that of determining the influence of those flaws which may remain in a fabrication, even one made to the highest standards of quality and of quality assurance. These aspects of the assessment of reliability, of the use of fracture mechanics to determine the effect of possible flaws, and the probabilistic and statistical aspects associated with such approaches form part of all the discussions of structural mechanics in reactor technology, particularly those related to pipework and pressure vessels.

Some aspects of such work require specialist input which we considered could best be achieved by arranging specialist seminars immediately after each SMIRT Conference, which could be attended not only by the interested delegates of the Conference itself but also by others coming for the Seminars especially.

One topic particularly appropriate for such treatment is that of Non-Destructive Examination (NDE) which by the use of such tools as visual examination, radiography, eddy currents and ultrasonics (especially ultrasonics) sets out to determine what flaws are in a finished structure, what is their size and where they are located. The use of such procedures has long formed part of the quality control of every high integrity fabrication, and together with the use of manufacturing techniques chosen and demonstrated to have a very low rate of flaw production, provide the required assurance of quality. The development of fracture mechanics has changed the role of NDE somewhat from that of being a watchdog on production procedures to that of detecting any significant flaws before they can lead to failure in service. This aspect has been extended by the use of such techniques on the completed reactor structure before commissioning and at intervals throughout its service life in the so-called in-service inspection procedures on which the ASME Boiler & Pressure Vessel Code Section XI gives considerable detailed guidance. It is against this background that I willingly agreed to organise this post-conference seminar on 'Non-Destructive Examination in Relation to Structural Integrity', intending to cover reports on recent relevant experience and developments.

On this occasion however, one particular aspect became of overriding importance. The use of NDE as a tool for detecting flaws in relation to fracture mechanics calculations raises the question of how reliable is NDE in such detection. The development of probabilistic fracture mechanics in particular makes it desirable to have more quantitative information on this reliability in actual application—a very different matter from the sensitivity or the potential detection ability of particular NDE techniques. Information of this type is very difficult to obtain as was indicated in the UK report on its study of the integrity of PWR pressure vessels (the 'Marshall' report), which had to make do with estimates that that Study Group had obtained from experienced operators. The difficulty of getting really relevant information on this subject is that it can only really be obtained by the comparison of the results of non-destructive examination with those of a comprehensive destructive examination in which the subject component is dissected until all the flaws are revealed and characterised, an operation that can rarely be afforded in practice. It is most convenient then for such work to be done on specially prepared representations of components into which deliberate but real flaws are introduced, these components being subjected to a round-robin of non-destructive examinations and subsequently with great care and precision examined destructively. Several such programmes have recently been initiated—in particular by the US Pressure Vessel Research Council (PVRC/HSST), by the US Electric Power Research Institute (EPRI), by the UK Welding Institute (WI) and by the Committee on the Safety of Nuclear Installations (CSNI) of the OECD Nuclear Energy Agency and the Commission of the European Communities. A major part of this seminar was therefore devoted to receiving status reports on each of these programmes. In particular there was presented a series of final reports on the CSNI Plate Inspection Steering Committee (PISC) work in which more than 30 European NDE testing institutions participated. This seminar and this proceedings volume thus became the medium for publication of an exceptionally important set of results from what is at present a unique and particularly relevant and extensive piece of collaborative research.

The attendance at the seminar was notable for the expertise of the delegates and for the good international coverage which was achieved. Vigorous discussion took place both in the meeting and between smaller groups outside. That in the meeting was, by agreement, recorded on tape, and I have used the transcripts of these tapes to produce the edited discussions presented in this volume. For practical reasons it was agreed that the transcripts would not be sent back to the speakers, with the result that the written version here given is my own responsibility and interpretation. I hope that I have recorded the most important points of general interest, that I have interpreted the comments correctly and that I have given them correct attributions. If not, I apologise for any errors. I hope that readers of this volume will find the discussion adds to their appreciation of the interesting and important papers which are given in the order of presentation. The first four papers cover recent developments in general survey methods and the following four papers cover aspects of recent development and experience with ultrasonic examination techniques. After these presentations on technique developments there are two papers on the assessment of the reliability of flaw detection by ultrasonics, the last one (Paper 10) being in five sections representing different aspects of the PISC trial. Finally there are two papers covering other reliability trials now in progress which have emphasis on flaw sizing and characterisation and the use of advanced NDE techniques.

I will close this preface by thanking all those responsible for writing, presenting and making these papers available for publication, and to the many people behind the scenes who helped in the seminar and in the preparation of these proceedings.

R. W. NICHOLS

Contents

Preface vii

List of Contributors xv

Session I: Review of Methods Available

1. Non-Destructive Testing for Field Welds: A Real Time Weld
   Quality Monitor 3
   F. W. KEARNEY

2. Application of Acoustic Emission as a Monitoring System
   during Hydrostatic Tests of Nuclear Reactor Components . 17
   E. VOTAVA

3. Acoustic Emission Testing of Pressure Vessels made of $2\frac{1}{4}$ Cr–1
   Mo Steel 19
   S. YAMAMATO, T. TSUKIKAWA, M. NAKANO, H. UEYAMA, J.
   WATANABE, K. OHNISHI and R. SAIKUDO

4. Spectral Analysis Approach for Interpretation of Acoustic
   Emission Signals for NDT and Monitoring of Structural
   Integrity 41
   C. R. L. MURTHY, B. DATTAGURU, T. S. RAMAMURTHY and
   A. K. RAO

5. Pressure Vessel Nozzle Inspection Using Adaptive Learning
    Techniques   45
    M. F. WHALEN and A. N. MUCCIARDI

6. Development of Ultrasonic Techniques for Sizing Defects .   59
    H. WÜSTENBERG and A. ERHARD

7. Ultrasonic Testing Applied to Austenitic Steel   .   .   .   85
    P. CAUSSIN

8. Problems Associated with Repetitive Inspection of Reactor
    Pressure Vessels and Research toward Solutions   .   .   107
    C. E. LAUTZENHEISER, A. R. WHITING and W. T. FLACH

**Session II: The Reliability and Efficiency of Ultrasonic Flaw Detection
Methods**

9. Results of the Pressure Vessel Research Committee Program
    on Reliability of Ultrasonics   115
    L. J. CHOCKIE

10. Plate Inspection Steering Committee (PISC) Reports .   .   133

    Report No. 1: A Description of the PISC Project   .   .   134
    A. L. ADAMS and A. DE STERKE

    Report No. 2: Ultrasonic Examination in the PVRC Plates   159
    A. C. PROT, G. DEUSTER and J. B. PEREZ PRAT

    Report No. 3: Destructive Examination of the PVRC Plates   170
    S. J. CRUTZEN and K. GOTT

    Report No. 4: Method of Evaluation and the Results of the
    PISC Trials   200
    S. J. CRUTZEN and G. W. PARRY

    Report No. 5: Discussion of NDE/DE and Summary
    Conclusions   223
    R. O'NEIL and P. CAUSSIN

11. Non-Destructive Inspection of Thick Section Materials Using
Advanced Non-Destructive Examination Techniques . . 233
   A. E. HOLT and J. W. BROPHY

12. Size Measurement and Characterisation of Weld Defects by
Ultrasonic Testing 251
   T. J. JESSOP and P. J. MUDGE

**Session III: Discussion of Requirements for Non-Destructive
Examination** 265

Index 291

List of Contributors

A. L. ADAMS
  UKAEA, SRD, Culcheth, Warrington, Cheshire WA3 4NE, UK

J. W. BROPHY
  Babcock & Wilcox Company, PO Box 1260, Lynchburg, Virginia 14505, USA

P. CAUSSIN
  Departement Etudes, Association Vinçotte, B-1640 Rhode-Saint-Genese, Belgium

L. J. CHOCKIE
  General Electric Company, Nuclear Energy Group, 175 Curtner Ave., San Jose, California 95125, USA

S. J. CRUTZEN
  Joint Research Centre, Ispra Establishment, 21020 Ispra, Varese, Italy

B. DATTAGURU
  Department of Aeronautical Engineering, Indian Institute of Science, Bangalore-560012, India

G. DEUSTER
  Fraunhofer Institut Zerstörungsfreie, Prüfv. (IZFP), Universität Gerbaude 37, 6600 Saarbrücken 11, FRG

A. ERHARD

Bundesanstalt für Materialprüfung (BAM), Unter den Eichen 87, D-1000 Berlin (West) 45, Germany

W. T. FLACH

Southwest Research Institute, PO Drawer 28510, 6220 Culebra Rd, San Antonio, Texas 78284, USA

K. GOTT

Studsvik Energiteknik AB, Fack 5-611-01, Nyköping 1, Sweden

A. E. HOLT

Babcock & Wilcox Company, PO Box 1260, Lynchburg, Virginia 24505, USA

F. W. KEARNEY

Department of the Army, Construction Engineering Research Laboratory, PO Box 4005, Champaign, Illinois 61820, USA

T. J. JESSOP

Research Laboratory, The Welding Institute, Abington Hall, Abington, Cambridge CB1 6AL, UK

C. E. LAUTZENHEISER

Southwest Research Institute, PO Drawer 28510, 6220 Culebra Rd, San Antonio, Texas 78284, USA

A. N. MUCCIARDI

Adaptronics, Inc., 1750 Old Meadow Rd, McLean, Virginia 22102, USA

P. J. MUDGE

Research Laboratory, The Welding Institute, Abington Hall, Abington, Cambridge CB1 6AL, UK

C. R. L. MURTHY

Department of Aeronautical Engineering, Indian Institute of Science, Bangalore-560012, India

M. NAKANO

Civil and Applied Mechanics Research Department, Chiyoda Chemical Engineering & Construction Co. Ltd, PO Box 10, Tsurumi, Yokohama, Japan

R. O'NEIL

UKAEA, SRD, Culcheth, Warrington, Cheshire WA3 4NE, UK

K. OHNISHI

Muroran Plant, The Japan Steel Works Ltd, Muroran, Hokkaido, Japan

G. W. PARRY

UKAEA, SRD, Culcheth, Warrington, Cheshire WA3 4NE, UK

J. B. PEREZ PRAT

Tecnatom, Cargetera Nacional No. 1 KM19, San Sebastian de los Reyes, Madrid, Spain

A. C. PROT

Commissariat à l'Energie Atomique, Centre d'Etudes Nucléaires de Saclay, Boîte Postale No. 2, 91 Gif sur Yvette, France

T. S. RAMAMURTHY

Department of Aeronautical Engineering, Indian Institute of Science, Bangalore-560012, India

A. K. RAO

Department of Aeronautical Engineering, Indian Institute of Science, Bangalore-560012, India

R. SAIKUDO

Muroran Plant, The Japan Steel Works Ltd, Muroran, Hokkaido, Japan

A. DE STERKE

RTD-BV Delftweg 144, PO Box 6107, Rotterdam 3008, The Netherlands

T. TSUKIKAWA

Civil and Applied Mechanics Research Department, Chiyoda Chemical Engineering & Construction Co. Ltd, PO Box 10, Tsurumi, Yokohama, Japan

H. UEYAMA

Civil and Applied Mechanics Research Department, Chiyoda Chemical Engineering & Construction Co. Ltd, PO Box 10, Tsurumi, Yokohama, Japan

E. VOTAVA

Kraftwerk Union AG, 8520 Erlangen, Postfach 32 20, Hammerbacherstr. 12 u 14, FRG

J. WATANABE

Muroran Plant, The Japan Steel Works Ltd, Muroran, Hokkaido, Japan

M. F. WHALEN

Adaptronics, Inc., 1750 Old Meadow Rd, McLean, Virginia 22102, USA

A. R. WHITING

Southwest Research Institute, PO Drawer 28510, 6220 Culebra Rd, San Antonio, Texas 78284, USA

H. WÜSTENBERG

Bundesanstalt für Materialprüfung (BAM), Unter den Eichen 87, D-1000 Berlin (West) 45, Germany

S. YAMAMOTO

Civil and Applied Mechanics Research Department, Chiyoda Chemical Engineering & Construction Co. Ltd, PO Box 10, Tsurumi, Yokohama, Japan

SESSION I
Review of Methods Available

1

Non-Destructive Testing for Field Welds: A Real Time Weld Quality Monitor

F. W. KEARNEY

US Army Construction Engineering Research Laboratory, Illinois, USA

SUMMARY

A weld quality monitor with real time output has been developed that designates defective weld areas. The device monitors arc voltage, current, speed, thermal spectra and acoustic emission and with an integral microprocessor computes the value of derived welding parameters. These computed values are compared to predefined optimum limits; this computed data is used for real time quality assurance.

1. INTRODUCTION

1.1. Background

During the welding process, changes in arc voltage, travel speed, and heat input can occur without the operator's knowledge. These changes can cause defects such as porosity, slag inclusions, incomplete fusion, and undercut in the deposited weld metal. The cost of locating and repairing these defects can be a major portion of construction costs; welding inspection can constitute 25 to 40 % of the weld fabrication cost. In addition, weld defects decrease service life of welded joints.

Consequently, it is necessary to monitor the welding parameters to detect, identify, and locate possible defects. A weld monitor with real time output would aid the inspector in designating suspect areas for non-destructing testing after welding. Further, a real time weld quality monitor could be used to interrupt welding when defects are occurring, thus precluding costly rework. To address this need, the US Army Construction

3

Engineering Research Laboratory (CERL) is conducting research to develop a field portable real time weld quality monitor (WQM).

In the initial phase of the study, the following requirements were established for the device:

1. Monitor the three primary signals from the weld system: arc voltage, current, and travel speed; compare them to preset limits; and alert the operator if the limits are exceeded.
2. Calculate the heat input, nugget area, and cooling rate from the three primary signals; compare these values with preset limits; and alert the operator if these limits are exceeded.
3. Be field portable.
4. Interface easily with *in situ* welding equipment.

Essentially, the WQM is intended to provide a mechanism to merge the welding engineer's design intent with the actual field welding process.

Following delineation of these requirements, a prototype WQM was designed, fabricated, and tested using input from a fully automatic gas metal-arc (GMA) welding machine. The automated GMA process was chosen to obtain close control and reproducibility of the welding variables for initial testing.

1.2. Objective
The objectives of the first phase of the study were; (1) to configure a portable, real time WQM System and, (2) conduct laboratory and field tests to determine the adequacy and field applicability of the design.

1.3. Approach
The design of the breadboard WQM was modified to incorporate improvements indicated by actual welding situations in the laboratory. Hardware was assembled and packaged for field use.

In the transitional period from laboratory prototype to field prototype, personnel in Government and the private sector were consulted and their suggestions were used to further improve the unit. The unit was then installed in a welding situation that would thoroughly test all modes of operation.

2. FACTORS AFFECTING WELD MECHANICAL PROPERTIES

In the development, testing and evaluation of the various generations of the weld quality monitor, certain basic welding parameters and relationships were used as guidelines.

2.1. Defects

Changes in the welding parameters of arc voltage, travel speed, and heat input can cause several types of defects of deposited weld metal.

Porosity is a void or gas pocket trapped in solidifying weld metal. The reduced solubility of the gas in the metal caused by the decreasing temperature forces the gases out of solution. The gases are originally introduced either by poor shielding, which contains air, or by chemical reactions in the molten weld metal. With stick electrodes, too long an arc resulting from excessive arc voltage can reduce the shielding effectiveness, thus introducing gas.

Slag inclusion is the entrapment of an oxide or other non-metallic material under the weld beam. The major source of slag is the coatings on stick electrodes. This defect is related to heat input.

Incomplete fusion is the failure of adjacent layers of the weld metal or weld baseplate to fuse. Incomplete fusion may result when the adjacent metal is not heated to the melting point because of insufficient heat input.

An undercut is a groove melted into the base plate at the toe of the weld and is caused primarily by excessive *travel speed* in relation to the welding current.

In addition to the defects caused by improper control, the heat generated by the welding process can cause the following changes in the base metal:

(1) Grain coarsening,
(2) softening ('annealing effects'),
(3) hardening (phase precipitation or transformation),
(4) segregation of constituents,
(5) grain boundary melting,
(6) loss of ductility,
(7) loss of toughness,
(8) residual stresses causing distortion or cracking.

The type of change which occurs depends on the chemical composition of the base metals and electrodes and heat history of the base plate.

In the two commonly used field welding processes—shielded metal-arc (stick electrodes) and gas metal-arc (bare wire)—the source of heat for melting the material is an electric arc. Control of the arc parameters will control the amount of heat generated, the length of time at an elevated temperature, and the cooling rate of the weld zone.

2.2. Base Metal Microstructure

The cooling cycle after a weld pass determines the microstructure of the weld metal and the heat-affected zone. With fast cooling rates, some steels become very hard because of a martensitic transformation. If the cooling is sufficiently slow, the metal may be more ductile and the structure ferritic and pearlitic. The type of steel generally determines which of these structures is desired. For low-carbon and low-alloy steels, the pearlitic structure is desirable, while for high-strength quenched and tempered steel, the martensitic structure is desirable.

Martensite is undesirable in low-carbon and low-alloy steels designed for yield strengths less than eighty ksi (552 MN/m^2) because of its hardness and low solubility for hydrogen at ambient temperatures. The combination of characteristics increases the likelihood of hydrogen cracking in the joints. By using low hydrogen (stick electrodes), the gas metal-arc welding system reduces this tendency towards hydrogen induced cracking.

2.3. Cooling Rate Control

Control of the cooling rate is essential in preventing undesirable microstructure in the weld and heat-affected baseplates. A mathematical combination of arc voltage, current, and travel speed known as heat input (HI) has been used as a means of controlling cooling rates for many years. The equation for calculating heat input is:

$$HI(J/in) = \frac{\text{voltage} \times \text{amperage} \times 60}{\text{travel speed (in/min)}} \qquad (1)$$

The normal maximum has been 55 000 to 60 000 J/in (21 654 to 23 622 J/cm) for the field processes mentioned above. Another means of controlling cooling rate has been preheat treatments. Dorschu [1] has shown that the relationship between heat input, preheat temperature, and cooling rate is:

$$CR = \frac{m(T - T_0)^2}{HI} \qquad (2)$$

where CR = cooling rate, T = test temperature, T_0 = preheat temperature, m = constants and HI = heat input.

Equation (2) indicates that the higher the preheat temperature and heat input the slower the cooling rate.

Schultz and Jackson [2] have shown that the cross-sectional area of the weld bead is a useful indicator of weld metal mechanical properties and that a relationship exists between the area and cooling rates. They also found that arc voltage has little or no effect on the nugget area and cooling rate.

The relationship that Schultz and Jackson have developed for nugget area, arc current, and speed is:

$$na = 122 \times 10^{-7} \frac{i^{1 \cdot 55}}{S^{0 \cdot 0903}} \tag{3}$$

where na = nugget area (in^2), i = arc amperage, and S = arc travel speed (in/min).

3. CIRCUIT DESCRIPTION

Figure 1 is a block diagram of the weld quality monitor showing the input signals from the welding arc. These signals are conditioned to standard

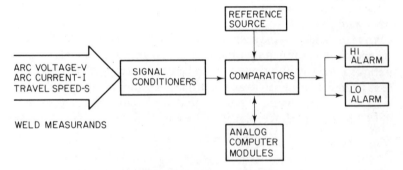

FIG. 1. Block diagram of weld quality monitor.

values and sent to the comparator module, which compares the input signals with a set of limit signals. If the input signals are too high or too low the appropriate alarm is triggered. Input signals are also transmitted to the analog computer module for calculation of the heat input, cooling rate, and nugget area. The calculated values are then compared to reference signals and the appropriate alarm is triggered if needed.

4. LABORATORY TESTS

4.1. Procedure

Each channel of the laboratory prototype monitor was individually tested with a variable signal similar in current and voltage level to the signal from a welding machine. The limits for each channel were set and the voltage tests were varied to simulate changes in the primary signal.

After each channel was tested successfully, the three simulated primary signals were fed into the monitor simultaneously. The limits were again set and the input voltages varied. All circuits including the analog computer section were checked for accuracy and reproducibility.

The monitor was then connected to the CERL welding machine to test the circuitry with actual signals after the limits were set; the welding arc was established on a test plate.

4.2. Results

Results of the laboratory testing showed that all channels performed satisfactorily both independently and in conjunction with each other. The warning lights were triggered when the input signal exceeded the limits set by the reference signal, and no difficulties were encountered when the limit spans were changed.

While investigating the signals of the three parameters (voltage, current, and speed), it was found that the voltage and amperage signals contained spurious noise signals. These signals were removed by; (1) incorporating filters in the data channels to eliminate the peaks and smooth out the signals thus reducing the chance of damage to components, and (2) replacing the shunt as the amperage signal source with a Hall effect solid state

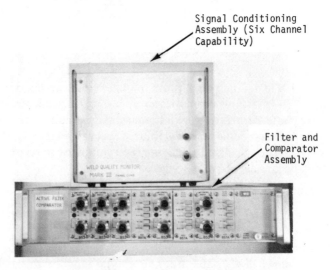

FIG. 2.   Modified prototype weld quality monitor.

transductor. (The advantage of using the transductor is that it is not directly connected to the welding machine as the shunt is; instead, it fits around the cable and measures the magnetic field generated by the current passing through the cable.) The transductor minimised amperage transient signal problems; filters were installed in all channels in field contingencies.

The modifications indicated by the laboratory testing program were incorporated into the monitor before field testing. The system assembled for field testing is shown in Fig. 2.

5. FIELD TEST

5.1. Site Selection

The general types of welding operations considered for field testing were shop fabrication which uses automated welding equipment, and field fabrication/repair, which involves manual or semi-automatic welding and is more dependent on the operator's subjective judgement.

In addition, it was decided that field tests would be more conclusive if the weld quality monitor were used in conjunction with some other form of non-destructive testing. Two sites were available that offered these combinations; Flint Steel Corp., Tulsa, Oklahoma, and a hydro-electric turbine shaft repair job at Ozark Hydro-Electric Plant, Ozark, Arizona. The field repair job at Ozark power plant was chosen since it would entail situations that could not be simulated during the CERL laboratory evaluations. It was felt that the time and space constraints of the field repair situation would assess the unit's adaptability most rigorously. In addition to the hardware evaluation, the field test would provide an opportunity for welding personnel from industry to appraise the WPM.

5.2. Test Operations

The WQM and auxiliary equipment were transported from CERL to the Ozark plant in a conventional automobile with no special handling. The equipment was set up by maintenance personnel and was ready for operation in less than one day.

The WQM was set up approximately 50 ft (15 m) from the repair location. The Hall effect current transductor is shown in Fig. 3. Installation of this device involves simple disconnection and reconnection of one of the leads from the welder power unit; no hard wiring is required.

The welding operation shown in Fig. 4 shows the weld quality monitor voltage sensing lead attached to the welding cable leading to the welding gun. The lead does not encumber the operator in any way.

F. W. Kearney

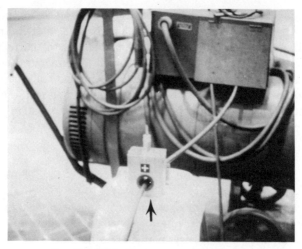

FIG. 3.   Hall effect current transductor.

Since no speed measurement system was available for this test, a precision voltage source was used to provide an equivalent signal to compute heat input and nugget area. For this mode of operation, a voltage corresponding to a particular welding speed is input to the analog computer module to compute heat input in nugget area (eqns (1) and (3)). For

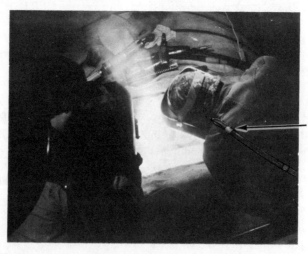

WQM Voltage
Sense Lead

FIG. 4.   WQM field test, WQM arc voltage sense lead attached to welding stick cable.

example, if the analog module were scaled for 1 V equal to 1 in/min, then a 6 V signal from the precision voltage source would be input for a welding speed of 6 in/min.

The signals taken at the output of the signal conditioners before filtering for inputting the comparators are not distorted and the response of the sensors to the voltage and current variations incurring in the arc is preserved in the transduction and the conditioning process. Thus, several data utilisation options are possible—from simple alarms to adaptive control systems.

5.3. Results

The central unit and associated sensors were interconnected and energised without disrupting the welding contractor or requiring welding equipment modification. This verified the adaptability and flexibility of the design objective. Installation of the system was accomplished by a ceramic engineer; an electrical engineer was not required.

The WQM was operated by non-electronic personnel (a welding engineer) with minimal instruction. The data display and printout were understandable to both laboratory and contractor personnel.

During the start up of the WQM, erratic operation was indicated by the visual display; the modular packaging method enabled the problem to be diagnosed and repaired rapidly by interchanging modules. Again, this was accomplished by non-electronic personnel using predefined trouble shooting procedures.

With the feasibility of the design intent of the WQM demonstrated, a concerted program was initiated to develop; (1) suitable speed measuring systems for manual welding situations, (2) specific radiometric measurement techniques involving acoustic emission and thermal spectral analysis, and (3) digital processing features using a microprocessor to facilitate programming the WQM.

6. OPTOELECTRONIC WELD EVALUATION

Direct quantitative measurements of certain parameters of welds in process have not been possible for several reasons. In particular:

(1) The high weld temperatures consume and destroy sensors proximate to the weld area,
(2) contacting sensors introduce a discontinuity of the weld process causing data of uncertainty,

(3)   in the case of manual welding, the subjectiveness peculiar to the welder is indeterminant and variable.

At the present time some indirect measurements are utilised such as thermocouples, etc., but these techniques exhibit time lags, averaging effects and other factors that mitigate the validity and reproducibility of the information obtained.

Because of this inability to measure directly and instantaneously the quantities relevant to a satisfactory weld, a research program was implemented to produce non-contacting instrumentation techniques that will be field applicable to directly monitor pertinent weld measurements such as cooling rate, weld speed, and heat input, to serve as input data to the CERL weld quality monitor.

Optoelectronic technology is used to detect the amplitude and wave length of radiation emitted by the welding arc. A photodetector, or an array of photodetectors is the primary sensor with appropriate circuitry to provide the required output information.

6.1. Physics of Welding Arc

For all practical purposes, the welding arc can be thought of as a gaseous conductor which changes electrical energy into heat. The welding arc can be defined as a particular group of electrical discharges that are formed and sustained by the development of a gaseous conductive medium. The current carriers for the gaseous medium are produced by thermal means and field emission.

The arc current is carried by the *plasma*, the ionised state of a gas composed of nearly equal numbers of electrons and ions. Mixed with the plasma are other states of matter, including molten metals, slags, vapors, and neutral and excited gaseous atoms and molecules.

Measured values of welding arc temperatures normally range between 5000 and 30 000 K, depending on the nature of the plasma and the current conducted by it.

The amount and character of spectral radiation emitted by arcs depend fundamentally upon the atomic mass and chemical structure of the gas, the temperature, and the pressure. Spectral analysis of arc radiation shows bands, lines, and continua. The analysis of radiation from organic type covered electrodes shows molecular bands due to the existence of vibrational and rotational states as well as line and continuum emission from excited and ionised states. The inert gas arcs radiate predominantly by atomic excitation and ionisation. As the energy input to arcs increases, higher states of ionisation occur, giving radiation from higher energy levels.

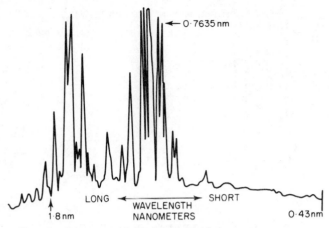

FIG. 5. Spectrum of the argon shielded gas tungsten arc.

The fundamental method utilised in the development of non-contracting sensors in this study, is to separate and quantify segments of weld spectra correlatable to specific weld parameters. The visible spectrum and a portion of the infrared spectrum emanating from the argon shielded gas tungsten arc are shown in Fig. 5.

6.2. Optional Electronic Transduction Methods

Two methods of segmenting or partitioning weld spectrum are; selection of photosensors having a spectral response only in sections of the spectrum to be measured and, use of optical filters to limit the wave length of radiation impinging on the photodetector. For this work the latter method was used; the radiation physics and adaptation of the optical electronics to the problem are illustrated in Fig. 6. Extreme flexibility was provided by various combinations of commercial photographic filters which made it possible to segment the arc spectra into approximately five bands which provided adequate resolution to quantify weld flaws. Two examples will briefly illustrate the procedure.

An analysis of the metallurgical phase diagrams associated with weld nugget area suggested that the normal (acceptable) weld spectrum and a deviant spectrum characterising a flaw would have wave lengths greater than 700 nm. To implement the 'front end' of the sensor system, a Wratten type 89b filter was selected coupled with a type TIL-63 phototransistor. This provided a sensor system with a photometric 'window' of approximately 700–1050 nm; thus the desired spectra were detected while

F. W. Kearney

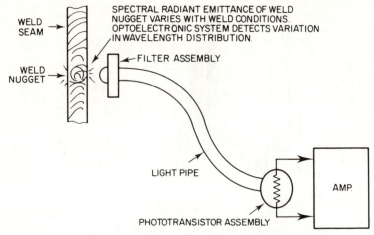

FIG. 6.   Optoelectronic system and application to welds.

extraneous spectra were attenuated. A fiber optic light pipe was the transmission device between the arc and the phototransistor.

Weld arc instability or 'sputtering' is one of the most common flaw inducing conditions encountered in practice. Laboratory testing using radiometers indicated that spectral lines emitted by an unstable arc were very dense in the visible range; to quantify this a ratton 57 cylinder was used in the front end with notable results.

Another flaw inducing condition that was detected by this 'poor man's photometer' was magnetic arc blow.

Present work is concentrated on developing rugged high temperature optical systems to provide durability for field use. To date the results are most encouraging; the fiber optic bundles are 1/16 to 1/8 in diameter and fortuitously have a pass band in the range required, specifically 0·4 nm to 1·9 nm.

7.   LARGE SCALE INTEGRATION (LSI) AND THE WQM

The primary factor that makes the WQM a practical and ubiquitous tool is the confluence of welding engineering and large scale integration electronics technology. Measurements and recordings of voltage, current and, more recently, acoustic emission data are becoming quite standard. The CERL WQM is innovative and unique in that it utilises this data for *in situ*, *real time* analysis for *continuous* and *instantaneous* quality assurance.

REFERENCES AND BIBLIOGRAPHY

1. Dorschu, K. E. (February 1968). Control of cooling rates in steel weld metal, *Welding Research Supplement.*
2. Schultz, B. L. and Jackson, C. E. (January 1973). Influence of weld bead area on weld metal mechanical properties, *Welding Research Supplement.*
3. Weber, R. A. and Jackson, C. E. 'Review of Weldability of Construction Materials', Interim Report M-168/ADA027383, CERL, 1976.
4. Weber, R., Kearney, F. and Joshi, S. 'Development of a Weld Quality Monitor', Interim Report M-183/ADA027644, CERL, July 1976.
5. American Welding Society, *Welding Handbook*, AWS, 1976.
6. Hackforth, H. L. (1960). *Infrared Radiation*, McGraw-Hill Book Co.
7. Sharpe, R. W. (1970). *Research Techniques in Non-Destructive Testing*, Academic Press.
8. Simon, R. E. (1974). *Electro-Optics Handbook*, RCA.

2

Application of Acoustic Emission as a Monitoring System during Hydrostatic Tests of Nuclear Reactor Components

E. VOTAVA

Kraftwerk Union AG, Erlangen, FRG

EDITOR'S NOTE

Dr Votava made a presentation on the above topic which was based on his paper 'Inspection of nuclear reactors by means of acoustic emission during hydrostatic test' which has subsequently been published in the book 'Acoustic Emission Monitoring of Pressurised Systems' edited by W. F. Hartman and J. W. McEiroy, ASTM STP 697, American Society for Testing and Materials, 1979.

For completeness, a brief summary of the presentation is provided here but readers are referred to the above publication for full details.

SUMMARY OF PRESENTATION

Choice of Techniques

An important aspect is the differentiation between different types of emission—the continuous noise caused by fluid flow or leakage and the 'burst' type emission pattern. The former can reduce the effectiveness of acoustic emission (AE) detection of defects and must be suppressed by such practices as acoustic decoupling of the tested object, control of leakage and avoidance of circulating water. 'Burst' type emissions due to frictional effects can be confused with flaw indications, and both accurate location and experience is needed to distinguish them. Control of the rate of pressure increase to less than 1 bar/min was found to be beneficial in reducing overlap of AE signals.

Great attention must be given to calibration by applying test signals on the test object, to calibrate the sensitivity of each channel and to determine wave propagation effects and location accuracy. It is also beneficial with respect to optimising sensor placing and checking the on-line evaluation and data storage systems. The equipment used in such tests was described. Results of trials showed two main effects influencing rigid attenuation—those purely due to distance (the attenuation then being proportional to the inverse of the square root of distance travelled) and scattering effects at areas of complex geometry such as the nozzles, where additional attenuation of 10 dB can occur. The location accuracy was found to be approximately equal to the wall thickness.

Two examples were described, one a PWR pressure vessel in which 16 sensors were put on the cylindrical part, seven on the bottom head and six on the closure head. These showed signals due to leak, and others at a welded-on lifting trunnion and at other points where surface defects (microcracks) were subsequently found by penetrant testing. Thus AE can be very sensitive; the microcracks so found were removed by grinding. Other indications, later examined and classified as not dangerous, were in the region of seam welds or closure head studs.

The entire pressurised system of a 3-loop PWR was examined using 72 sensors during a system pressure test. In addition to two leaks, 48 indications were recorded. Some of these came from the region of a pump coated with thick and brittle paint which was thought to show local flaking which produced the AE. Other signals came from the bouncing of water droplets coming from a leak on the closure head. Others were identified as frictional effects.

These investigations have shown that AE is a sensitive method, that it can find small leaks, that it can arise from frictional and other effects that need experience for identification, and that it can find flaws not first found by other NDE methods.

3

Acoustic Emission Testing of Pressure Vessels Made of $2\frac{1}{4}$Cr–1Mo Steel

S. Yamamoto, T. Tsukikawa, M. Nakano, H. Ueyama

Chiyoda Chemical Engineering and Construction Co. Ltd, Yokohama, Japan

and

J. Watanabe, K. Ohnishi and R. Saikudo

The Japan Steel Works Ltd, Muroran, Japan

SUMMARY

Applicability of the acoustic emission testing to pressure vessels made of $2\frac{1}{4}$Cr–1Mo steel has been studied in an extensive cooperative project among specialists of the acoustic emission technique, pressure vessel fabrication, material and fracture mechanics. The study program included a fundamental laboratory tensile test and a hydrostatic test of a heavy wall test vessel. The obtained results have shown that; (1) if a pressure vessel is fabricated with good quality control required by the ASME Code, there is no active emission during the hydrostatic test before service, (2) if a pressure vessel fails in brittle manner without any formation of a stable crack, there will be few warning emissions prior to the fracture, and (3) if acoustic emission testing is carried out carefully in accordance with the ASME or ASTM standard procedure, minute stable (ductile) crack growth can be detected by experienced acoustic emission testing specialists and failure of the pressure vessel can be avoided.

1. INTRODUCTION

AET (Acoustic Emission Testing) is one of the major topics among those who are engaged in testing pressure containing equipment, such as pressure vessels, pipings and tankages. AET is considered a good non-destructive examination tool which supplements or replaces conventional ultrasonic, radiographic and other non-destructive techniques. ASME and ASTM have respectively issued a proposed standard [1] and a standard recommended practice [2].

If AET is properly planned and performed in accordance with those standards, the emission sources can be readily located. However, AET provides no information on the size, shape and orientation of defects, though such information is necessary for the application of fracture mechanics. Fracture mechanics is increasingly used for the safety analysis of pressure containing equipment. The ASME and ASTM standards give their interpretation and classification of emissions, but they are rather arbitrary and are not based on the fracture mechanism of materials.

In this study, applicability of AET to pressure vessels made of $2\frac{1}{4}$ Cr–1 Mo steel has been studied with particular attentions to the following:

(1)   The detection of AE from the weld defects and discontinuities created in the course of fabrication.
(2)   The detection of AE from the defects induced during the operation.
(3)   The interpretation of AET results based on fracture mechanism of the steel.

The steel chosen was $2\frac{1}{4}$ Cr–1 Mo steel because it is widely used for refinery pressure vessels and because AE behaviour varies with material [3] and little has been known for this particular steel in this regard.

For this very interdisciplinary work, extensive studies on a fundamental laboratory tensile test and a hydrostatic test of a test pressure vessel were carried out with cooperation of specialists in various fields, such as acoustic emission technique, pressure vessel fabrication, material and fracture mechanics.

2.   ACOUSTIC EMISSION BEHAVIOUR OF $2\frac{1}{4}$ Cr–1 Mo PRESSURE VESSEL STEEL

2.1. Background and Objectives

At the planning stage of this study the following facts were known:

(1)   There was no active nor intense acoustic emission during the hydrostatic testing of heavy wall $2\frac{1}{4}$ Cr–1 Mo steel pressure vessels built under proper quality control.

(2) In general, acoustic emission behaviour depends on the material tested [3], and $2\frac{1}{4}$Cr–1Mo steel is not an active material [4].

(3) Acoustic emission from defects has a close relation to material behaviour at the crack tip under loading [5].

A model of the cracking process from a pre-existing crack is presented in Fig. 1 [6]. It is a plot of J versus crack extension Δa, where J is the J-integral [7] which is the energy flow to the crack tip region per unit crack growth.

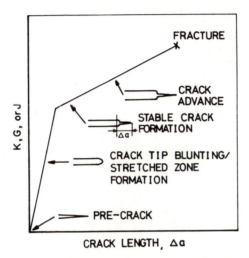

FIG. 1. Schematic diagram of crack growth.

When a structure with cracks is loaded, the crack tip becomes blunted, and a stretched zone is formed; then ahead of the blunted crack a stable crack starts to grow. The stretched zone and the stable crack can be observed under a scanning electron microscope (Fig. 2). When a structure fails in a brittle manner, there is no stable crack formation, and crack tip blunting may be small.

Recent studies show that the total acoustic emission counts from a crack have some relationship with the stress intensity factor K_I at the crack tip as shown in Fig. 3 [5] [8].

Based on this knowledge, the objective of this study was the collection of information needed for the effective application of AET to heavy wall $2\frac{1}{4}$Cr–1Mo steel pressure vessels through studies on the acoustic emission behaviour of the steel with respect to the fracture process of the steel. It was

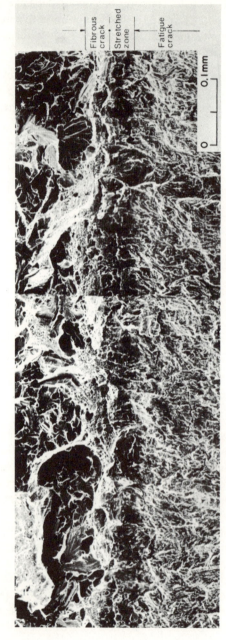

Fig. 2.   Scanning electron micrograph of a crack tip.

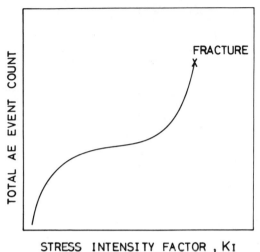

FIG. 3.   Stress intensity factor K_I versus total AE event count.

also intended to separate areas where AET is successfully used from those where AET cannot be a useful tool.

In order to fully understand hydrostatic test results from an artificially flawed test vessel, studies on pre-cracked tensile specimens were carried out [9].

3.   EXPERIMENTAL

3.1. Material

Three normalised and tempered $2\frac{1}{4}$Cr–1Mo steels, whose chemical composition is shown in Table I, were selected on the basis of temper embrittlement susceptibility. The *J*-factor [10], a parameter for temper embrittlement susceptibility of the steels, ranges from 471 for Steel A to 246 for Steel C; the larger the *J*-factor, the greater the susceptibility.

3.2. Tensile Test

A part of Steel A was postweld heat treated and step-cooled [11] to simulate the thermal history that the test reactor is to receive as mentioned later. Tensile specimens were taken from the heat treated Steel A and as-received Steel C as shown in Fig. 4. These specimens were re-designated as Steel A' and Steel C'. As shown in Table II, these two steels have similar

S. *Yamamoto* et al.

TABLE I
CHEMICAL COMPOSITION OF TEST MATERIALS (PERCENTAGE BY WEIGHT)

Material	C	Si	Mn	P	S	Ni	Cr	Cu	Mo	Al	As	Sn	Sb	J-Factor[a]
Steel A	0·14	0·44	0·63	0·018	0·014	0·19	2·72	0·24	1·08	0·005	0·027	0·026	0·0015	471
Steel B	0·16	0·22	0·65	0·015	0·015	0·28	2·51	0·24	0·99	0·005	0·037	0·027	0·0045	365
Steel C	0·15	0·24	0·61	0·011	0·010	0·20	2·26	0·18	1·15	<0·005	0·018	0·018	—	246

[a] J-factor = (Si + Mn) × (P + Sn) × 10^4 [10].

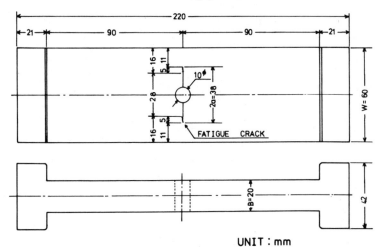

UNIT : mm

FIG. 4.   Tensile specimen.

tensile properties but considerably different impact toughness. The tensile specimens were pre-cracked by fatigue and then tested at room temperature.

3.3. Hydrostatic Test

A heavy wall pressure vessel was fabricated of $2\frac{1}{4}$ Cr–1Mo steel in accordance with the ASME Code Section VIII, Division 2. The size of the

TABLE II

MECHANICAL PROPERTIES OF MATERIALS FOR TENSILE TEST

Material	Room temperature tensile properties[a]				CVN test result[b]	
	Yield[c] strength kg/mm²	Tensile strength kg/mm²	Elongation %	Reduction of area %	FATT[d] °C	CVN_{us}[e] kg-m
Steel A'	44·3	63·1	25·9	55·0	112	14·2
Steel C'	53·6	68·1	26·8	74·7	−18	20·8

[a] 14 mm diameter, 50 mm gauge length.
[b] 2 mm V-notched.
[c] 0·2% offset.
[d] 50% fracture appearance transition temperature.
[e] CVN energy at upper shelf temperature where 100% ductile fracture is first experienced.

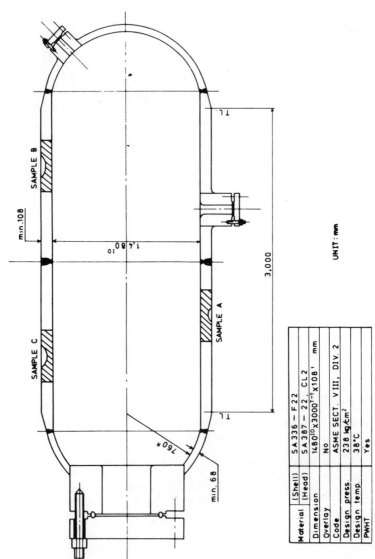

Material	(Shell)	SA336 − F22
	(Head)	SA387 − 22, CL2
Dimension		1480^{ID}x3000^{T-T}x108^t mm
Overlay		No
Code		ASME SECT. VIII, DIV. 2
Design press.		238 kg/cm²
Design temp.		38°C
PWHT		Yes

UNIT : mm

FIG. 5. Test vessel.

test vessel is 1480 mm inside diameter, 108 mm wall thickness and 3000 mm tangent-to-tangent length as shown in Fig. 5. Two shell courses were made of steel plates and welded together. Chemical composition and mechanical properties of the plate and weld metal are shown in Table III.

After intermediate postweld heat treatments, various kinds of weld discontinuities were deliberately introduced into major weld seams [12], and

TABLE III
CHEMICAL COMPOSITION AND MECHANICAL PROPERTIES OF SHELL PLATES AND WELD METAL

Material	Chemical composition (% weight)						
	C	Si	Mn	P	S	Cr	Mo
Plate	0·15	0·25	0·51	0·013	0·012	2·44	1·03

Material	Mechanical properties					
	Room temperature tensile properties[a]				CVN test result[b]	
	Yield[c] strength kg/mm^2	Tensile strength kg/mm^2	Elongation %	Reduction of area %	FATT[d] °C	CVN_{us}[e] kg-m
Plate	47·3	63·4	30·8	75·5	−60	20·6
Weld metal					−5	11·3[f]

[a] 14 mm diameter, 50 mm gauge length.

[b] 2 mm V-notched.

[c] 0·2% offset.

[d] 50% fracture appearance transition temperature.

[e] CVN energy at upper shelf temperature where 100% ductile fracture is first experienced.

[f] Alternative CVN specimen (thickness: 7 mm, width: 10 mm).

then final postweld heat treatment was performed. Non-destructive examinations after the PWHT confirmed the kind, size and location of the discontinuities (Table V later in the text). A hydrostatic test was carried out to study the acoustic emission behaviour from the weld discontinuities during the hydrostatic test required by the Code.

After the hydrostatic test, three open holes were made on the shell wall of the reactor into which the three Steels A, B and C were welded. These three steel samples were fatigue cracked [13] prior to the welding. The reactor with the three test steels was then subjected to postweld heat treatment and step-cooling treatment. Because of the different susceptibility of the steels to temper embrittlement, this enabled the hydrostatic testing of virtually three vessels of different fracture toughness by one actual reactor vessel. Thus, special care was taken in this program in order to:

(1) study the AE behaviour associated with fracture process in connection with the fracture toughness of $2\frac{1}{4}$ Cr–1 Mo steel,
(2) match the fracture toughness of the samples to the possible toughness of actual pressure vessels in service, and
(3) test the three samples in one hydrostatic test at an economically favorable temperature, i.e. ambient temperature, which was 10 °C on the day of the hydrostatic test.

The hydrostatic test was conducted twice for this sample-implanted reactor: first to the pressure specified by the Code and at the second time until the burst of the reactor.

Mechanical properties of the three samples and shell plate after the step-cooling treatment are shown in Table IV. A wide variety of toughness was obtained with small variation in tensile properties.

3.4. Acoustic Emission Test

A four-channel NORTEC system was used in the tensile test for the observation of AE signals. An AET system named as MAESA (Multi-channel Acoustic Emission Source Location Analyser) was used in the

TABLE IV

MECHANICAL PROPERTIES OF PRE-CRACKED SAMPLES AND SHELL PLATES AFTER STEP-COOLING

| | Room temperature tensile properties[a] | | | | CVN test result[b] | |
	Yield[c] strength kg/mm^2	Tensile strength kg/mm^2	Elongation %	Reduction of area %	FATT[d] °C	CVN_{us}[e] kg-m
Steel A	44·2	63·5	29·3	67·0	130	16·5
Steel B	45·5	62·8	30·3	69·7	80	14·5
Steel C	47·9	62·7	28·7	71·2	45	18·5
No. 1 shell	43·9	59·5	30·1	75·7	9	19·8
No. 2 shell	41·7	58·7	30·5	73·7	2	18·8

[a] 14 mm diameter, 50 mm gauge length.
[b] 2 mm V-notched.
[c] 0·2 % offset.
[d] 50 % fracture appearance transition temperature.
[e] CVN energy at upper shelf temperature where 100 % ductile fracture is first experienced.

hydrostatic test. This system uses the CDL (Coincidence Detection Location) method to distinguish acoustic emission signals from the background noise and to analyse the location of signal sources. The system has six arrays consisting of 24 sensors, and the area covered by each array is divided into 1280 zones. It is controlled by a Nova 840 mini-computer with 40 KW core memory and dual 1·2 MW disk memory units.

At the burst test, the NORTEC system was used in addition to the MAESA for Sample A. The NORTEC system had a spacial filter to eliminate the signals from the sources other than Sample A. Signals received were analysed in the same way as in the laboratory tensile test.

4. TEST RESULTS

4.1. Acoustic Emission from Weld Discontinuities

Table V shows AET results obtained from weld discontinuities during the hydrostatic test. It may be concluded from the results that:

(1) noticeable acoustic emission was observed only from the discontinuities that exceed the allowable limit by the Code in their nature and size,

(2) some slag inclusions and blow holes did not show active emissions despite their rejectaneous size,

(3) ultrasonic examination after the hydrostatic test revealed increased echo heights for three of five discontinuities that had emitted acoustic signals.

4.2. Acoustic Emission from Cracks

Figures 6 and 7, plots of the calculated stress intensity factor K_I versus total AE energy count, show AET results from pre-cracked tensile specimens of Steels A' and C', respectively. The results have revealed the following interesting findings.

(1) In Fig. 6, the embrittled Steel A' exhibits three regions, I, II, and III. In Region I, acoustic emission activity increases sharply with the increase of the stress intensity factor K_I whereas in Region II the activity is very small and there exists a plateau. After Region II, Region III follows until the specimen breaks. In this region, the acoustic emission activity shows a rapid increase again.

(2) When the stress intensity factor K_I approaches the fracture toughness K_{Ic}, Region III begins.

TABLE V
SUMMARY OF NDT AND AET RESULTS

Weld discontinuity		Size	UT.RT results Location			UT difference Location			AE results Location		
Type	ASME code acceptance		1/4t	2/4t	3/4t	1/4t	2/4t	3/4t	1/4t	2/4t	3/4t
Slag inclusion (SL)	Yes	Length 19 mm	○		○	○		○	○		○
	No	Length 76 mm	▲	▲	○	○		■	○	○	●
Blow hole (BH)	Yes	Total area 75 mm²/6 in	○			○					○
	No	Total area 300 mm²/6 in	▲		▲	○			○		○
Lack of fusion (LF)	No	Length × depth 50 × 10 mm			▲	○			○		○
	No	Length × depth 50 × 30 mm	○			○			○	○	○
Weld crack (CR)	No	Length × depth 50 × 10 mm	○	○	○	○		■	○		●
	No	Length × depth 50 × 30 mm	○		○			■	○	○	●
Incomplete penetration (IP)	No	Length × depth 50 × 10 mm	○			○					●
	No	Length × depth 50 × 30 mm	○		○	○		○	○		○

○ ▲ ■ ● discontinuities which were introduced in the test vessel;
▲ discontinuities which produce large indications;
■ discontinuities which showed clear difference before and after the hydrostatic test;
● discontinuities which showed noticeable acoustic emission.

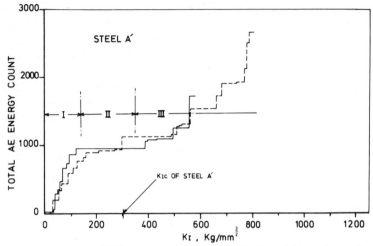

FIG. 6. K_I versus total AE energy count of pre-cracked Steel A′ tensile specimens.

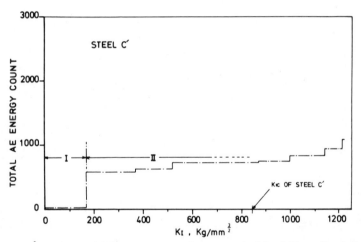

FIG. 7. $\dot{K}_I$ versus total AE energy count of a pre-cracked Steel C′ tensile specimen.

(3) In tough material Steel C′, (Fig. 7) Regions I and II are observed, but transition to Region III is not clearly identified. The acoustic emission in Region I is not so active as in the case of Steel A′, and there is a long plateau before the fracture of the specimen.

The following findings were also obtained from the hydrostatic test for the burst of the test vessel.

(1)   Figure 8 shows a plot of K_I [14] versus total AE event count per unit crack length for Samples A and C. Steel A, which has a considerably lower fracture toughness (233 kg/mm$^{3/2}$) compared with expected K_{Ic} for actual pressure vessel (600 kg/mm$^{3/2}$ or higher) clearly shows Region III, but the distinction between the other two regions is not clear. The activity of acoustic emission in Region III becomes rapidly intensified as K_I approaches the K_{Ic} of the material.

(2)   Figure 9 shows the same plot for Sample B, which has an intermediate fracture toughness. Regions I, II and III are clearly identified, and Region III begins when the stress intensity factor comes into the vicinity of the fracture toughness of the material as in the case of Steel A.

(3)   Steel C, an excellently tough steel, shows low acoustic emission activity as observed for the pre-cracked tensile specimen.

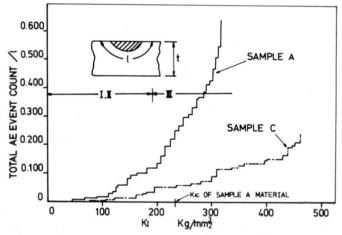

FIG. 8. K_I versus total AE event count per unit pre-crack length: Test vessel Samples A and C.

Scanning electron micrographs of the crack tip areas of Samples A and B are shown in Fig. 10. A stretched zone and stable crack similar to those in Fig. 2 are observed. Figure 11 is a plot of the crack opening displacement versus hydrostatic pressure for three samples, and the departure from the linear portion of the curve indicates the occurrence of non-elastic deformation at the crack tip, and this is supported by the scanning electron micrographs, Fig. 10.

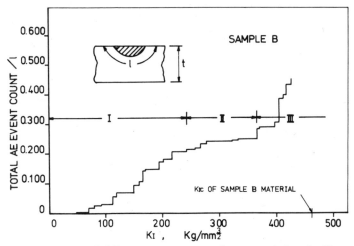

FIG. 9. K_I versus total AE event count per unit pre-crack length: Test vessel Sample B.

Figure 12 shows the relationships between pressure, total AE event count and elapsed time during the hydrostatic test. It clearly manifests the presence of the Kaiser effect. The hydrostatic test was conducted twice as mentioned earlier, i.e. first to the pressure required by the Code and secondly until the reactor burst. At the second test, acoustic emission was not active until the pressure reached the previous level.

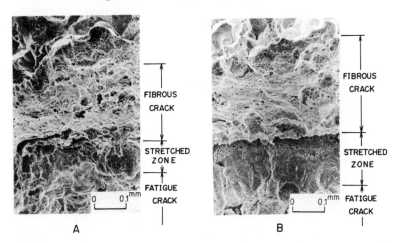

FIG. 10. Scanning electron micrographs of pre-crack tips of Samples A and B.

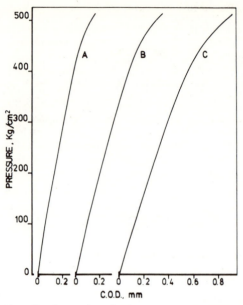

FIG. 11.   Crack opening displacement at the crack tips.

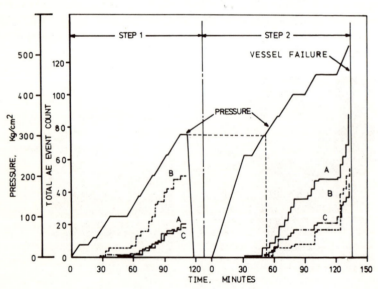

FIG. 12.   Time versus pressure and total AE event count plots: Test vessel with pre-cracked samples.

The results obtained in this test lead to the following conclusions:

(1) This study confirmed the recent finding by others [5] [8] that there is rapid increase of acoustic emission activity when the stress intensity at the crack tip approaches the fracture toughness K_{Ic} of the material tested. This occurs in Region III and is believed to be the onset of stable crack growth from the fracture process viewpoint.

(2) There are two preceding regions where acoustic emission activity begins with relatively rapid increase (Region I) and then reaches a plateau (Region II). For a brittle material, the activity in Region I is high and the plateau in Region II lasts for only a short time. For a tough material, the activity in Region I is low and there is very long plateau extending over to Region III. These two regions are considered to be caused by the preparative fracture process for the onset of stable crack, such as stretched zone formation, plastic zone extension, and separation of non-metallic inclusions from the matrix.

(3) The presence of the Kaiser effect was confirmed.

4.3. AET of Pressure Vessels Made of $2\frac{1}{4}$ Cr–1Mo Steels

This study on the acoustic emission behaviour of $2\frac{1}{4}$ Cr–1Mo steel has revealed several important points to be considered as to the application of AET to pressure vessels made of this steel. These will be discussed for three cases; 4.3.1. AET during hydrostatic test, 4.3.2. AET under brittle fracture condition, and 4.3.3. AET under in-elastic fracture condition.

4.3.1. AET During Hydrostatic Test

Table V shows that such defects as cracks, lack of fusions and incomplete penetrations which are not allowed by the ASME Code can be the source of acoustic emission during hydrostatic test. The laboratory test results and the results obtained from the hydrostatic test of the test vessel show that the emissions from such defects start to occur when plastic deformation begins prior to stable crack growth. Consequently, the stress intensity factor at the tip of the defects must be high enough to produce active acoustic emissions, and this condition would not exist in the pressure vessels which are designed, fabricated using specified materials and inspected in accordance with the Code. It may be concluded that acoustic emission during hydrostatic testing of such pressure vessels will be of low activity and low intensity.

Table V also shows that blow holes and slag inclusions can cause acoustic emission. The emission from slag inclusions is considered to occur due to the friction between slag inclusion and matrix and the cracking of the inclusions themselves. The emission from non-destructively found large blow holes may be associated with the linkage of many closely dispersed porosities. The emission from these defects starts at a relatively low pressure and becomes inactive at an early stage of the hydrostatic test. Signals from such defects can be distinguished by experienced acoustic emission engineers from those emitted from cracks.

4.3.2. AET Under Brittle Fracture Condition

It was found in this study that in the case of brittle fracture without any plastic deformation, blunting or stretched zone formation, there will be no noticeable acoustic emissions. This infers that AET is not a useful tool to avoid brittle fracture. It is ironical that AET is most needed to avoid unexpected brittle fracture, yet this is not possible. However, complete brittle fracture is very seldom, and in many cases small plastic deformation will proceed the brittle failure.

TABLE VI
CALCULATED BURST PRESSURE FOR STEELS A, B AND C

| Sample | Crack size | | K_{Ic} at $10°C^a$ $kg/mm^{3/2}$ | Calculated burst pressure kg/cm^2 |
	Depth, a mm	Length, 2c mm		
A	51	99	233	369
B	51	187	462	556
C	63	205	713	796

^{a} Converted from J_{Ic}

Table VI lists the crack length, K_{Ic} (measured using specimens taken out of the samples after the burst test), and expected burst pressure calculated based on linear fracture mechanics. The actual burst pressure was $523\,kg/cm^2$, much higher than the pressure calculated for Steel A. Figure 11 demonstrates the presence of in-elastic fracture mechanism.

4.3.3. AET Under In-elastic Fracture Condition

In this case, AET can be effectively used to detect growing cracks and to prevent the failure of pressure vessels. In other words, for the effective use of

AET, one must ensure that the pressure vessel in question is being operated or being tested under an in-elastic (ductile) fracture condition.

Recent development in linear and non-linear fracture mechanics has helped establish fracture safe analysis of pressure vessels made of $2\frac{1}{4}$ Cr–1 Mo steel [15] [16]. However, it is still a difficult task to ensure there is no brittle fracture condition because of insufficient information on material properties, and the size, shape, location and orientation of flaws.

When the presence of a brittle fracture situation is eliminated, most possibly through proper selection of pressurising temperature, AET can be a useful tool to detect crack growth. ANSI/ASTM E569-76 'Standard Recommended Practice for Acoustic Emission Monitoring of Structures During Controlled Stimulation' [2] provides good guidelines for AET.

This practice stipulates, as a source classification; (1) critically active or critically intense, (2) intense, (3) active but not intense, and (4) low activity and intensity. Based on the present study, it is felt that this classification needs more clarification in connection with Regions I, II and III as found in the present study because they relate to the fracture process at the crack tip. It must be pointed out that Region II is critical in terms of prevention of final failure despite its low emission activity, because it is a clear indication of plastic deformation at the crack tip that prepares the onset of stable crack growth which then leads to the final failure.

5. CONCLUSIONS

In order to find the effectiveness of AET, the acoustic emission behaviour of $2\frac{1}{4}$ Cr–1 Mo steel was studied employing tensile tests of pre-cracked specimens and hydrostatic tests of a heavy wall test vessel with weld discontinuities and pre-cracked samples. The acoustic emission data obtained were analysed in relation to the fracture process of the material tested.

The following conclusions may be drawn from the results of the present study.

(1)   In general, the acoustic emission behaviour of $2\frac{1}{4}$ Cr–1 Mo pressure vessel steel relative to the stress intensity factor K_I at the crack tip is divided into three regions.

(a)   Region I: initial increase of the acoustic emission activity, which is believed to be caused by the fracture process at the crack tip.

(b)   Region II: plateau on the K_I versus acoustic emission activity plot between Regions I and III, where little activity is observed.

(c)   Region III: rapid increase of the acoustic emission activity until fracture, which is thought to be associated with the formation of a new stable crack at the pre-crack tip and its growth.

(2)   Acoustic emission activity and intensity in these three regions depend on the toughness of the material.

(3)   For the effective use of AET, the following need to be considered.

(a)   AET in the hydrostatic testing of pressure vessels built in accordance with the ASME Code and under good quality control will serve as a double checking of its quality level.

(b)   Prevention of brittle fracture of pressure vessels by AET is difficult, because preceding plastic deformation at the pre-existing crack is small and accompanying acoustic emission activity is therefore small.

(c)   In in-elastic fracture cases, which are believed to be common in real incidences, AET is a useful tool for crack growth detection.

(4)   In order to make interpretations and classifications of AET results more reasonable, the acoustic emission behaviour of materials in conjunction with their fracture process must be more fully understood. Improvement in AET equipment is also required.

ACKNOWLEDGEMENTS

The authors wish to express their gratitude to Mr Yudo Ohshio and his colleagues of Chiyoda Chemical Engineering and Construction Co. and to Mr Shunji Mima and his colleagues of Japan Steel Works for their significant support in this study. The authors also wish to thank Dr Tadao Iwadate of Japan Steel Works for his contributions to the fracture mechanics portion of this study.

REFERENCES

1. The American Society of Mechanical Engineers, 'Proposed Standard for Acoustic Emission Examination During Application of Pressure', 1975.

2. The American Society for Testing and Materials, 'Standard Recommended Practice for Acoustic Emission Monitoring of Structure During Controlled Stimulation', ANSI/ASTM E569–76, 1976.
3. Eisenblatter, J. (1974). 'A Survey of Acoustic Emission Research in Europe and Investigations Conducted at Battelle Frankfurt', Proc. 2nd Acoustic Emission Symposium, Session 7.
4. Bentley, P. G. *et al.*, (1973). Preprint of 'Acoustic Emission and Pressure Vessel Failure', Second International Conference on Pressure Vessel Technology, part II, ASME, p. 643.
5. Clark, G. and Knott, J. F. (1977). Acoustic emission and ductile crack growth in pressure vessel steels, *Metal Science*, **11**, 531.
6. Landes, J. D. and Begley, J. A. 'Recent Developments in J_{Ic} Testing', ASTM STP 632, American Society for Testing and Materials, p. 57, 1977.
7. Rice, J. R. (1968). A bath independent integral and approximate analysis of strain concentration by notches and crack, *Trans. ASME*, **35**, 379.
8. Ying, S. P. and Grigory, S. C. 'Acoustic Emission Monitoring of One-Inch-Thick and Six-Inch-Thick Tensile Specimens', Tests of 6-Inch-Thick Tensile Specimens Fifth Technical Summary Report HSSTP-TR-24, Southwest Research Institute, San Antonio, Texas, 1972.
9. Tsukikawa, T., Yamamoto, S. and Watanabe, J. *et al.*, (June, 1979). 'Acoustic Emission Testing during a Burst Test of a Thick Walled $2\frac{1}{4}$ Cr–1 Mo Steel Pressure Vessel', presented at the 3rd US National Congress on Pressure Vessel and Piping, San Francisco, California.
10. Murakami, Y., Watanabe, J. and Mima, S. (Aug., 1978). 'Heavy Section Cr–Mo Steels for Hydrogenation Services', presented at the 17th C.I.N. Annual Conference of Metallurgists, Montreal.
11. Olsen, R. J. *et al.*, (1974). 'Temper Embrittlement of Hydro Cracker Reactor Steels', Technical Report of SOCAL, Presented at the API Task Group Meeting on Temper Embrittlement, Chicago.
12. Ishii, Y., Kihara, H. and Tada, Y. (Aug., 1968). On the relation between the non-destructive testing information of steel welds and their mechanical strength, *J. Nondestructive Testing*, **16**, 319.
13. Abbatiello, A. A. and Derby, R. W., 'Notch Sharpening in a Large Tensile Specimen by Local Fatigue', ORNL-TM-3925, Oakridge National Laboratory, Nov. 1972.
14. Kobayashi, A. S. and Moss, W. L. (1969). Stress intensity magnification factors for surface-flawed tension plate and notched round tension bar, *Fracture*, 31.
15. Watanabe, J. *et al.*, 'A Fracture Safe Analysis of Pressure Vessels Made of $2\frac{1}{4}$ Cr–1 Mo Steel', Corrosion/76, Paper No. 126, National Association of Corrosion Engineers, Houston, Texas, 1976.
16. Spän, H. (1977). 'Material Problems, Testing and Inspection, Corrosion Protection and Operating Experience', Preprint of Third International Conference on Pressure Vessel Technology, Part III: Discussions, ASME, p. 9.

4

Spectral Analysis Approach for Interpretation of Acoustic Emission Signals for NDT and Monitoring of Structural Integrity

C. R. L. Murthy, B. Dattaguru, T. S. Ramamurthy and A. K. Rao

Indian Institute of Science, Bangalore, India

SUMMARY

Some results from detailed spectral analysis of AE (Acoustic Emission) from zircaloy specimens are presented. The mean normalised energy spectral density has been found to be a reliable criterion for identification of flaw size. Certain other typical results in the time domain which exhibit correlations between AE parameters and flaw size are also included. This study indicates the necessity for a comprehensive analysis of AE signals for deriving reliable information which is valuable for the purpose of NDT and structural integrity monitoring.

1. INTRODUCTION

The changes occurring in a material during loading tend to release energy which propagates as stress waves, which are termed acoustic emissions. Materials emit stress waves while undergoing deformation or fracture. Such acoustic signals from a specimen or a component contain considerable information regarding the presence and severity of defects, and the state of damage, deterioration or fracture in the material. Therefore, effective methods of interpretation of these data are valuable for non-destructive testing and inspection procedures and for structural integrity monitoring.

The most commonly used method of characterising AE signals is through the measurement of amplitude-based parameters like counts, count rates and amplitude distributions. The limitations of these methods of data

Paper prepared for, but not presented at the Seminar.

analysis in providing definitive information on the source, nature and extent of damage are being increasingly recognised. It is more realistic to postulate that the simultaneous measurement and analysis of a series of spectral and amplitude parameters can bring out valuable correlations between the AE signals and material, configuration, loading and damage parameters. What is more significant is that by such an approach the severity of a defect can be assessed and damage can be recognised at very low loads and at early stages of structural deterioration. Such a possibility enhances the scope of this technique for applications in research, testing, inspection and integrity monitoring. This postulation has formed the basis for a programme of work at the Indian Institute of Science.

The conceptual ideas in this direction of pattern recognition are being developed in the laboratory through static and fatigue tests on materials like wood, tin and zircaloy with controlled defects at specific locations. For wood and tin the analysis was carried out in the audio frequency zone. Results on spectral analysis of AE from wood and some of the basic findings on spectral and multi parameter characterisation of AE from tin have been reported earlier [1, 2]. Typical results of further studies on tin and zircaloy are presented in this short paper.

Analyses of Acoustic Emission from zircaloy, tin and wood during static tensile tests have confirmed the postulation that structural defects can be identified at small loads. Analysing emissions in the initial stages of loading, it was found possible to correlate the changing patterns of AE parameters to the controlled defects introduced into the specimens. Like many natural phenomena, AE is a random process. Consequently the parametric variations thereof should be considered statistically.

2. EXPERIMENTS

Extensive experiments on zircaloy are underway because of its importance in reactor technology. Tensile tests were carried out on zircaloy specimens at 6 mm/min strain rate. The defects were introduced into the specimens as edge cracks of different lengths. Emissions from these tests were recorded on a high speed analog magnetic tape recorder which has a frequency response of 2 MHz on direct recording at 120 in/s speed. The data was later time expanded by 256 times to make it compatible for processing on the available hybrid computer system. The frequency range of analysis was 125 kHz to 1 MHz.

A program package was developed for use on a DEC-10 digital computer which computes the number of events, cumulative counts, count rate, interval between events, rise time and fall time, energy in the time domain, and frequency domain parameters such as peak spectral amplitude and energy in different bands. Certain simple criteria based on these parameters, have been worked out to sort out the events. A set of events which carry the information about the severity of the defect has been identified. Significant differences in the spectral characteristics were observed with different severities of the defect.

3. RESULTS

Typical results are as follows. Analyses of defective and non-defective specimens have indicated that the severity of the defect can be identified from; (1) a distinct change in energy in the specified bands in the frequency domain, (2) a distinct shift in the predominant frequency in the spectrum, and (3) the percentage of events which occur with extremely small gaps between pairs of consecutive events.

A simple hypothesis test was conducted on the mean normalised energy spectral density (MNSD) in three bands to identify the severity of the introduced defects. The success or failure of such a hypothesis test is presented in Table I. The result shows that the defect configuration is well identified from the MNSD in band 3 and it can be observed that, in the first and second bands it is possible to make a distinction only when the difference in the size of the defects is significantly large. The variation of the percentage of the closely spaced events in zircaloy and tin with defect size is shown in Fig. 1.

TABLE I

RESULTS OF HYPOTHESIS TESTING ON THE MEAN
NORMALISED ENERGY SPECTRAL DENSITY

Specimen comparison	*Band 1*	*Band 2*	*Band 3*
Plain and 1/8 in crack	S	S	S
1/8 in crack and 1/4 in crack	F	F	S
Plain and 1/4 in crack	S	S	S

S—Success; F—Failure.

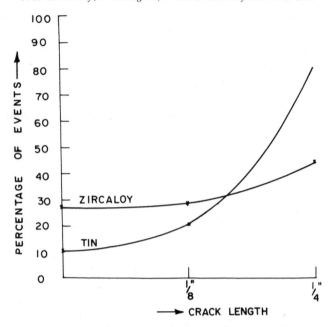

FIG. 1.   Percentage of events with small gap for 3 mm of elongation.

ACKNOWLEDGEMENTS

The authors acknowledge the co-operation extended by the Aeronautics Research and Development Board and the Power Projects Engineering Division of Atomic Energy Commission and the Aeronautical Development Establishment for carrying out the work presented in this paper.

REFERENCES

1. Eshwar, V. A., Dattaguru, B., Yegnanarayana, B. and Rao, A. K. (March 1977). 'A Preliminary Study on the Use of Spectrum Analysis in Acoustic Emission Testing', paper presented at the International Conference on Fracture Mechanics and Technology, Hong Kong.
2. Murthy, C. R. L., Dattaguru, B. and Rao, A. K. (March 1979). 'Multi-parameter Characterization of Acoustic Emission Signals', paper presented at the International Conference on Fracture Mechanics in Engineering Applications, Bangalore, India.

5

Pressure Vessel Nozzle Inspection Using Adaptive Learning Techniques

M. F. WHALEN and A. N. MUCCIARDI

Adaptronics, Inc., McLean, Virginia, USA

SUMMARY

Thermal fatigue cracks which grow on the inner radius of feedwater nozzles have been difficult to characterise by conventional ultrasonic inspection methods. Common problems with nozzle inspections are long metal distances, complicated geometries, and low signal levels. Crack detection capability can be improved an order of magnitude by utilising signal processing methods applied in other scientific fields such as radar, sonar, and seismology. Crack depth can also be inferred accurately by examining specific characteristics in the power spectrum of the crack echo transient. The ALN 4000 Multi Purpose Processing System developed under EPRI sponsorship combines the most up-to-date advances in microprocessor and LSI technology with a powerful signal processing software repertoire to achieve reliable and complete nozzle inspection with unambiguous detection for cracks as small as 4 mm in depth.

1. CRACK DETECTION

The ability to detect small cracks in nozzle forgings is clearly dependent on the signal-to-noise level of the received crack echo. If the signal is large compared to the noise, the crack can be detected easily. If the signal is buried in background noise, the waveform must be processed to recover the crack echo. The following signal enhancement methods are being used to increase signal-to-noise levels:

(1) Bandpass filtering: digitally filtering signal components outside of the transducer bandwidth; the filter passband characteristics can be changed easily to accommodate any transducer bandwidth.

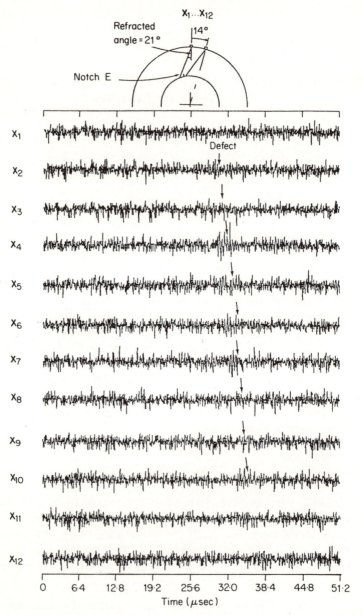

FIG. 1.   Unfiltered ultrasonic waveforms—COM–ED mock-up—notch 'E' (depth = 4 mm).

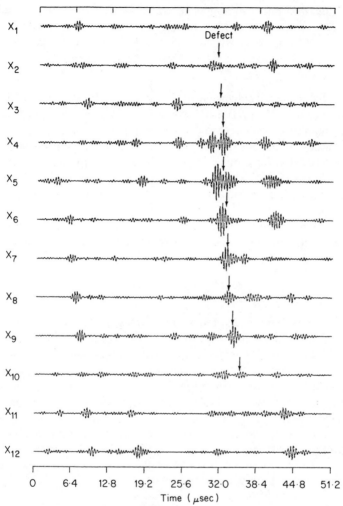

FIG. 2. Non-linear beamformed and matched filtered waveforms—notch 'E'
(depth = 4 mm).

(2) Signal averaging: summing of several pulse–echo waveforms while
holding the transducer at a fixed position; the random noise
components in the received data will cancel but the coherent signal
transients will add.

(3) Match filtering: convolving a known defect response with a noisy
waveform to recover a known crack response.

(4) Beamforming: averaging several pulse–echo waveforms recorded at slightly different orientations relative to the defect; each waveform is delayed before averaging so the signals add coherently; beamforming reduces coherent noise sources such as grain scattering.

The effect of signal enhancement is dramatic, as illustrated in Figs 1 and 2. Figure 1 shows 12 unprocessed ultrasonic RF waveforms recorded over a 14° segment of a circumferential scan which passes over a 5 mm (0·157 in) deep saw cut on the inner radius of the Commonwealth Edison calibration nozzle. Note that the data are extremely noisy and the signal level of the defect is below the noise level. Figure 2 shows the same 12 waveforms after match filtering and beamforming. Note that the defect response is clearly observable.

After S/N enhancement, the signal is detected automatically by comparing the average signal power to a predetermined threshold.

2. CRACK SIZING

Most attempts to size nozzle cracks ultrasonically have been based on peak amplitude measurement of the rectified time echo transient. With this method, the peak is compared to a calibration notch threshold after distance–amplitude correction of the instrument. The echo amplitude can be affected by so many factors that crack sizing in practical situations is rarely reliable. A more reliable sizing approach is to make use of the diffracted wave from the crack tip as well as the main reflection from the corner reflector formed by the nozzle inner surface and the crack base. The time difference (Δt) between the arrival of the diffracted wave and the arrival of the corner response is a function of the crack depth (d), the angle of incidence (θ), and the velocity of propagation (c) where,

$$t = \frac{2d\cos\theta}{c} \tag{1}$$

Since these arrivals are opposite in phase, a 'ripple' (i.e. successive maxima) period (Δf) in the power spectrum will result such that,

$$\Delta f = \frac{1}{\Delta t} = \frac{c}{2d\cos\theta} \tag{2}$$

If good approximations for the velocity and angle of incidence can be

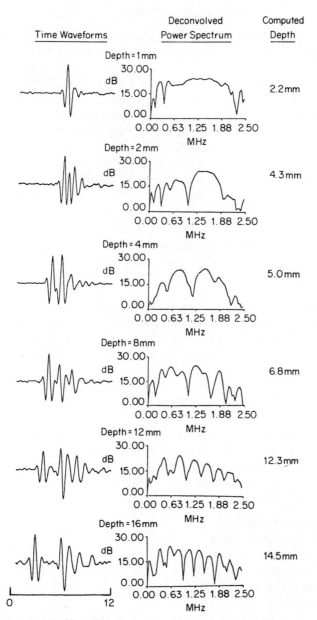

FIG. 3.   Time waveform and power spectra responses from calibration block saw cuts at various depths (angle of incidence was 45°, centre frequency was 1 MHz and the computed depth was calculated using eqn. (2)).

obtained, the crack depth can be measured directly from Δt or Δf. However, the measurement of Δt will be difficult if the two arrivals overlap. Therefore, measurement of Δf is preferred since the ripple period can, in principle, still be measured even when the two arriving wave packets overlap.

Examples of ultrasonic responses from semi-elliptical saw cuts, whose depths were measured according to eqn (2), are shown in Fig. 3. Six defects at the depths shown were machined into one side of a triangular carbon steel block. Pulse–echo waveforms were recorded from the other side of the block such that the angle of incidence was 45°. Note the two distinct pulses in the time waveform for the 16 mm-deep defect. The earlier pulse is due to diffraction at the defect's tip. The second arrival, which is opposite in phase, is caused by the corner reflector formed by the crack base and specimen surface. Note the appearance of the ripples in the power spectra. Also observe how the ripple period decreases with increasing crack depth. The right column shows the computed depth from eqn (2), above, after computing d from the average ripple period. The computed and true depths compare very well.

This diffraction method is presently being investigated to size saw cuts and thermal fatigue cracks in nozzle inner radii. The ripple period estimate is being included with other spectral features as inputs to Adaptive Learning Networks. The network output is an estimate of the crack depth.

3. NOZZLE GEOMETRY PROGRAM

The Feedwater Nozzle Geometry Program (FwN GP) is an analysis tool which locates the inner diameter (ID) exit point of the main ultrasonic beam given: (1) the transducer location on the outer diameter (OD); (2) the refracted angle; and (3) six geometry measurements taken from the nozzle. The six parameters include:

(1) plate thickness;
(2) inner pipe diameter;
(3) outer pipe diameter at the nozzle bore;
(4) blend radius;
(5) inner radius;
(6) vessel curvature.

The FwN GP was written initially to locate precisely the position of cracks on the ID, once detected by a transducer on the OD. The complex structure of the nozzle and the use of a refracted angle make it very difficult to determine the exit point without such a program. The geometry program provides several other uses:

(1) calculation of the metal path and window functions;
(2) determination of theoretical delays for beamforming;
(3) analysis of mechanised UT scan patterns.

The main ultrasonic beam is described as a unit vector which is determined uniquely by the transducer position and the refracted angle. The pipe bore, inner radius, and vessel plate are described mathematically in the program as three connecting surfaces. The intersection of the unit vector with the proper surface is found parametrically to yield the ID exit point.

The inner radius can be described mathematically as a torus (donut) which is bent around the inside of the vessel curvature. The pipe bore and vessel plate are described as simple cylinders. The program decides which surface is applicable.

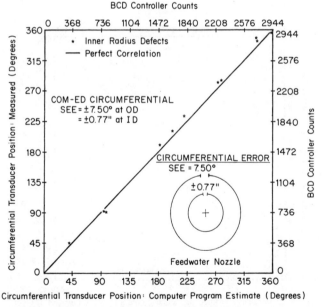

FIG. 4.   Comparison of the measured (circumferential) transducer on the OD with that estimated by the Adaptronics FwN geometry computer program for the Commonwealth–Edison mock-up (the measured data were recorded in August 1978 at Maywood, Illinois).

4.   EVALUATION ON EXPERIMENTAL DATA

The scan patterns used on Jersey Central Power & Light (JCP&L) and Commonwealth–Edison (COM–ED) mock-ups were simulated with the FwN GP to help analyse the recorded data. This resulted in a means for evaluating the program's accuracy on experimental data. Figure 4 shows the measured circumferential transducer position for 11 defects versus the position estimated by the FwN GP. The data points were taken from the COM–ED mock-up. The standard error of estimate is 7·5°. This means the circumferential error in locating cracks is about ±0·77 in (±19·5 mm) at the ID. Figure 5 shows the measured versus estimated transducer position for the axial data. The axial error is 0·44 in (11 mm) at the ID. Error estimates were obtained for the JCP&L data with results very similar to the COM–ED results. On both nozzles, the position of cracks on the ID could be located to within an area of about the size of a matchbook cover. Locatability is essential for tight cracks which are not detectable by penetrant testing.

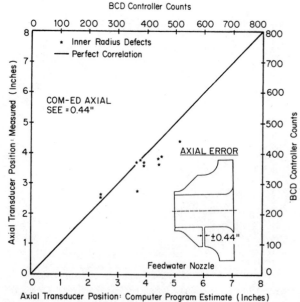

FIG. 5.   Comparison of the measured (axial) transducer position on the OD with that estimated by the Adaptronics FwN geometry computer program for the Commonwealth–Edison mock-up (the measured data were recorded in August 1978 at Maywood, Illinois).

5. BEAMFORMING WITH THEORETICAL DELAYS

Beamforming is a signal processing operation used to enhance the signal-to-noise ratio of a target by adding coherently more than one waveform when the transducer is moved relative to the target. The FwN GP was used to generate the theoretical delays (via estimates of the metal path from transducer to defect) needed to add the signals coherently.

The program outputs the location of the transducer and the location of the exit beam on the inner radius. These locations are three-dimensional

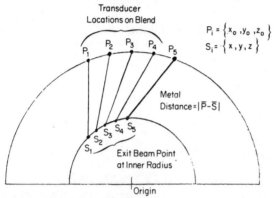

FIG. 6. Illustration of the nozzle geometry program outputs for a circumferential scan simulation: (1) The location of the transducer on the blend radius (P), and (2) the exit point of the main refracted longitudinal beam on the inner radius (S).

points in space relative to some fixed origin. A diagram of five transducer locations (P) along a circumference and the corresponding inner radius points (S) is given in Fig. 6. The metal distances (M) between any point, P, and any point, S, can be computed by taking the vector difference:

$$M = [(P_x - S_x)^2 + (P_y - S_y)^2 + (P_z - S_z)^2]^{1/2}$$

By computing the metal distances from several transducer locations to a specified exit point (S_3) as shown in Fig. 7, the theoretical delays about, say, point P_3 can easily be calculated by subtracting the metal distance, $|\bar{P}_3 - \bar{S}_3|$, from all others and dividing the remainder by the velocity of the ultrasonic wave in the base metal.

The theoretical delays were checked against the delays observed in actual data and were found to agree very closely. The theoretical delays were subsequently generated for all transducer positions along the inner radius and bore for both the JCP&L and COM–ED mock-ups.

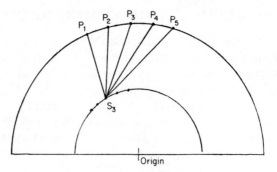

FIG. 7.   Illustration showing how the theoretical delays were computed from the
nozzle geometry program's output.

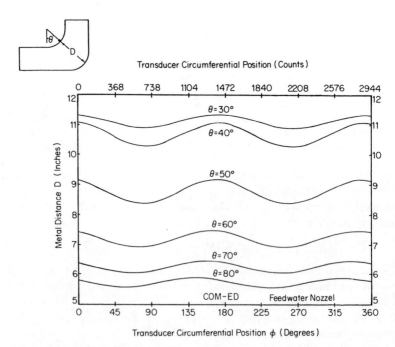

FIG. 8.   Metal distance as a function of circumferential transducer position at six
angular positions (θ) on the blend radius for the Commonwealth–Edison feedwater
nozzle mock-up, (these data were generated by the Adaptronics FwN geometry
computer program).

6. OTHER USES OF THE GEOMETRY PROGRAM

The program has been useful in analysing mechanised scan patterns. Figure 8 shows how the metal distance '*D*' varies during circumferential scans from the blend radius for several angular positions on the blend. A 20·65° refracted angle was used. Note that when θ is at about 50°, the metal

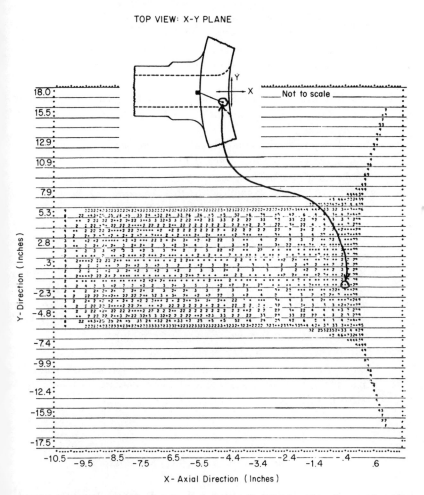

FIG. 9. Inspection points of the main beam on the ID (viewed in the *x-y* plane) for a mechanised ultrasonic inspection of the Commonwealth–Edison feedwater nozzle mock-up as simulated by the Adaptronics nozzle geometry computer program.

distance changes almost one inch depending on the transducer's circumferential position. This variance is due to the vessel's curvature. At $30° < \theta < 50°$, the transducer is viewing the inner radius 'knuckle'. In Fig. 9, the inner surface of the nozzle is mapped out by the geometry program; the vessel curvature is followed quite well.

7. CONCLUSIONS

The major accomplishments of this work have led to the following:

(1) development of a crack detection algorithm which can detect inner radius defects as small as 4 mm in depth when inspecting from the blend radius;

(2) use of frequency domain information instead of rectified time and amplitude to determine crack depth;

(3) application of signal processing techniques used in fields such as radar, sonar, and seismology to the ultrasonic RF waveform to enhance the signal-to-noise ratio; techniques such as match filtering, beamforming, and signal averaging have improved ultrasonic signals more than an order of magnitude over conventional systems;

(4) development of the ALN 4000 Multi Purpose Processing System to perform automatic mechanised nozzle inspection; the ALN 4000 employs state-of-the-art LSI circuitry including two Z80 microprocessors, a 20 MHz A/D converter, a 115 ns multiplier/ accumulator, and five arithmetic function chips;

(5) formulation of a feedwater nozzle geometry program which mathematically defines the inner and outer surfaces on a nozzle; this program determines metal distances, scan protocols, and location of defects on the inner surface.

ACKNOWLEDGEMENT

This work was supported by the Electric Power Research Institute (EPRI) under Contract No. RP1125–1. The guidance and support of the EPRI Program Manager, Dr Gary J. Dau, are gratefully acknowledged.

BIBLIOGRAPHY

Cleveland, D., Barron, A. R. and Mucciardi, A. N. Frequency domain methods for reducing transducer variability, submitted to the *Journal of Nondestructive Evaluation*, September 1979.

Cleveland, D., Barron, A. R. and Mucciardi, A. N. Methods for determining the depth of near-surface defects, submitted to the *Journal of Nondestructive Evaluation*, September 1979.

Shankar, R. and Mucciardi, A. N. Near-surface defect detection, submitted to *Materials Evaluation*, July 1979.

6

Development of Ultrasonic Techniques for Sizing Defects

H. WÜSTENBERG and A. ERHARD

*Bundesanstalt für Materialprüfung (BAM),
Berlin (West), Germany*

SUMMARY

Flaw detection with ultrasonic pulse–echo methods can be realised with suitably adapted parameters at almost all technically relevant flaw types in metallic materials with a good detectability. The evaluation and analysis of indicated reflectors concerning their location, kind and size must use a multitude of information sources in order to deliver unambiguous interpretations about the importance of quality and safety. Whereas conventional ultrasonic pulse–echo methods determine flaw location from time of flight, beam angle and probe position almost always with sufficient accuracy, the evaluation of kind and size of a flaw from amplitude and echo dynamic is unreliable. Specialised analysing methods must try to derive discriminating criteria for different kinds of defect (voluminous, planar) and length as well as depth extension as more or less abstract flaw data. Another analysing possibility is the use of flaw imaging. However results from analysing—or imaging—techniques based on a pulse–echo–reflection mode are influenced by the reflection behaviour of the defects and, therefore, are only partly reliable. This paper reports on experiences with different sizing techniques (acoustical holography, focusing probes, shadow arrangements, evaluations of echo-dynamic patterns) and indicates the areas of application.

1. INTRODUCTION

In the past 20 years ultrasonic non-destructive inspection has seen a tremendous increase of application in almost all technical constructions, but the poor flaw sizing capability of most of the ultrasonic techniques

59

seems to be a serious limitation, if an evaluation critical for the safety of the object and strongly depending on flaw dimensions is needed. The well-known advantages of ultrasonic methods—good detectability of almost all kinds of defects in technical constructions and in all cases a sufficiently exact description of the flaw position—have been the reason for the widespread use of ultrasonic pulse–echo methods.

The evaluation of the results is mainly based on more or less abstract specifically ultrasonic criteria which often have a very weak correlation to the real flaw dimensions. An evaluation based only on an acoustically gained image of the flaw is seldom achieved. Figure 1 demonstrates these two possibilities of evaluation [1]. Many national codes and specifications [2–4] evaluate ultrasonic results based on a classification, as indicated at the top of Fig. 1. An evaluation according to the analytical method in Fig. 1 for

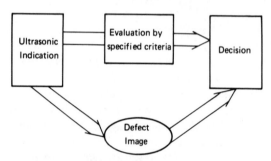

FIG. 1.   Decision finding at UT inspection.

determining acoustically the flaw dimensions—this can be done via the production of an acoustical image or by a precise measuring procedure for length and depth extensions—may also have a limited reliability because an acoustical description differs from a metallographic presentation for many reasons. The most important reason is the fact that results gained from reflected pulses are based on the specific reflectivity of a defect [5–8]. An alternative consists of a pitch and catch mode which uses the acoustical shadow of a defect [9].

Since the development of ultrasonic techniques has been advanced during their use in non-destructive testing by the requirements of the practical application, some physical background has only been regarded on a very simplified basis. In particular the flaw sizing problem—from the beginning based on amplitude and half value extension—has been further developed and improved on by experimentally gained experiences. The fundamental limitations of an amplitude based evaluation and even of an evaluation based on the half value extension or a determination derived from echodynamic patterns have been pointed out by many authors in the past [10–26].

Other approaches better adapted to the purpose of flaw dimensioning are mostly intended to improve the conventional techniques. For a long time, it has been obvious, that a reliable flaw sizing with ultrasonic methods needs specially adapted procedures using the physical laws of wave propagation, reflection and diffraction without doubtful simplifications. This led to the development of more sophisticated techniques, such as acoustical holography. Due to its historical development, flaw dimensioning technology with ultrasound must respect conventional and semi-conventional techniques as well as highly sophisticated procedures restricted more or less to the analysis of ultrasonic indications and not well suited to the detection of defects.

2. SOURCES OF INFORMATION AND EVALUATION OF ULTRASONIC INDICATIONS

In Fig. 2 the information which can be used during an evaluation and the most important evaluation and defect sizing methods are listed. Ultrasonic techniques use the probe position on the object producing a maximum echo amplitude, the echo amplitude, the time of flight, phase and sometimes the

Techniques	Probe position X, Y, φ	beam direction α	Echo Amplitude	Time of Flight	Phase	Pulse-Shape or Spectrum
DAC or DGS (AVG) Method	X	X	X	(X)		
Echodynamic pattern (half value a. others)	X	X	(X)	X		
Combined Evaluation	X		X	X	(X)	(X)
Focus-Probes	X	X	X	(X)		(X)
Ac. Holography	X		X		X	
Synthetic Aperture	X		X	X		X
Shadow Techn. Pitch a. Catch, Scattering	X	(X)	X	X	X	
Pattern Recognition (ALN etc.)	X	X		(X)		X

FIG. 2. Sources of information for the evaluation of UT-indications.

pulse shape (in time or frequency domain). Amplitude and time of flight are related to the probe position. This relationship can be measured during the scanning of a reflector. The resulting dynamic behaviour delivers information which is used for the evaluation of many conventional specifications [10–13].

The maximum echo amplitude—e.g. with the help of the DGS(AVG) method described in terms of equivalent reflector sizes ($\simeq$ diameter of circular disc reflectors)—has often a very weak correlation between size and amplitude [14–26]. The amplitude together with echodynamic behaviour can be used to judge indications statistically if sufficient experience is available. This procedure becomes very questionable if objects with a strongly fluctuating sensitivity due to coupling or attenuation are to be inspected, e.g. with coarse grained stainless steels or cladded surfaces [28]. By combining the basic information from an ultrasonic inspection, a lot of flaw sizing problems can be reduced to some kind of a 'puzzle game' which must interpret data gathered by relatively simple measurements, e.g. time of flight, amplitude, echodynamic behaviour and pulse shape. Such puzzle games must be regarded as a specific family of ultrasonic flaw dimensioning methods. In Fig. 2 they are described as combined evaluation techniques.

Focusing probes and acoustical holography are almost classical analytical ultrasonic techniques. Thanks to progress in computer technology, the synthetic aperture focusing technique can also be taken into account.

For many problems, where the above mentioned puzzle games become cumbersome, pattern recognition techniques like the adaptive learning procedure may represent a better solution.

The first six techniques in Fig. 2 and all known applications of pattern recognition are based on the reflection of an ultrasonic pulse at the defect. According to Fig. 3, three main types of reflection can be discriminated; the geometric reflection, the tip reflection and the diffuse reflection. The geometric reflection represents the energy reflected back from a planar or homogeneously curved surface within the main lobe of a reflected sound field. Diffusely reflected energy comes from a rough surface with a roughness $R_a > \lambda/5$, which means that diffuse reflection has only a minor importance for UT-inspection at frequencies below 5 MHz. The energy diffracted at corners, tips and linear boundaries is described as tip reflection.

The production of a not ambiguous image of the defect surface, e.g. by focusing probes, acoustical holography or synthetic aperture, needs either a geometric main lobe reflection or a diffusely reflected beam. Tip reflections

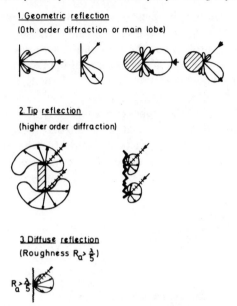

1.Geometric reflection
(0th. order diffraction or main lobe)

2.Tip reflection
(higher order diffraction)

3.Diffuse reflection
(Roughness $R_a > \frac{\lambda}{5}$)

FIG. 3.   Reflection of ultrasonic waves at defect surfaces (schematic).

from a boundary or a corner lead to point-like images from irregularities of the flaw surface. Unfortunately such tip reflections are in general the most important part of the reflected energy, if the defect orientation and the beam direction are not sufficiently matched. Therefore alternatives to acoustic imaging procedures based on the energy reflected back from the defect, such as shadow images, could be a helpful option in special cases. Many analysing techniques like focusing probes or acoustical holography can also be used in a shadow arrangement [9].

3.   EVALUATING AND SIZING TECHNIQUES

In the following some of today's most important defect evaluating and sizing techniques are described and evaluated.

3.1. Methods Based on an Amplitude Evaluation (DGS Method, DAC Evaluation)

The echo amplitude—being influenced by a large number of factors e.g. coupling, attenuation, defect orientation, shape, type, size, location, sound field, frequency—can only be regarded as a useful measure for the size of a reflector for small defects ($> 2\lambda$) and for constant coupling conditions (Fig. 4). There is a large gap between the amplitude-based flaw size estimation, (e.g. with the help of the equivalent flaw size of the DGS diagram [14–26]) and methods using the echodynamic pattern for deriving half-value or 20 dB drop extensions remains according to Fig. 4, if one takes into account the sound beam diameters of the probes currently in use, which must represent a certain compromise between reliable defect detection and analysis of indications [30]. Most of the practically important defects are situated within this gap. The necessity of further development for specialised analysing of ultrasonic techniques is again underlined by this fact. Despite

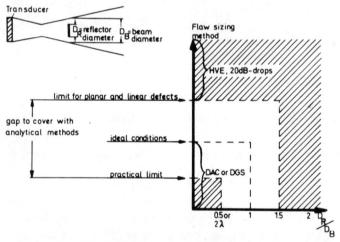

FIG. 4.   Range of applicability for conventional ultrasonic flaw sizing methods.

the limited suitability of the echo amplitude for sizing, it should be mentioned that, nevertheless, the amplitude must be used in the judgement of an ultrasonic indication for all techniques, e.g. in terms of the equivalent flaw sizes of the DGS diagram or of DAC levels as a threshold for defining negligible indications and important ones [27]. For example the signal to noise ratio, that is the relationship between echo amplitudes from really existent separations and grain structures or geometric reflectors, is one of the most important quality criteria for an ultrasonic technique.

3.2. Echodynamic Evaluation

From the amplitude and time of flight, (if recorded in relation to the probe

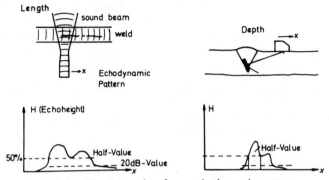

FIG. 5(a). Flaw extension from echodynamic pattern.

movement as echodynamic plots) a lot of information about the position, shape and orientation of a defect can be derived. In addition the use of probes with different refraction angles and in some case also a tandem technique helps to produce a conclusive evaluation as far as shape and orientation of a defect is concerned [1, 34, 34a]. Figures 5 and 6 illustrate some procedures for the evaluation of echodynamic plots. Figure 5(a) illustrates a widely used procedure for deriving length and depth extensions of defects. Half-value, 20 dB drops or other extensions can be determined. The best theoretical fitting to the real extensions is given by the half-value extension. Of course, the accuracy is limited by the beam diameter which can be reduced by focusing probes. However, Fig. 5(b) shows also that the applications to volumic defects cannot deliver reliable results. Planar or linear defects (e.g. slag inclusions) are correctly sized, if large enough and if adequately orientated towards the beam. The possibility of determining the extension of flaws in depth with beam diameters which in practice are

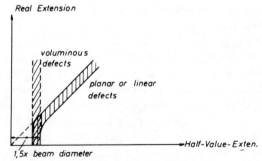

FIG. 5(b). Flaw extension from echodynamic pattern.

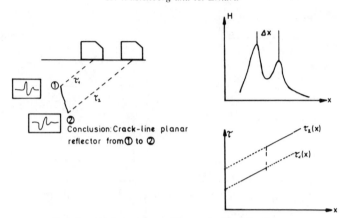

FIG. 6.   Defect sizing with crack tip reflections.

usually greater than the expected extensions, is according to Fig. 5(b) rather limited. Defect sizing based on the echo amplitude plots is useful in connection with focusing probes. Without sharper focused sound fields only the use of crack tip reflections seems to offer in many cases a possibility of sizing the depth extension (see Fig. 6) [29, 37].

3.3. Combined Evaluation

In many cases the reliability of the echodynamic evaluation can be improved simply by better use of the information offered by conventional ultrasonic techniques. This may be demonstrated in Fig. 6, using a dynamic plot of the amplitude together with the time of flight [29]. The example of Fig. 6 represents the reflection of an ultrasonic beam on a crack-like flaw. Two main sources of indications must be discriminated, one from the upper and one from the lower crack tip. Monitoring the time of flight will show in such cases, that one amplitude indication traced during the measurement of the dynamic behaviour is produced from two different locations, in the case of Fig. 6 from the upper and the lower crack tip.

In order to discriminate cracks from, for example, two slag inclusions, it seems necessary to also take into account the pulse shape which differs from the upper and the lower crack tip. This is shown in the lower part of Fig. 6. The phase behaviour of the reflectivity at the upper and lower crack tip differs in a typical way, which cannot be produced at two voluminous slag inclusions placed on the upper and the lower crack tip positions [31–33].

Another hint to the existence of a planar defect can be derived from the equivalent reflector sizes, evaluated with a DGS diagram and measured for different beam angles, including a tandem arrangement. Large differences between, for example, tandem and 45° and 0°, lead to the conclusion that a planar reflector of a certain size must be the reason [7]. One of the main applications of crack tip reflections for defect sizing is the use of spectroscopy [36]. Silk and Dijkstra describe different approaches to size cracks starting at the surface or within the body [29, 37, 38]. De Vadder and others have presented a combination of focusing probes and crack tip reflection behaviour in order to discriminate between different kinds of reflectors [40] (See also Fig. 6). The echo amplitude received from crack tips has been measured [41]. Crack tip reflections are connected with an inhomogeneous surface wave on the defect and can therefore be strongly influenced in amplitude by applied stresses. A defect detection based only on the tip reflection can be hazardous, if stresses are present. In References 29 and 39 results are presented of sizing defects in welds found with these techniques.

It seems that in fortunate situations—this means without interfering influences from the flaw and object geometry—the deviations between the real flaw sizes (especially extensions in depth) and ultrasonically measured values can be lower than 1 mm. The disadvantage of this method is that a very special defect geometry is required with the corresponding preliminary knowledge from previous measurements. A general applicability cannot be acknowledged.

The discrimination between volumic and planar defects can use three different types of information from the echo amplitude plot [34, 34a, 35] (Fig. 7(a) and (b)).

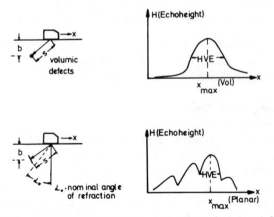

FIG. 7(a). Discrimination between volumic and planar defects.

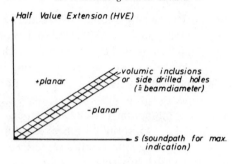

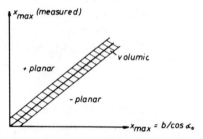

FIG. 7(b).   Discrimination between volumic and planar defects.

1. The shape of the curve (smooth for volumic reflectors, wavy with interference peaks for planar reflectors).
2. The half-value extension (compared, for example, with that of side drilled holes of similar depth).
3. The shift of the maximum amplitude position to a position that can be forecast from the angle of refraction and defect depth.

The time of flight plots (See Fig. 6) can be used to discriminate between structural noise and defect indications, for an exact depth determination by a triangulation calculation and in fortunate cases for a defect sizing [34].

3.4. Flaw Imaging Methods
3.4.1. Focusing Probes

The simplest way to image a defect is by using a focused sound field. For nuclear components with large wall thickness, Saglio and others have first use focused sound fields produced by large immersion-coupled probes [43]. The increasing demand for the application of focusing probes under practical circumstances in shops during fabrication initiated the development of contact coupled probes with perspex or other plastic wedges (Fig. 8)

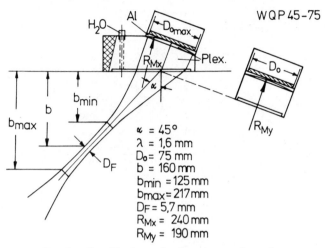

FIG. 8. Specific data of a focusing angle probe.

[45–49]. The commonly used diameters of the focal spot range from 2 mm ϕ (4 MHz shear waves) up to 12 mm (1 MHz shear waves). Such probes can be operated at depths from 20 mm up to 600 mm. However, a disadvantage is that nearly all probes available today are restricted to a given depth range depending on the focalisation factor. An actually discussed possibility to overcome this drawback is the use of dynamically focusing systems [50] or of systems based on the phased array technology which may change not only the depth range of the focal spot area but also the angle of refraction. Practically available and experienced in many places are focusing probes in an immersion as well as in a direct contact coupled form.

The application of focusing probes may lead to the direct production of an image or of dynamic patterns according to the different scanning lines (see Fig. 9). As demonstrated in Figs 9 and 10 the interpretation of a received echodynamic pattern with focusing probes is so much better than a pattern from other probes that the curves show a steeper rise and fall. This means that threshold levels with a relative threshold defined, e.g. by 6 dB of the maximum amplitude, or an absolute threshold defined by a reference reflector amplitude will not influence the results too strongly. Nevertheless, it is necessary to apply a special interpretation technique [48, 52] (Fig. 10) in order to avoid underestimations of the flaw size. If a defect shows a greater uninterrupted flaw area at a 12 dB drop than at 6 dB, then the 12 dB drop extension or the 18 or 24 dB drop extension should be taken as the real maximum extension of the defect in the scanning line, if one subtracts from

H. Wüstenberg and A. Erhard

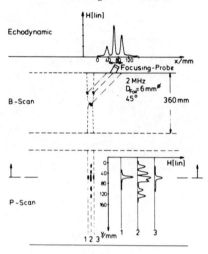

FIG. 9. Echodynamic B- and C-scan presentation of weld defects by focusing
probes.

the chosen extension respectively one time, two times or three times the
beam diameter. Regarding this special interpretation technique, quite good
results could be gained by focusing probes on heavy components. In many
practical cases, the accuracy lies in the order of one wavelength. An example
of the possibilities and limitations of focusing systems in a pulse reflection

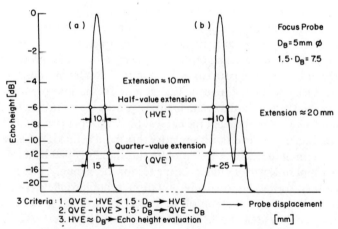

FIG. 10. Determination of the half- and quarter-value extension by the focus
technique.

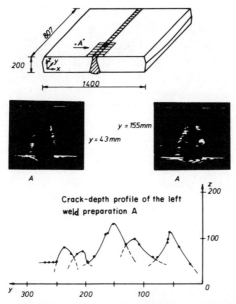

FIG. 11.   Defect imaging with superimposed sector-scan (compound scan).

mode is shown in Fig. 11 [51]. A crack has been scanned with a phased array focusing system with about 5 mm ϕ spot diameter at 2 MHz. The size of the defective area can be estimated, but the shape and type cannot. The size can be derived, only because a compound scan, with a lot of different defect observation angles is applied.

3.4.2. Acoustical Holography

The application of acoustical holography [55–65] for flaw imaging must take into account, that a long wavelength holography can not deliver the well-known three-dimensional images of the object. The relationship between wavelength and aperture size greatly reduces the longitudinal resolution. Nevertheless, acoustical holography will deliver images with a well-defined lateral resolution, which can be easily adapted to the need of a practical case. The principle of acoustical holography is described in Fig. 12 together with an example using so-called linear holography. The scanning device is guiding a probe along a line. This probe is excited by a quasi monochromatic pulse and produces a widespread sound field, at least in the plane containing the aperture line. The received echoes are multiplied with two reference signals, one 0° and one 90° shifted against the transmitting

H. Wüstenberg and A. Erhard

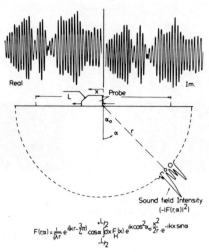

$$F(r\alpha) = \frac{1}{i\lambda r} e^{i(kr-\frac{3}{2}\pi)} \cos\alpha \int_{-L/2}^{+L/2} dx\, F_H(x)\, e^{ikcos^2\alpha_0\frac{x^2}{2r}} \cdot e^{-ikx\sin\alpha}$$

FIG. 12(a). Numerical reconstructed holography.

pulse and thus delivering a real and an imaginary part of the received echo at a number of sampling points along the aperture. Both are stored in a computer. With the help of quadratic phase functions, the computer defines a reconstruction plane and observation angle from which we can calculate according to the formula indicated in Fig. 12, the sound field intensity in the area of an expected defect. From the profile of such a sound field intensity,

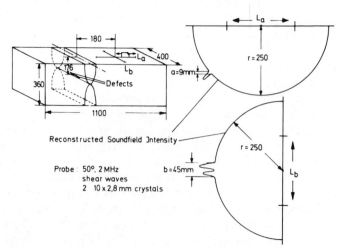

FIG. 12(b). Reconstructed linear holograms of a weld defect.

defect sizes can be derived. The most important advantage of acoustical holography is the fact that this technique can be applied to practical cases without the preparation of special probes adapted to the defect position. If the main disadvantage of acoustical holography, the weak resolution in the direction of the sound beam, interferes with the aim of a defect analysis, then the application of focusing probes, a multi-frequency holography or a synthetic aperture focusing technique may be possible alternatives [53, 54, 66, 67]. According to the experience gained during the past years with acoustical holography, it seems that acoustical holography will be of great value only because the lateral resolution needed for a special case can easily be realised with this approach. In most cases it is possible to reach, with acoustical holography, accuracies in the order of 1/2 to 1 wavelength. Figure 12(a) shows the hologram and the reconstruction of a real defect in a weld.

3.4.3. *Synthetic Aperture Focusing Technique (SAFT)*

A third imaging technique presently under development will be presented here—the synthetic aperture focusing technique [66, 67]. Figure 13 shows the principle of this approach. The synthetic aperture technique needs the storage of the high-frequency (hf) echo signal, received by a probe producing a similar sound field as a holographic probe in Fig. 11. The sampling points along an aperture line or an aperture surface must be

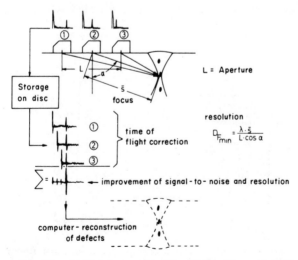

FIG. 13. Artificial aperture (after Frederick *et al.* [66]).

spaced at a similar distance as is necessary for the acoustical holography. The hf wave forms of the reflectograms (A-scans) are digitised and stored in a computer. After storage by the computer, it is possible to shift the different A-scans by predetermined delay times corresponding to a focalisation at the position where the reconstruction is to be carried out. By this procedure, synthetic focusing on arbitrary points of the volume is possible. The synthetic aperture focusing technique combines the advantages of acoustical holography and the focusing probe method, but it has a new drawback, that is the need of a highly sophisticated computer device with very large storing capacities and a relatively large reconstruction time. The accuracies and reliabilities of this technology may be expected to be in the same range as for acoustical holography. The synthetic aperture technique should replace acoustical holography only in the cases where a longitudinal resolution is necessary; for instance, welds with geometric indications, clusters of defects, and similar problems.

In Fig. 3 the basic limitations of ultrasonic imaging techniques based on the reflection of the defect have been considered. Due to the range of the applied wavelength, reflection from corners and tips of the defect contribute more to the production of the flaw image than the surface roughness or the main lobe of the reflected beam. This means, that for defect imaging an adaptation of the observation angle to the flaw orientation is also necessary [27, 29], otherwise ambiguous interpretations cannot be avoided, as shown in Fig. 14 for a defect scanned with a focused sound field.

In Fig. 15 a very important case is demonstrated, where crack sizing is

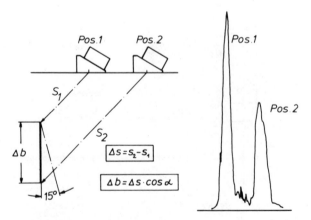

FIG. 14.   Determination of the extension in depth of planar reflectors (reflector perpendicular to the surface, $\pm 15°$).

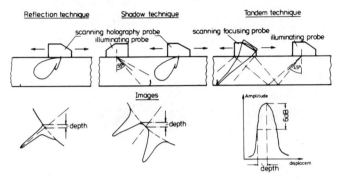

FIG. 15. Crack sizing with imaging methods.

difficult [68]. Surface defects cannot be ascertained by imaging techniques from the defective surface. Arrangements with a half skip distance according to Fig. 15 are necessary. With such a position, an important role is played not only by a crack tip reflection but also by the corner effect. Experience has shown that techniques influenced by corner effect reflections at cracks near the surface have a very limited range of accuracy [68]. One general conclusion is that the application of imaging techniques based on a reflection at the defect is more strongly restricted in the case of near surface reflectors.

3.5. Shadow Techniques

The only possibility of overcoming the drawback of flaw sizing techniques in a pulse reflection mode is the application of a through transmission arrangement. In this case the reflectivity of the defect will not be used but the shadow as in X-ray applications. It should be remembered here that the first acoustical images were produced by a through transmission arrangement [69]. Perhaps in the future through transmission techniques like those employed in medical practice [70] may also play an important role in analysing defects in thick-walled nuclear components. Meanwhile, focusing probes or acoustical holography may be used in a slightly modified arrangement as demonstrated in Fig. 16 [9]. The advantage of a holographic arrangement is that a depth focusing by the computer is possible for a certain range of accuracy. The shadow images reconstructed by acoustical holography deliver projections of the defect perpendicular to the observation angle.

Similar reconstructions to the one demonstrated in Fig. 16 in the case of acoustical holography, are also possible with the help of focusing probes.

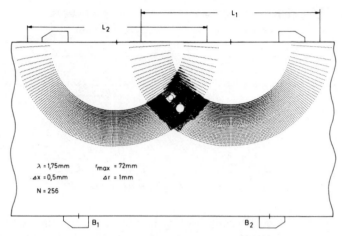

FIG. 16. Acoustic holography in double through transmission. (Diameter of the
side drilled holes, $D_1 = 4$ mm, $D_2 = 6$ mm.)

The advantage of the arrangement shown in Fig. 16 is that the dimensions
producing the maximum shadow extensions correspond quite well to the
mechanical separation represented by the defect. At least two scanning
positions are necessary to deliver sufficiently defined estimates on the
probable flaw extension area. Shadow techniques can also be applied at half
the skip, e.g. for surface cracks (see Fig. 15). One principal disadvantage is
that an evaluation of the flaw type is no longer possible. The volumic or
planar decision must be based on the orientation dependency of an
indication produced in a reflection pulse–echo mode.

Another technique using such a shadow effect has been presented in

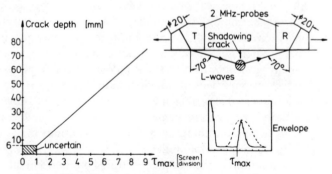

FIG. 17. Crack size estimation by scattered waves.

connection with the crack depth determination of near surface cracks [71–73]. The arrangement of this technique using the forward scattering of longitudinal waves is demonstrated in Fig. 17. Changing the distance between both probes, the indication of the scattered energy will increase if the crossing over of both beams is situated under the lower crack tip. Crack depths larger than 6 mm can be determined with an accuracy better than 1 mm.

The shadow technique seems to be, for the time being, the only one delivering valuable results even in cases where the defect orientation, situation or shape may limit the accuracy of other techniques.

3.6. Pattern Recognition Techniques

An entirely different approach to the problem of defect sizing is that of pattern recognition (simulearning, adaptive learning, low frequency scattering) [74–78]. As an example of such an approach, the adaptive learning network task will be described for a collection of objects, with all typical characteristics (interfering echo indications, defect indications, materials properties etc.), echo indjcations, if possible in the form of hf A-scans, are recorded. Typical characteristics of such A-scans are determined in terms of characteristic values, derived, for example, with the help of spectrum analysis. The correlation of such values in nonlinear combinations to the presence of a defect and to characteristic parameters of the defect, like type and size, is analysed by a suitable program. The combination obtained by the computer evaluation can afterwards be used by a hardware network to evaluate on line the results of an inspection procedure. It is obvious that such a procedure is especially valuable for similar objects where some typical defects must be analysed. The restriction of such approaches to objects with a more or less reproducible situation must be taken into account.

4. CONCLUSIONS

In the present contribution, we have tried to point out the most important approaches to the problem of defect sizing with ultrasound. Not all the possibilities reported in the literature have been described but the principal limitations for the method included in this contribution may also be valid with some minor changes for other possibilities.

Since defect sizing with ultrasound has been carried out by many practical engineers with too simple approaches, confidence in ultrasonic techniques has declined. Applying ultrasound to nuclear components means that the sizing of defects will be a key point. Therefore, a lot of new developments and new experience have been gained in the last ten years. One major conclusion can be drawn from all the past evidence: there are rare cases where only one approach will deliver accurate and reliable enough results to be used, for instance, for fracture mechanical analyses. In general, it should be taken into account that for almost all situations of detected defects, the use of more than one ultrasonic approach and in some cases also approaches with other NDT techniques are recommended.

The choice of the ultrasonic defect sizing techniques must be adapted to the special case. There is no approach which solves all problems. Since in practice a lot of methods must be available, an economic compromise between the applicability range of a special technique and the expense should be considered. The more highly sophisticated approaches, in particular, should be taken into account in this situation.

REFERENCES

1. Mundry, E., Wüstenberg, H., Neumann, E., Kutzner, J. and Nabel, E. (1975). Entwicklungstendenzen in der Ultraschallprüftechnik, *Schweißtechnik*, **12**, 204–9.
2. American Society of Mechanical Engineers, Boiler and Pressure Vessel Code, Section XI.
3. German Code RHP 5/3.
4. KTA-Regel 3201.
5. Wüstenberg, H., Kutzner, J. and Engl, G. (1976). 'Dependence of Echo Amplitude on Defect Orientation in Ultrasonic Examinations', 8th World Conf. on NDT, Cannes, France, 6–11 Sept.
6. Ermolov, J. N. (April 1972). The reflection of ultrasonic waves from targets of simple geometry, *Nondestructive Testing*, 87–91.
7. Shcherbinskii, V. G. and Belyi, V. E. (May–June 1975). New informative index for the nature of flaws in ultrasonic inspection, *Soviet Journal of Nondestructive Testing*, **11**(3), 279–88.
8. Wüstenberg, H., Kutzner, J. and Kaps, U. (1976). 'Flaw Size Determination in Ultrasonic Inspection by Evaluation of the Echodynamic Pattern', 8th World Conf. on NDT, Cannes, France, 6–11 Sept.
9. Kutzner, J. and Zimpfer, J. (1977). Einsatz der akustischen Holographie zur Erzeugung von Schattenbildern, *Materialprüfung*, **19**(5), 165–92.
10. Schlengermann, U. and Frielinghaus, R. (1973). Beitrag zur Fehlergrössen-bestimmung mit Ultraschall durch Fehlerabtastung mit relativer Schwelle, *Materialprüfung*, **15**(2), 50–6.
11. Schlengermann, U. and Frielinghaus, R. (1974). Beitrag zur Fehlergrössen-bestimmung mit Ultraschall durch Fehlerabtastung mit fester Schwelle, *Materialprüfung*, **16**(10), 319.

12. Wüstenberg, H. and Mundry, E. (1971). Beitrag zur Halbwertstiefenausdehnung von Reflexionsstellen in der Materialprüfung mit Ultraschall, *Materialprüfung*, **13**(10), 329–35.
13. Trumpfheller, R. (1966). Abnahmeprüfungen an Schweissnähten nach dem Ultraschallprüfverfahren, *Schweissen und Schneiden*, **18**(6), 268–79.
14. Skorupa, A. *et al.*, (1977). 'Influence of Types of Weld Flaws on Assessment of their size by the DGS Method', International Institute of Welding Annual Assembly 1977, Copenhagen, Denmark. Coll. Comm. V.
15. Stelling, H. A. and Büttner, K. (1974/75). Die Ermittlung von Einflussgrössen auf die Ersatzfehlergrössenbestimmung von realen Schweissfehlern, *Mitteilungsblatt für die amtl. Materialprüfung in Niedersachsen*, No. 14/15.
16. Schröder, K. (1975). Ultraschall-Schweissnahtprüftechnologie für spezielle Schweisskonstruktionen zur Fehlergrössenbestimmung mittels AVG-Methode, *ZIS Mitteilungen*, **17**(8), 923–32.
17. Skorupa, A., Hyrnik, E. and Jedrzejczak, Z. (1972). Bestimmung der wirklichen Fehlergrösse in Stumpfschweissnähten mit Hilfe der AVG-Skalen, *Krautkrämer. Mitteil. zur zerstörungsfreien Werkstoffprüfung mit Ultraschall*, No. 26, 433–4.
18. Richter, H. U. (1969). Zur Bestimmung der wirklichen Ungänzengrösse bei der Ultraschallprüfung von Schweissverbindungen, *ZIS Mitteilungen*, **11**(8), 1235–42.
19. Fujimori, T. (1976). 'Method of Setting Signal Level for Detection in Ultrasonic Angle Beam Testing for Welds in Steel Structures', 8th World Conf. on NDT, Cannes, France, 6–11 Sept.
20. Buken, G. and Krächter, H. (1968). Zur Frage der Fehlergrössenbestimmung in Schweissnähten nach dem Ultraschall-Reflexionsverfahren, *Materialprüfung*, No. 10, 329–37.
21. Rechner, W. (1969). Praktische Ultraschallergebnisse bei der Fehlergrössenbestimmung nach dem AVG-Diagramm, *ZIS Mitteilungen*, No. 8, 1227–34.
22. Richter, H.-U., Linke, D. and Rühe, E. (1969). Zur Bestimmung der Ungänzengrösse bei der Ultraschallprüfung von Schweissverbindungen, *Schweisstechnik Berlin*, **19**.
23. Jedrzejczak, Z. and Skorupa, A. (Sept. 1970). Forschungsergebnisse der polnischen technischen Überwachung bei der Verwendung von AVG-Skalen für die Fehlergrössenbestimmung an Schweissverbindungen', Vorausdrucke, 3. Symposium der Werkstüffprüfung, Pula, Yugoslavia, Vol. 1, No. 16.
24. Linke, D. (1969). Zur Anwendung des AVG-Diagramms bei der Bestimmung der Ungänzengrösse in der Ultraschall-Schweissnahtprüfung, *ZIS Mitteilungen*. **11**(8).
25. Tietz, H.-D. (1970). Informationen über die Fehlergrösse bei der Ultraschall-Materialprüfung und die Einflussfaktoren, *Feingerätetechnik*, **19**(11), 508–9.
26. Link, M. (1977). 'Flaw Evaluation of Welds on Reactor Components', International Institute of Welding Annual Assembly 1977, Copenhagen, Denmark, Coll. Comm V.
27. Wüstenberg, H., Mundry, E. and Kutzner, J. (1976). 'Considerations Concerning the Relationship Between Flaw Detection and Evaluation in Ultrasonic Inspection', Nondestructive Examination Conference, Washington, DC, 18 Nov.

28. Wüstenberg, H. and Mundry, E. (1974). 'Limiting Influences on the Reliability of Ultrasonic In-service Inspection Methods', Conference Proceedings, Periodic Inspection of Pressurised Components, Institution of Mechanical Engineers, London, 4–6 June.
29. Dijkstra, F. H. (1977). 'Flaw Evaluation with Particular References to Flaw Size Estimation', International Institute of Welding Annual Assembly 1977, Copenhagen, Denmark, Coll. Comm V.
30. Mundry, E. and Wüstenberg, H. (1976). 'Criteria for Optimization of Ultrasonic Inspection Systems for Defect Detection and Defect Evaluation', Paper presented at Specialists Meeting on the Ultrasonic Inspection of Reactor Components, at Risley, United Kingdom, 27–29 Sept, organised by OECD.
31. Freedman, A. (1976). 'The Use of Linear System Theory on Acoustic Radiation and Scattering Analysis', Proceedings of Institute of Acoustics Conference on Recent Developments in Underwater Acoustics, March–April, Portland, Dorset.
32. Nabel, E. and Mundry, E. (1978). Evaluation of echoes in ultrasonic testing by deconvolution, *Materials Evaluation*, **36**, 59–61 and 77.
33. Proegler, H. and Kräske, W. 'Anwendung der Ultraschall-Spektrometrie zur Ermittlung von Fehlerart und Fehlergrösse bei der Schweissnahtprüfung', Bericht No. 706, Abschlussbericht BFI, Düsseldorf, July 1978.
34. Barbian, O. A., Klocke, U. and Lotze, W. (1978). 'Fehlerrandrekonstruktion mit Hilfe von Laufzeitortskurven—Ergebnisse von automatischen Prüfungen an Körpern mit natürlichen und künstlichen Fehlern', Proceedings 1st European Conference on NDT, 24–26 April, DGZfP.
34a. Werneyer, R., Walte, F. and Klein, M. (1978). Mathematisches Modell zur Fehlerrekonstruktion bei der Ultraschall-Impulsecho- und Tandemprüfung und Ergebnisse aus Modellversuchen, *Materialprüfung*, **20**(2), 68.
35. 'Möglichkeiten und Grenzen der Fehlerklassierung und Fehlergrösseneinschätzung durch Auswertung der Echodynamik', Technischer Bericht der BAM zum Forschungsvorhaben RS 2703, April 1977 BAM/Berlin.
36. Whaley, H. L. *et al.*, (1977). Measurement of flaw size in a weld sample by ultrasonic frequency analysis, *Materials Evaluation*, **35**(3), 44–50.
37. Silk, M. G. (1976). 'Accurate Crack Depth Measurement in Welded Assemblies', 8th World Conf. on NDT, Cannes, France, Paper 2B16.
38. Charlesworth, J. P. and Silk, M. G. (1977). 'The Role of Ultrasonic Time Domain Analysis in the Sizing of Welds Defects', International Institute of Welding Annual Assembly 1977, Copenhagen, Denmark, Coll. Comm V.
39. Silk, M. G. (May 1979). The transfer of ultrasonic energy in the diffraction technique for crack sizing, *Ultrasonics*, 113–21.
40. de Vadder, D. (1978). 'Dimensioning Badly Oriented Flaws by Means of Focused Probes', 1st International Symposium on Ultrasonic Materials Characterisation, NBS Gaithersburg, Maryland, USA, June 7–9.
41. Wüstenberg, H. and Kutzner, J. (1978). 'Ultraschallanzeigen von Risskanten', Proceedings 1st European Conference on NDT, 24–26 April, DGZfP.
42. Harumi, K. Personal Information presented at 9th World Conference on NDT, Melbourne, 19–23 Nov. 1979.
43. Saglio, R. and Roule, M. 'Focused Ultrasonic Transducers', DMECN-DT-ECS-STA-NT 74, August 1971.

44. Varcin, M. (1975). 'Contrôle Non Destructif Ultrasonore Par Palpeurs Focalises', Compte rendu semestriel d'activité pour la CECA, Bruxelles.
45. Wüstenberg, H., Kutzner, J. and Möhrle, W. (1976). Fokussierende Prüfköpfe zur Verbesserung der Fehlergrössenabschätzung bei der Ultraschallprüfung von dickwandigen Reaktorkomponenten, *Materialprüfung*, **18**(5), 152–61.
46. Wüstenberg, H., Kutzner, J. and Kaps, U. (1977). Empfindlichkeitseinstellung beim Einsatz fokussierender Prüfköpfe in der Ultraschallprüfung an ebenen und gekrümmten Oberflächen, *Materialprüfung*, **19**(10), 441–4.
47. Wüstenberg, H. (March 1978). 'Erfahrungen beim praktischen Einsatz von fokussierenden Prüfköpfen', Seminar Zerstörungsfreie Prüfung in der Kernreaktortechnik, Ultraschallprüfung, IzfP, Saarbrücken.
48. Schulz, E., Wüstenberg, H., Erhard, A. and Möhrle, W. (1979). 'Praktischer Einsatz der Fokuskopftechnik in der Ultraschall-Prüfung', Vortrag bei Vortragstagung Zerstörungsfreie Materialprüfung, der DGZfP, Lindau, Bodensee, FRG, 21–23 Mai.
49. Schlengermann, U. (1974). Schallfeldausbildung bei ebenen Ultraschallquellen mit fokussierenden Linsen, *Acustica*, **30**(6).
50. Dietz, D., Parks, S. J. and Linzer, M. (1978). 'Expanding-Aperture Annular Array', 1st International Symposium on Ultrasonic Materials Characterisation, NBS, Gaithersburg, Maryland, USA, June.
51. Gebhardt, W. and Bonitz, F. (1979). 'Experimente zur Anwendung phasengesteuerter Gruppenstrahler in der Werkstoffprüfung', Vortrag: Vortragstagung Zerstörungsfreie Materialprüfung, der DGZfP, Lindau, Bodensee, FRG, 21–23 Mai.
52. Foulquier, H., Roule, M., Saglio, R. and Touffait, A. M. (1976). 'Application of Focused Ultrasound to Measure the Dimensions of Defects in Welds', Proceedings 8th World Conf. on NDT, Cannes, France, 6–11 Sept. Paper 3H11.
53. Ermert, H. and Karg, R. *Multifrequency Acoustical Holography*, to be published by IEEE.
54. Karg, R. and Ermert, H. (1974). Ein multifrequentes, quasi-holographisches Abbildungssystem im Mikrowellenbereich, *Nachrichtentechnische Zeitschrift*, **27**, 369–72.
55. Collins, H. D. and Gribble, R. P. 'PVRC Plate-Weld-Specimen 201 Inspection by Acoustic Holography', Holosonics, Inc. Report, 22 pp., Sept. 1972.
56. Holt, A. E. (1976). 'Characterization of Defects in Thick-Walled Pressure Vessels Using Acoustic Holography', 3rd Conference, Periodic Inspection, London, pp. 165–71.
57. Schmitz, V. and Wosnitza, M. (1978). 'Erfahrungen beim Einsatz der Ultraschall-Holographie mit numerischer und optischer Rekonstruktion', Tagung Zerstörungsfreie Materialprüfung der DGZfP, Mainz, FRG, 24–26 April.
58. Ando, Y. *et al.*, 'Study of Flaw Size Measurement by Acoustical Holography', NUREG/TR-0034, August 1978, 35 pp.
59. Aldridge, E. E. *et al.*, (1977). Ultrasonic holography in the inspection of rotor forgings, *NDT International*, **10**(3), 115–20.
60. Kutzner, J., Zimpfer, J. and Wüstenberg, H. (1978). 'Parameterwahl bei der numerischen Ultraschall-Holographie', Tagung Zerstörungsfreie Materialprüfung der DGZfP, Mainz, FRG, 24–26 April.

61. Kutzner, J. and Wüstenberg, H. (1976). Akustische Holographie in Tandemanordnung ein Hilfsmittel zur Fehleranzeigeninterpretation in der Ultraschallprüfung, *Materialprüfung*, **18**(12), 462–5.

62. Kutzner, J. and Wüstenberg, H. (1976). 'Akustische Linienholographie'; Vortrag Vortragstagung Zerstörungsfreie Materialprüfung der DGZfP, 24–26 May, Lahnstein.

63. Wüstenberg, H., Mundry, E. and Kutzner, J. (1978). 'Experiences with Flaw Size Estimation by Ultrasonic Holography with Numerical Reconstruction', Proceedings International Conference on Nondestructive Evaluation in the Nuclear Industry, Salt Lake City, Utah, USA, 13–15 February.

64. Posakony, G. J., Becker, F. L., Crow, V. L., Doctor, S. R., Davis, T. J. and Hildebrand, B. P. (1979). 'An Ultrasonic Linear Array System for Pulse Echo and Holographic Imaging of Flaws in Solids BN-SA-942', Proceedings Conference on Periodic Inspection for Pressurized Components, organised by the Institution of Mechanical Engineers, London, 8–10 May.

65. Flora, J. H., Holt, A. E. and Brophy, J. W. (1979). 'Defect Characterization with Computerised Ultrasonic Holography', Proceedings Conference on Periodic Inspection for Pressurized Components, organised by the Institution of Mechanical Engineers, London, 8–10 May.

66. Frederick, J. R., Ganapathy, S., van den Broek, C. and Elsinga, M. B. (1979). 'Improved Characterization of Discontinuities in Thick-Walled Pressure Vessels', Proceedings Conference on Periodic Inspection for Pressurized Components, Institution of Mechanical Engineers, London, 8–10 May.

67. Jackson, J. L. 'Program for Field Validation of the Synthetic Aperture Focussing Technique for Ultrasonic Testing (SAFT-UT)' Midyear Progress Report, NUREG/CR-0290, 1978.

68. Wüstenberg, H., Erhard, A. and Kutzner, J. (1978). 'Detection and Analysis of Near-Surface-Cracks by Ultrasound', Proceedings 1st International Symposium on Ultrasonic Materials Characterization, Gaithersburg, Maryland, USA, 7–9 June.

69. Pohlmann, R. (1939). Über die Möglichkeit einer akustischen Abbildung in Analogie zur optischen, *Zeitschrift für Physik*, **113**, 697–709.

70. Suarez, J. R., Marich, K. W., Holzemer, J. F., Taenzer, J. and Green, P. S. 'Biomedical Imaging with the SRJ Ultrasonic Camera', *Acoustical Holography*, Vol. 6 (Edited by N. Booth), Plenum Pub Co., London, 1977.

71. Böttcher, B., Schulz, E. and Wüstenberg, H. (1973). 'A New Method for Crack-Depth Determination in Ultrasonic-Materials-Testing', 7th International Conference on NDT, Warschau, Poland, June.

72. Wüstenberg, H. and Schulz, E. 'Risstiefenbestimmung bei der Ultraschall-prüfung mit der Streuanzeigentechnik', vorgetragen beim Unterausschuss Zerstörungsfreie Prüfung beim Werkstoffausschuss des VDEh, Oct. 1973.

73. de Raad, J. A. (RTD Rotterdam), (1975). 'ISI-Experience on Reactor Pressure Vessel with Cracks', Lecture held on May 24th in San Antonio, Texas, USA during PSI and ISI Seminar, organised by Southwest Institute.

74. Rose, J., Mast, P. and Niklas, L. (1975). The Potential of 'Simulearning' in Flaw Characterization, *Brit. J. NDT*, **XVII**(6), 176–81.

75. Mucciardi, A. N., Loew, M. H. and Elsley, R. K. (1978). 'Application of Adaptive Learning Networks to Ultrasonic Signal Processing: Classifying

Flaws in Multi-Layered Adhesively Bonded Structures', 1st International Symposium on Ultrasonic Materials Characterization, National Bureau of Standards, Gaithersburg, Maryland, USA, June.

76. Gubernatis, J. E., Domany, E., Huberman, M. and Krumhansl, J. A. (1975). 'Theory of Scattering of Ultrasound by Flaws', Proceedings 1975 Ultrasonics Symposium (IEEE, NY, USA) p. 107.

77. Pao, Y. H. and Sachse, W. (1974). Interpretation of Time Record and Power Spectra of Scattered Ultrasonic Pulses in Solids, *J. Acoust. Soc. Amer.*, **56**, 1478.

78. Thompson, R. B. and Evans, A. G. (Sept. 1976). Goals and Objectives of Quantitative Ultrasonics, *IEEE Transactions on Sonics and Ultrasonics*, **SU-23**(5).

7

Ultrasonic Testing Applied to Austenitic Steel

P. Caussin

Association Vinçotte, Belgium

SUMMARY

The physical background of the interaction of ultrasonic waves with an austenitic structure is reviewed in terms of effect on the attenuation and the velocities of waves. It is shown that no general rule can be drawn from available data. The examination techniques in use and under development are described. The emphasis is put on the performances of dedicated search units routinely used in the field.

1. INTRODUCTION

Austenitic stainless steels are used to manufacture a large variety of industrial components such as pipes, valves, pumps, etc. Weldments are also made to join these parts or to attach them to other carbon steel items. These welds are usually made of stainless steel or inconel alloys. The austenitic steels are sophisticated materials and justification for their use in delicate components is in regard to the safety and reliability aspects. They are mainly used in nuclear and petro-chemical plants.

These steels, as any other materials, need to be inspected to assess their structural integrity. Ultrasonic testing is one of the possible techniques. In some cases it is the only technique practically applicable. This mainly concerns components of the primary and auxiliary circuits of nuclear plants.

For a long time it has been recognised that most stainless steel items can be very difficult to inspect with ultrasonics. Researches were conducted in the author's organisation, as in other laboratories, to improve the technique. In the early 70s, the first encouraging results were obtained which made possible the inspection of welds in the primary circuits of nuclear plants [1].

This communication is based upon results gained through house research programmes and field practice as well as upon information collected for a state-of-the-art report prepared for the OECD (Organisation for Economic Co-operation and Development)/CEC (Commission of European Communities)—CSNI (Committee on the Safety of Nuclear Installations) Working Group on Safety Aspects of Steel Components in Nuclear Installations [2]. The next paragraph will deal with the physical background of the technique and will be followed by a short description of methods in use and under development. The actual performances and remaining problems will then be reviewed.

2. PHYSICAL BACKGROUND

The fundamental background of the ultrasonic technique is the interaction between high frequency acoustic waves and their sustaining material. In this section the main facts will be described about the structure of austenitic stainless steels and their influence upon the attenuation and the velocity of ultrasonic pulsed waves.

2.1. Microstructure of Austenitic Stainless Steels

The austenitic stainless steels of concern (ASME types 304 and 316) are obtained by adding a suitable amount of nickel and chromium to a molten low carbon steel. This alloy is then poured. When cooling down, various microstructures can build up depending on the exact chemical composition and the casting method. Dendritic, columnar and equiaxed structures are possible. In that process, large grains develop. When structurally refined either by heat treatment or cold or hot working, the grains can be shortened and become equiaxed. Nevertheless, forming and forging processes can induce another oriented structure parallel to the direction of the metal flow. In welds, the grains grow by epitaxy along the heat dissipation lines. Figure 1 shows two different microstructures of centrifugally cast ASTM A351–CF8M steels. Figure 2 shows a multi-pass weld joining a cast and an extruded pipe made of ASME type 316 stainless steels. These figures point out the diversity of structures which can be present even in nominally identical items.

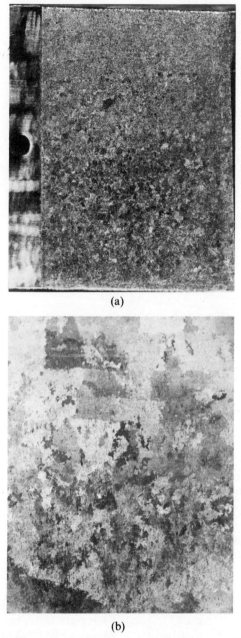

(a)

(b)

FIG. 1.   Full thickness macrographs of centrifugally cast austenitic steel pipes, 800 mm diameter, 62 mm thick. Material: ASTM A 351–CF8A. (Internal surfaces at top of macrographs, external surfaces at bottom.)

FIG. 2.   Macrograph of a 35-mm thick butt weld. Left: ASME TP316 extruded
pipe. Right: ASTM A351–CF8M cast pipe.

2.2. Ultrasonic Attenuation in Austenitic Structures

2.2.1. Grain Size

The austenitic grain size is generally recognised as the most important factor regarding the ultrasonic attenuation. Early in 1963, Holmes [3] pointed out that the attenuation factor α increases with the average grain size, D. Further studies [4, 5] showed that scattering played the most important rôle in the attenuation of ultrasonic waves and was a function of the grain size to wavelength ratio (D/λ). Other experiments [6] revealed that dependence can be thrown out when the steel contains a ferritic phase. Other conflicting results were reported [7]. Furthermore, simple experiments can demonstrate that samples with very different grain size have similar attenuation factors as in the case of the steels shown at Fig. 1.

Those observations indicate that if the grain size of austenitic steel items is clearly responsible for the difficulties encountered when ultrasonically testing them, this parameter has not an isolated character and must be associated with other structural peculiarities.

2.2.2. Grain to Wave Orientation

It was measured by X-ray diffractometry that in welds the grains preferentially grow parallel to the $\langle 100 \rangle$ crystallographic axis [8, 9] and form elongated zones. It has for a long time been recognised that the ultrasonic waves undergo less attenuation when directed along the main axis of the grains than when propagating transversally. This point was recently verified by Kupperman *et al.* [9, 10]. The difference increases with the frequency.

These observations are in agreement with the ones of Murray [6] but she specified that the attenuation was also minimum at an incidence angle of 60° with regard to the grain axis. A maximum in attenuation also appeared at 30° in both ferritic and austenitic cast steels. The difference was 3 to 10 dB/mm in stainless steel and 6 to 15 dB/mm in ferritic steel. Baikie *et al.* [8] also found that the ultrasonic waves underwent less attenuation when directed towards the grains with a certain angle. They measured a minimum attenuation factor (0·05 dB/mm) at 45° of incidence and a maximum one (0·4 dB/mm) at 0 and 90° of incidence. These observations were recently confirmed [2, 7]. One nevertheless observes in some results [2] that the attenuation factor, if minimum at 45°, is also less important at 0° than at 90° (Table I). The

TABLE I
LONGITUDINAL WAVE ATTENUATION FACTOR IN DENDRITIC, AUSTENITIC STRUCTURES (dB/mm) (FOLLOWING YONEYAMA *et al.* [24])

| *Wave to grain orientation* | *Frequency* | |
	2 MHz	5 MHz
0°	0·25	0·5
45°	0·15	0·22
90°	0·43	0·75

above results show that the situation is not yet very clearly understood. If it is obvious that the orientation of the ultrasonic beam in regard to the austenitic grains plays a rôle, the present observations cannot be used to draw a general conclusion. It was also suggested that some attention be paid to the possible effect of velocities and beam geometry [2].

The above considerations mainly concern longitudinal waves. The situation for transverse waves seems to be less disturbing. Indeed, the transverse waves can be polarised in different directions orthogonal to the propagation direction. Serabian [11] and Kupperman *et al.* [9, 10, 12] showed that transverse waves are less attenuated than longitudinal waves of equal wavelength when the polarisation vector is parallel to major interfaces encountered or to the grain axis.

2.2.3. Carbide Precipitates
In general, it is recognised that the carbide precipitates content has no

major influence on attenuation. Nevertheless, it was observed [2] that the presence of precipitates at the grain boundaries increased the dependence of the attenuation factor on the wavelength of transverse waves.

Other experimenters [2] did not observe any effect of carbide precipitates content but pointed out that when the stainless steels are heat treated above 1100 °C the carbides leave the grain boundaries and enter in solid solution. This process could destroy the preferred orientation of the grains and the structure would become highly attenuating in all directions.

2.2.4. Ferrite Content

There is a big controversy about the effect of the ferrite content in austenitic welds and castings. Holmes and Beasley [13] and Neumann *et al.* [5] did not record any effect of the ferrite content upon attenuation even in the range of 5 to 30% in 18/11 type stainless steel. On the other hand Richter [4] and others [2] reported an exponential decreasing effect of ferrite content in the range of 0 to 20%. According to Murray [6], 5% of ferrite kills the influence of the grain size and no ferrite allows the grain size effect for $D > \lambda$.

Juva and Haavisto [7] recorded contradictory effects of the ferrite content. They suggested that the ferrite distribution could be more important than its content. It is also recognised that less than 5% of ferrite could lead to the appearance of microcracks (USAEC's Regulatory Guides 1.31 and 1.44). Thus it is possible that the adverse effect of a low ferrite content upon attenuation is due to microcracking of the structure.

2.2.5. Microcracks

In austenitic stainless steels microcracking is associated with a liquation process and is enhanced by a low ferrite content and thermal cycling. Only a few papers [2] deal with the microcrack content effect. They all point out that it dramatically increases the attenuation in welds.

2.2.6. Propagation Mode

As a general rule, all experimenters [2] measured, in stainless steel, a stronger attenuation of transverse waves than of longitudinal waves. On the other hand, Neumann *et al.* [5, 14] and others [2] found similar attenuation factors for longitudinal and transverse waves in worked materials provided the wavelength is kept constant.

Recently Kupperman *et al.* [9, 10, 12] showed that the attenuation of transverse waves mainly depends upon the wave polarisation in regard to the propagation direction in crystallographically oriented structures such as welds and castings. Optimal polarisation would assure less attenuation for transverse waves than for longitudinal ones.

2.2.7. *Wavelength and Frequency*

Many experimental results have been published on the effect of either the frequency or wavelength upon wave attenuation [2]. Every one confirms that the attenuation increases with the frequency. Romer *et al.* [15] specified that the importance of this effect depends on the structure of the material. For instance, plotting the attenuation factor versus frequency revealed similar slopes for worked base material and castings but at an order of magnitude of difference. The same plot showed a much higher slope for welds but at intermediate levels between base materials and castings.

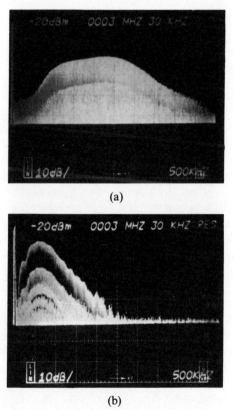

(a)

(b)

FIG. 3. Spectrum analysis of bottom wall echoes from 60-mm thick test blocks (a): carbon steel; (b): ASTM A351–CF8A centrifugally cast austenitic steel.

Serabian [11] also showed that dendritic structures can behave like stopband filters preventing some frequencies to propagate.

The frequency of ultrasonic waves propagating in a centrifugally cast structure (ASTM A351–CF8A) was studied by Caussin and Cermak [16, 17]. They used a 2·25 MHz, 25·4 mm diameter normal probe. Frequency spectra of bottom wall echoes obtained in carbon steel and the cast austenitic steel, both 60 mm in thickness, are presented at Fig. 3. They also showed that a beam can be partitioned in fillets having different frequencies. This phenomenon leads to a beating effect causing the echoes to oscillate with an amplitude ratio of ± 2 dB.

TABLE II
FREQUENCY DEPENDENCE OF THE S:N RATIO IN FINE
GRAIN STAINLESS STEEL (FOLLOWING ERMOLOV AND
PILIN [18])

Reflector shape	Near field	Far field
Disc	$f^{1-n/2}$	$f^{2-n/2}$
Sphere and cylinder	$f^{1-n/2}$	$f^{1-n/2}$

$n = 2$ to 4 depending on the scattering process.

Ermolov and Pilin [18] made a theoretical analysis of the signal-to-noise (S:N) ratio encountered when ultrasonic testing fine grain austenitic steels ($D < \lambda$). They found that the S:N ratio should vary with the frequency and depends upon the shape and the position of the reflector either in the near or the far field. The frequency dependence is indicated in Table II. They also indicated that the flaw echoes are less sensitive to frequency variations than the structural noise. Furthermore Mech and Michaels [19] noticed that the flaw echoes are more broad banded than the noise.

2.2.8. Ultrasonic Beam Profile

It is known that for measuring the grain size of metals, it is necessary to enlarge as much as possible the volume of material covered by the emitted ultrasonic pulses. For ultrasonic testing of austenitic steels, it therefore seems obvious that conversely an as thin as possible ultrasonic beam should be used [18]. In specific experiments Richter [4] agreed with that conclusion and promoted the use of twin crystal transmitter–receiver (T–R) probes. In such a design the energy going back to the receiver is expected to come only from the zone where the beams relate to each crystal overlap.

Grebennikov and Sotnichenko [20] reduced still further the beam spread by a focusing technique. They got very good results with a focused angle probe, 1·2 MHz, transverse wave. Such probes were intensively developed in France. Elliptic crystals have also been used by Just *et al.* [21] to obtain longitudinal wave angle probes emitting beams with a circular cross-section. Nevertheless, Iotchev and Pawloski [22] showed that a coarse structure can substantially modify the geometry of an ultrasonic beam. To illustrate that effect, the beam spread of a 2·25 MHz, 25·4 mm diameter normal probe was compared using the blocks corresponding to Fig. 3. Figure 4 shows the difference which can exist. In welds, Edelmann and

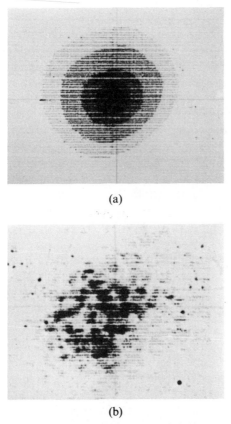

(a)

(b)

FIG. 4. Beam spread of a 25·4 mm diameter, 2·25 MHz normal beam probe at 60 mm of metal path. Limits at 2, 6, 14 dB drop. (a): fine grain carbon steel; (b): centrifugally cast austenitic steel.

Hornung [23] and Yoneyama *et al.* [24] showed that a columnar structure could entrap the beams and orient them in a completely different way. For instance, an angle probe could be transformed in a straight beam probe.

The above measurements show that although improvements were achieved by better design of ultrasonic beam profiles, a coarse austenitic structure can strongly deviate and scatter the ultrasonic beams.

2.2.9. *Ultrasonic Pulse*

It is generally agreed that an as short as possible ultrasonic pulse should be used for ultrasonic testing of austenitic steel structures. This point is confirmed by the theoretical work of Ermolov and Pilin [18].

2.3. Ultrasonic Velocities in Austenitic Structures

In practical tests the ultrasonists have very often experienced strong differences in ultrasonic velocities. Usually no straightforward correlation could be found between austenitic steel pieces, even though produced in the same way. Baikie *et al.* [8] associated this fact with the presence of a crystallographically oriented structure. Indeed, in that case, the velocities depend upon the elastic constants related to the crystallographic axes. They found that the fastest direction of propagation was at 50° of incidence in regard to the grain axis. These grains were supposed to be parallel to the $\langle 100 \rangle$ crystallographic axis. Kupperman and Reimann [10, 12] made the same kind of analysis for longitudinal waves and two transverse waves polarised in orthogonal directions. For a single crystal of an ASME 304 type stainless steel, they calculated that the velocities ranged as follows:

$$\text{Transverse waves: } v_t = 2120\text{–}4040\,\text{m/s}$$

$$\text{Longitudinal waves: } v_1 = 5320\text{–}6570\,\text{m/s}$$

They also observed, like others [2], that less attenuation was encountered when the waves propagated with a higher velocity. This fact implies that the wavelength is proportionally longer. In any case the practical range of velocities measured by most experimentalists [2] fits very well the one calculated by Kupperman and Reimann. It should also be borne in mind that such a range causes the refracted beam angle associated with angle probes to widely vary from piece to piece and even in one single piece of austenitic steel according to the relative orientation of the beam in regard to the austenitic structure. The error could be as high as 30 % of the nominal angle or, for a 70° angle probe, the waves could not exist any more due to total reflection. When the velocities vary in a piece, this fact implies that the waves can be reflected, refracted, and mode converted in many different ways leading to increased attenuation and apparent beam curvature. This effect could explain the wave guide property of dendrites and the deviation of beams.

3. TECHNIQUES

Most of the techniques described below are still at a development stage. Only special probes are routinely used with standard equipment.

3.1. Special Probes

The first improvement in the inspection technique of austenitic steel components was gained through the use of special probes. Nevertheless, standard transverse wave angle probes are still in use for the inspection of welds (less than 20 mm thick) and of heat-affected zones through a fine grain base material. Frequencies used are 2 to 5 MHz [16, 17]. Special transverse wave angle probes were also developed [2] for the inspection of thin items. A refracted angle of 45° with a 1·5 MHz central frequency and a medium bandwidth were estimated to be more effective in that case.

In thicker materials, the longitudinal wave angle probes were found more suitable [1]. Now normal and miniature probes are commercially available. Their frequencies range from 1 to 4 MHz, and their angle from 45 to 70°.

Several designs exist:

(1) TR probes are often used as they give a better signal-to-noise ratio in adverse conditions, but their use is often limited because of their larger size.
(2) Focused probes either single or twin crystal are also commercially available—the focusing effect is obtained through either an acoustic lens or a semi-spherical transducer.
(3) Special beam shaping is obtained with the aid of elliptical [21] or annular [15] transducers.

Recently Kupperman *et al.* [9] proposed transverse wave probes with a polarisation direction orthogonal to the usual one. However it is still very difficult to effectively couple such waves to the piece to be inspected.

3.2. Synthetic Beam Forming

Frederick *et al.* [25] developed a computerised technique providing high resolution in the inspected volume. This technique is called Synthetic Aperture Focusing Technique for Ultrasonic Testing (SAFT–UT) and could compete with sharp focus probe, phased array probe, and acoustic holography. Phase combination, convolution and averaging methods are used to artificially generate a sharp focus beam in the material. Application to stainless steel is in progress.

3.3. Pulse Wobbling

To improve the signal-to-noise ratio Crostack and Steffens [26] proposed to modulate in amplitude the radio-frequency pulse exciting a wide band transducer. The modulating signal is the first, second or third power of a triangle. In that way the frequency bandwidth of the emitted pulse can be optimised. This special excitation method is coupled to a tuned receiving circuitry. When the emitter and the receiver are set up in the proper way, peculiar for each inspected structure, the signal-to-noise ratio enhancement can reach several decibels. Deutsch and Vogt [27] proposed equipment based on that principle.

3.4. Pulse Compression

In order to transfer more power into the inspected piece, Linzer (quoted by Caussin [2]) proposed a pulse compression technique. A swept frequency pulse is emitted with the aid of a wide band transducer. Such a pulse can be very long and severely affect the resolution. To restore that resolution the received echoes are connected to a dispersive filter. The frequencies travel at different speeds and are compressed in time at the filter output. Till now a compression ratio of 8 has been achieved.

3.5. Beam Variation

Considering that in the far field the flaw echoes vary with the beam spread and the noise echoes do not, Ermolov and Pilin [18] proposed to periodically modify the beam shape. Therefore only varying echoes will be associated with flaws. This technique requires that the power be kept constant at the emission.

3.6. Accumulation Techniques

Koryachenko [28] observed that when the conditions at the emission are constant, the noise is stochastic in one single period but correlated at identical moments in each period. When destroying the correlation it is possible to use an accumulation (averaging) technique to improve the signal-to-noise ratio. Accordingly it is proposed to periodically shift the excitation frequency and to accumulate the signals during several periods.

Ermolov and Pilin [18] and Linzer (quoted by Caussin [2]) dealt with that problem in the opposite way. They observed that when moving the probe slightly a flaw echo is less affected than the structural noise. Hence it is proposed to accumulate several periods during the probe movement (spatial averaging).

3.7. Multi-frequency Analysis

Considering that the flaw echoes are less sensitive to frequency variation than the structural noise, Ermolov and Pilin [18] proposed to emit wide band pulses and to receive them through a series of frequency filters. It is expected that the flaw echoes will have equivalent amplitude at the output of several filters whereas the noise amplitude will vary more drastically. This technique requires that the beam be kept equal to itself even when changing the frequency.

3.8. Frequency Analysis

Mech and Michaels [19] investigated the efficiency of using the power spectral density and its momentums of the 0th to the 2nd order:

$$M_i = \int_0^\infty w^i p(w)\, \mathrm{d}w \qquad i = 0, 1, 2 \tag{1}$$

where

$$p(w) = A_w^2 + B_w^2 \tag{2}$$

with A_w and B_w representing the Fourier transform coefficients. In a practical experiment they showed that M_2 (eqn (1)) best distinguished the flaw echoes.

3.9. Cross Correlation Technique

Mech and Michaels [19] experimented with a cross correlation method taking a calibration echo as the reference. This method was not found to be more effective than the standard A-scan presentation.

3.10. Crack Tip Measurement

de Raad and de Sterke [29] and Silk *et al.* [30] proposed the use of a scatter interception technique (also called the time domain measurement technique) for measuring the depth of cracks lying perpendicular to the testing surface. This method seems to be effective in fine grain materials but leads to large uncertainty for subcladding cracks for instance.

3.11. Adaptive Learning Network

Shankar *et al.* [31] developed a computerised system based upon advanced signal analysis methods. In this system, called the Adaptive Learning Network, a computer is trained to recognise signal attributes. First, the system is taught a series of typical cases. The system then adapts its decision network to provide a diagnosis. The system is used for the detection and the evaluation of intergranular stress corrosion cracking (IGSCC) of small pipes. Good results were obtained in the laboratory. A field system was developed and will be evaluated.

4. PERFORMANCES

The new techniques such as those described in Sections 3.2 to 3.11 are not yet regularly applied in the field. Thus, the information given below mainly concerns the application of special probes and procedures in a straight pulse–echo technique.

4.1. Flaw Detection

Referring to the physical limitations outlined in Section 2, one is obliged to acknowledge that flaw detection in austenitic structures is still questionable and at least far lower than in carbon steel. At the present time, each particular situation must be evaluated and laboratory tests performed to assess the efficiency of the planned technique. During field tests, the status of the art allowed the following conclusions to be drawn:

(1) For inspecting thin components, less than 15 mm in thickness, miniature transverse wave angle probes proved to be able to disclose flaws of 1 mm in height as well as full thickness cracks [16, 17]. Figures 5 and 6 are examples of these performances. These are often impaired by the presence of spurious echoes. Their shape can sometimes enable them to be recognised. In practice, simple modifications of the weld preparation and of the welding procedure often eliminated the problem.

(2) For thicker components, transverse wave angle probes can still be used when the base material is finely grained. Their efficiency is nevertheless limited to the heat-affected zones. The welds require longitudinal waves at 2 or 4 MHz. The detectability achieved with such a probe and an ASME procedure is illustrated at Fig. 7 [17].

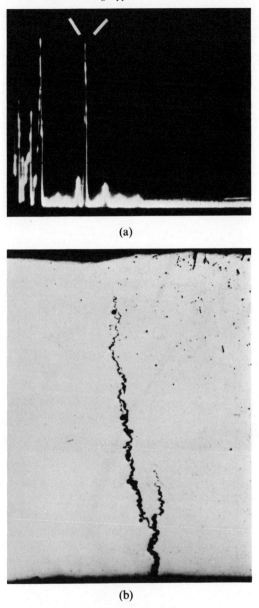

(a)

(b)

FIG. 5.   Detectability of a crack situated in the heat-affected zone of a 5·5 mm thick
weld. (a): ultrasonic response obtained with a standard 70° angle probe, 4 MHz; (b):
macrograph.

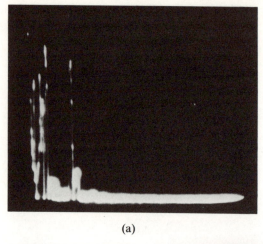

(a)

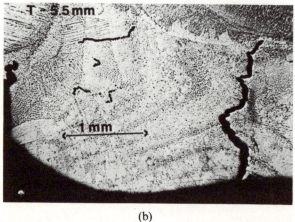

(b)

FIG. 6. Detectability of root defects in a 5·5-mm thick weld. (a): ultrasonic response obtained with a standard 70° angle probe, 4 MHz; (b): macrograph.

(3) For cast pieces, low frequency longitudinal wave probes are mandatory. Till now a sensitivity as required by the ASME code was obtained in castings up to 100 mm in thickness, even in centrifugally cast pieces. In this case, 1 MHz, T–R probes are necessary (Fig. 8).

4.2. Flaw Location
Due to the anisotropy of the velocity distribution in austenitic structures,

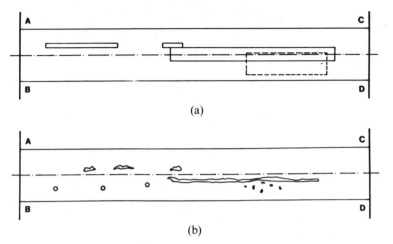

(a)

(b)

FIG. 7. 'C-scan' results of the ultrasonic (a) and radiographic (b) examination of a 49·2-mm thick butt weld.

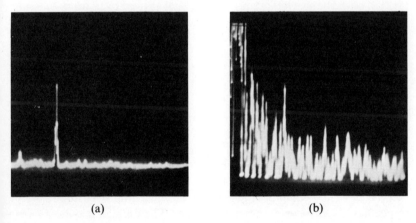

(a)   (b)

FIG. 8. Echoes from a 4·7-mm diameter, 30-mm deep hole drilled in a centrifugally cast block. (a): longitudinal wave, 1 MHz, 45° angle probe; (b): standard, 2 MHz, 45° angle probe.

it is generally recognised that the accuracy of flaw location in those structures is rather poor. Iotchev and Pawloski [22] proposed a theoretical explanation of the observed curved wavepath of ultrasonic beams. This is based on the propagation theory in layered media. Other authors [24] insisted on the wave guide effect of dendrites.

Further, the problem is amplified by the use of longitudinal wave angle probes. Indeed, we cannot avoid a transverse wave beam being simultaneously emitted [1]. When testing through a low attenuation base material, this can lead to a rather confusing situation as the 'parasitic' beam travels at about half the velocity of the main beam and it carries a not negligible energy.

Although these phenomena impair the reliability of the technique for location, in practice quite acceptable results were obtained as shown at Fig. 7.

4.3. Flaw Identification

It is generally recognised that the present technique does not allow the identification of detected reflectors [2].

4.4. Flaw Sizing

Due to the anisotropy of velocity and attenuation, the classical sizing methods, such as DGS, 6 or 20 dB drop, etc., are rejected by most experts [2]. Till now, the sharp focus probes have not proved to be more accurate. Only the ALN technique provided good results in specific tests. It is still to be evaluated during field tests.

5.   CONCLUSION

The physics of the interaction of ultrasonic waves with an austenitic structure is still not largely understood. One can only retain from present studies the fact that the austenitic microstructure and the ultrasonic beam characteristics play a definite rôle in the detectability and evaluation of structural flaws. The structure also generates varying wave velocities. Nevertheless, new equipment was developed which improved quite a bit the inspectability of austenitic steel components. The simplest and most widely used in the field are special probes emitting refracted longitudinal waves at low frequencies (1 to 4 MHz). They allow inspection of items up to 100 mm in thickness, even if they are centrifugally cast. The ASME code sensitivity can be achieved but the actual performances of a given equipment should always be evaluated and new probes eventually designed to meet special conditions.

At present, the ultrasonic technique allows detection of flaws higher than 1 mm in items 5 to 100 mm thick. The reliability of this performance was not studied and is expected to vary widely from case to case. The ability to locate flaws, although low in principle, seems to be quite acceptable in practice. Till now, acceptance of flaws was based mainly upon the echo amplitude, although large variations were expected.

The present study suggests that researches be conducted to:

(1) analyse the interaction of ultrasonic waves with the austenitic structures,
(2) eliminate the spurious echoes in welds with insufficient preparation (root geometry, welding procedure),
(3) improve the inspectability of thick castings, and
(4) assess the reliability of performances.

REFERENCES

1. Pelseneer, J. P. and Louis, G. (July 1974). Ultrasonic testing of austenitic steel castings and welds, *Br. J. NDT*, 107–113.
2. Caussin, P., 'Ultrasonic Testing of Austenitic Stainless Steel Structures', Vinçotte report to OECD/CEC-CSNI-Working Group on Safety Aspects of Steel Components in Nuclear Installations, OECD-NEA. Ref. SINDOC (78) 190, Revision 2, Sept. 14, 1978.
3. Holmes, E. (1963). Ultrasonic scatter in austenitic stainless steel, *Appl. Mat. Research*, 181–4.
4. Richter, H. V. (1968). Zur Ultraschallprüfung austenitischer Schweiss-verbindungen (Teil I–II), *Die Techniek*, No. 23, 610–19, 692–6.
5. Kuhlow, B., Roemer, M., Neumann, E. and Matthies, K. (1976). Ultrasonic Testing of Austenitic Steel Weld Joints', Proceedings 8th World Conference on Non-destructive Testing, Cannes, France, September 6–11.
6. Murray, R. M. (June 1969). Ultrasonic attenuation in austenitic steels—A review of the association's work, *J. of Research SCRATA*, 31–43.
7. Juva, A. and Haavisto, M. (Nov. 1977). On the effect of microstructure on the attenuation of ultrasonic waves in austenitic stainless steels, *Br. J. NDT*, 293–7.
8. Baikie, B. L., Wagg, A. R., Whittle, M. J. and Yapp, D. (March 1976). 'Ultrasonic Inspection of Austenitic Welds', Paper for presentation at the IAEA, IWGFR on in-service inspection at Bensberg, 6 p.
9. Kupperman, D. S., Reimann, K. J. and Fiore, N. F. (April 1978). Rôle of microstructure in ultrasonic inspectability of austenitic stainless steel welds, *Mat. Eval.*, 70–74, 80.
10. Kupperman, D. S. and Reimann, K. J. (1976). 'Effects of Microstructure on Ultrasonic Examination of Stainless Steel', Paper presented at the CSNI Specialists' Meeting on the Ultrasonic Inspection of Reactor Components, Risley, September 27–29, 10 p.
11. Proceedings of NDE Experts Workshop on Austenitic Pipe Inspection. Electrical Power Research Institute (EPRI) SR-30, Special Report, 123 p., (February 1976).

12. Kupperman, D. S. and Reimann, K. J. (Jan. 1978). Effect of shear-wave polarization on defect detection in stainless steel weld metal, *Ultrasonics*, 21–27.
13. Holmes, E. and Beasley, D. (1962). The influence of microstructure in the ultrasonic examination of stainless steel welds, *J. Iron and Steel Inst.*, 283–90.
14. Neumann, E., Wustenberg, N., Nagel, E. and Leisner, W. (1974). 'The Ultrasonic Testing of Welds in Austenitic Steels', Proceedings of the Int. Conf. on Quality Control and Non-destructive Testing in Welding, London, November 19–21, Paper 21, pp. 115–120.
15. Romer, M., Just, T., Matthies, K. and Neumann, E. (1978). 'Erfachungen bei der ultraschallprüfung ebener und gekrümmtes austenitischer Bauteile', Vortrafstagung und Ausstellung Zerstorungsfreie Materialprüfung, Mainz, FRG, 24–26 April.
16. Caussin, P. and Cermak, J. (1978). 'Field Efficiency of Ultrasonic Testing of Austenitic Steel Components', Proceedings of Nuclex 78, Basle, Switzerland, October 2–9, 10 p.
17. Caussin, P. and Cermak, J. (1979). 'Performances of the Ultrasonic Examination of Austenitic Steel components', Presented at the Conference on Periodic Inspection for Pressurized Components, London, May 8–10.
18. Ermolov, I. N. and Pilin, B. P. (Dec. 1976). Ultrasonic inspection of material with coarse grain anisotropical structures, *NDT Int.*, 275–80.
19. Mech, S. J. and Michaels, T. E. (July 1977). Development of ultrasonic examination methods for austenitic stainless steel weld inspection, *Mat Eval.*, 81–86.
20. Grebennikov, V. V. and Sotnichenko, A. L. (Dec. 1971). Influence of ultrasonic frequency and focusing on the condition for flaw detections in austenitic welds, *Welding Production*, No. 18, 34–7.
21. Just, T., Romer, E., Neumann, E. and Mundry, E. (1978). 'Vergleich der Leistungsfähigheit verschiedener Ultraschallprüftechniken für groskristalline Werkstoffe mittels statistischer Methoden', Vortrafstagung und Ausstellung Zerstörungsfreie Materialprüfung, Mainz, FRG, 24–26 April.
22. Iotchev, B. and Pawloski, Z. (1976). 'Effect of Material Acoustic Anisotropy on the Shape of Ultrasonic Wave Beam', Paper presented at the 8th World Conf. on NDT, Cannes, France, 6–11 September, No. 3F10, 7 p.
23. Edelmann, X. and Hornung, R. (1977). Erfahrungen im Prüfen von austenitischen Schweissverbindungen mit Ultraschall, *Mat. u. Techn.*, No. 1, 19–29.
24. Yoneyama, H., Shibata, S. and Kishigami, M. (Feb. 1978). Ultrasonic testing of austenitic stainless steel welds—False indications and the cause of their occurrence, *NDT Int.*, 3–8.
25. Frederick, J. R., Vandenbroek, C. J. H., Fairchild, R. C. and Elzinga, M. B., 'Improved Ultrasonic Non-destructive Testing of Pressure Vessels', Univ. of Michigan Report to US-NRC, NUREG/CR-0135, R5, May 1978. 94 p.
26. Crostack, H.-A. and Steffens, H.-D. (1978). 'Untersuchungen zur Steuerung von Ultraschallimpulsen und ihr Einsatz in der zerstörungsfreien Werkstoffprüfung', Vortragstagung und Ausstellung Zerstörungsfreie Materialprüfung, Mainz, FRG, 24–26 April.

27. Deutsch, V. and Vogt, M. (1978). 'Verbesserte Lösung verscheidener Ultraschallprüfprobleme durch Wahl eines optimalen Sendespektrums', Vortragstagung und Ausstellung Zerstörungsfreie Materialprüfung, Mainz, FRG, 24–26 April.
28. Koryachenko, V. D. (Jan–Feb 1975). Statistical processing of flaw detector signals to enhance the signal-to-noise ratio associated with structural reverberation noise, *Sov. J. NDT.*, 69–75.
29. de Raad, J. A. and de Sterke, A. (1976). 'Ultrasonic Monitoring of Sub-cladding Cracks', Proceedings of the 3rd Conference on Periodic Inspection of Pressurized Components, London, 20–22 September, Paper C195/76, pp. 13–18.
30. Silk, M. G., Lidington, B. H., Montgomery, P. and Hammond, C. G. (1976). 'Ultrasonic Time Domain Measurements of the Depth of Crack-like Defects in Ferritic and Austenitic Steel', Paper presented at the CSNI Specialists' Meeting on the Ultrasonic Inspection of Reactor Components, Risley, 27–29 September, 10 p.
31. Shankar, R., Mucciardi, A. N., Lawrie, W. E. and Stein, R. N., 'Development of Adaptive Learning Networks for Pipe Inspection', Adaptronics Report to EPRI, Ref. EPRI NP-688, FR 770, March 1978.

8

Problems Associated with Repetitive Inspection of Reactor Pressure Vessels and Research toward Solutions

C. E. LAUTZENHEISER, A. R. WHITING and W. T. FLACH

Southwest Research Institute, Texas, USA

SUMMARY

Over the past 10 years, technology has successfully developed equipment and ultrasonic techniques for the inspection of reactor pressure vessels (RPVs); and the detection of flaws and reproducibility of data have been satisfactorily demonstrated. However, accurate sizing, location, and analysis of the flaws remain a principal problem. Intensive research is underway to improve the techniques and the hardware for flaw analysis. Examples of the reproducibility of data taken during the inspection of RPVs and advanced computer-assisted, ultrasonic inspection techniques for precise flaw analysis are discussed.

1. INTRODUCTION

Research and development activities over the past 10 years have been successful in providing equipment for inspection of reactor pressure vessels (RPV) and ultrasonic techniques capable of detecting flaws of concern. Reproducibility of data is satisfactory as has been demonstrated on many reactors. The principal problem remaining is the accurate sizing, precise location, and analysis of the flaws detected. Current methods for analysis of the data, although computer-assisted, require very experienced personnel; and the results are a matter of judgement. New analytical methods currently being researched should provide more uniform and precise sizing, location, and analysis of flaws. The following paragraphs describe the reproducibility obtained on a series of inspections of a RPV and some of the research efforts aimed at improving flaw sizing, location, and analysis.

2. REPRODUCIBILITY OF INSPECTION DATA

The series of inspections of the Pilgrim Unit 1 RPV will be used as an example of the reproducibility of the data.

2.1. Preservice Inspections

In 1971 Southwest Research Institute (SwRI) performed the preservice inspection of the Pilgrim Unit 1 RPV using the manual ultrasonic method. Indications were noted in some of the nozzle-to-shell welds. One of the indications was in the N2 nozzle. The indication was marginally acceptable based on signal amplitude and was 'fingerprinted' for use during future inspections.

2.2. First Inservice Inspection

The first inservice inspection of the N2 nozzle was made in September 1974 using remote mechanised equipment. The recorded data indicated an amplitude of approximately twice that obtained on the preservice inspection, but the length of the indication was essentially unchanged. This increase in amplitude was of serious concern, and major efforts were made to duplicate the original inspection as far as possible. The principal difficulty in total duplication was that the preservice inspection was done manually, and, because of the lack of sufficient access, the inservice inspection was performed with remote mechanised equipment. After checking the installed insulation, it was found possible to perform a very restricted manual ultrasonic inspection in one small area. This inspection was made and confirmed that, in fact, the amplitude had essentially doubled. Therefore, the increase in amplitude was due to reasons other than the change in ultrasonic technique.

After a careful review of the data, it was the general opinion that the increase in amplitude was due to a change in the reflectivity of the flaw; in other words, the actual size of the flaw which produced the indication had not changed even though the amplitude of the reflected signal had increased. Although it could not be conclusively demonstrated that a microscopic change had or had not occurred in the size of the flaw, related research work was presented that showed that ultrasonic signal reflections could increase without any change in true flaw size. The primary reason given was that the small amount of stress relieving, resulting from plant operation, relaxed the compressive residual stresses to allow the flaw surfaces to separate very slightly. This would ultrasonically uncouple the flaw surfaces and reflect ultrasonic energy which might have otherwise been transmitted across the flaw when under compressive stress.

During the regulatory review of these data, SwRI personnel stated that they believed it was technically possible to reproduce the data so as to provide a size accuracy ± 3–4 mm when very strict controls were placed on the performance of the successive inspections.

2.3. Second Service Inspection

Insofar as amplitude was concerned, data reproducibility on the second inspection was reasonably good, with the major difference being that the maximum amplitude was noted at a different location. Dimensions, however, calculated in accordance with Section XI, showed no change in size within the ± 3–4 mm tolerance.

2.4. Subsequent Inservice Inspections

SwRI repeated the inspection on the N2 nozzle in 1977, and the data again showed no change within the ± 3–4 mm tolerance. In fact, successive inspections have shown the response to the flaw to be more stable. The 1976 and 1977 inspections have resulted in a very close reproduction of results. This stabilisation of results tends to support the earlier postulations that the change in reflectivity occurred as a result of very small mechanical changes brought about by the first few years of plant operation. This ability to reproduce the data is a tribute to the designer of the remote mechanised equipment and to the use of detailed procedures rigorously imposed.

3. DATA ANALYSIS

One of the most critical aspects of the chronology discussed above involves the interpretation and analysis of data by very experienced personnel. Even with experienced personnel, large variations in flaw size are possible. The large variations in estimation of flaw size when the size is based on personal judgement is illustrated by the Edwin I. Hatch unit situation. During the preservice inspection, a flaw was detected in one of the N2 nozzle-to-shell welds. The data used for the analysis were obtained by SwRI, and these data were analysed by personnel from the vessel manufacturer, the nuclear steam supply system supplier, and SwRI. The estimated size of the flaw ranged from less than 1 mm for one organisation to as much as 18 mm for another organisation. The actual size of the flaw was 18 mm which was determined during excavation for repair.

4. SIZING, LOCATION, AND DATA ANALYSIS RESEARCH

Although detection of flaws and reproducibility of the data are satisfactory, it is evident that this is not true with regard to sizing, location, and analysis of the flaws. Intensive research is underway leading to improved techniques and hardware designed to enhance the analysis of ultrasonic data. Areas of research in which significant results are being achieved include real-time radiographic imaging, synthetic aperture imagery, and adaptive learning or pattern recognition techniques. The following paragraphs describe some of these efforts.

4.1. Real-Time Imaging

There are many situations where it is difficult, if not impossible, to differentiate between the ultrasonic signal from a flaw and from a metallurgical artifact. A real-time imaging (RTI) system for high-energy radiographic applications is being developed by SwRI under sponsorship of the Electric Power Research Institute (EPRI). This system will permit resolution of ultrasonic indications by conjunctive moving of a high-energy source and the RTI device. Once the location of the high-energy source and RTI device is established, an exposure can be made on radiographic film for detailed diagnosis and permanent record. An important adjunct of this system is a portable linear accelerator (LINAC) being developed by SwRI under sponsorship of EPRI. This is a man-portable, 4 Mev unit specially designed for inservice inspection applications.

4.2. Synthetic Aperture Focusing Technique

Under the sponsorship of the United States Nuclear Regulatory Commission, SwRI is developing an ultrasonic imaging system based on the synthetic aperture focusing technique (SAFT) for ultrasonic applications. The SAFT system employs a computer to generate inspection results equivalent to that which would have been obtained from a large, perfectly focused search unit. The advantages SAFT provides over other methods include very high axial and lateral resolution, the capability to compensate for the defocusing effects of curved surfaces, and a high degree of signal averaging which improves signal-to-noise ratios. Prototype hardware has been developed, and results to date indicate a substantial increase in the accuracy of flaw sizing and locating, and of determination of flaw character.

4.3. Pattern Recognition Technique (Adaptive Learning)

Conventional ultrasonic data rely solely on information available in an amplitude domain, i.e. time of flight, reflector amplitude. Received RF signals are processed by the ultrasonic instrument and displayed as analog signals. The processing and display operations inherently lose significant and intelligent bits of information such as frequency spectra, pulse shape, and so forth. Recent advances in computerised analysis of RF wave forms reflected from flaws have led to the development of sophisticated, but easily used systems which simplify the flaw sizing and clarification problems. This is accomplished via a complex comparative matrix of data parameters in both the frequency and amplitude domains in which discrete and unique variables characteristic of a real flaw, such as a fatigue crack, can be identified. Having once 'educated' the comparative matrix algorithms with advance data, real indications can be analysed by applying the identical algorithms with minimal compensations for specific field test variables. A significant research program by Adaptronics, Inc. under the sponsorship of EPRI has yielded significant and promising results in this area.

5. CONCLUSIONS

It is the author's opinion that available mechanised equipment and flaw detection techniques are adequate. Further development will optimise the equipment and techniques, but a major breakthrough is unlikely.

Major progress will occur in the general area of flaw analysis and will principally be due to the use of sophisticated computer techniques to replace the judgement analysis by personnel.

The Reliability and Efficiency of Ultrasonic Flaw Detection Methods

9

Results of the Pressure Vessel Research Committee Program on Reliability of Ultrasonics

L. J. CHOCKIE

General Electric Company, California, USA

SUMMARY

An industry and government cooperative program was organised by the Pressure Vessel Research Committee (PVRC) over 10 years ago to address the question 'how effective are currently used inspection techniques and what new inspection techniques may be applied to weldments and fabrication of vessels fabricated of heavy-section steels?' Although the program is still in progress, significant results have been obtained in cooperation with the Nuclear Regulatory Commission's Heavy-Section Steel Technology Program and the Edison Electrical Institute Program on New Methodology. One of the most significant results is the application of the linear elastic fracture mechanics methods as applied to assess the structural integrity of nuclear reactor pressure vessels and the requirement that nondestructive examination methods measure the length, depth and position of flaws in the structure. Ultrasonic examination methods, offering the most promise, have been developed as a result of the PVRC program and are now mandatorily required for nuclear reactor vessels and components. Twelve large test blocks, each containing intentionally placed flaws, were fabricated for the PVRC program; and, as improvements in the reliability of detection and analysis evidenced themselves, some blocks were sectioned to prove the capability or to identify the need for more work. Three blocks were donated to the European PISC Program and a similar arrangement has now been developed for exchange of test blocks with Japan. The data from this continuing program have been analysed and are being reanalysed to provide a more definitive assessment of ultrasonic reliability and to determine what further improvements are necessary.

1. INTRODUCTION

Modest Pressure Vessel Research Committee (PVRC) studies assessing the variables concerning safety of heavy-walled steel pressure vessels were given impetus by the Advisory Committee on Reactor Safeguards letter, prepared by Chairman W. D. Manly, November 24, 1965. The recommendation in the ACRS letter that work should be done to reduce the probability of reactor pressure vessel failure still further, prompted the Pressure Vessel Research Committee to address three important questions:

(1) What are the properties of and how effective are inspection techniques for heavy-section steels and weldments?
(2) What effect do flaws and the variation of properties have on the behaviour of vessels fabricated of heavy-section steels?
(3) What inspection techniques may be effectively applied to vessels in service?

The response to the generation of answers to these questions was twofold. The AEC funded the Heavy-Section Steel Technology (HSST) Program managed by Oak Ridge National Laboratory. Industry funded an Industry Cooperative Program (ICP) which was directed and managed by PVRC.

The HSST program concentrated on material testing and analytical studies in 12 tasks whereas the ICP work was divided into 10 projects. Projects 3 (in part) and 8 to 10 dealt specifically with nondestructive examination. Chockie and Larson [1] presented a summary of the original scopes as shown below. Discussions of progress and accomplishments will come later; however, it should be noted that after 10 years some of the programs are still being carried out.

1.1. Project 3: Effects of Process Variables on Mechanical Properties

The effects of process variables on the mechanical properties of heavy-section steels 10 to 12 in (25 to 30 cm) in thickness will be studied. Included in this project are studies of the 'scatter' of test data, variation of properties at different locations in the plate, effect of rolling reduction ratio, property dependence on heat treatment, and identification of discontinuities detected by nondestructive inspection.

1.2. Project 8: Development of Improved Ultrasonic Testing of Weldments

Ultrasonic testing is currently employed to inspect welds in many applications; however, the equipment and techniques have not been generally accepted because of the inability to detect, define and interpret indications. A sophisticated method will be developed for the ultrasonic inspection of weldments. It is proposed that the weld will be automatically scanned and the resultant ultrasonic data will be fed into a computer which will analyse the data and provide a readout of exact flaw size and location. The equipment will also mark the location of the flaw on the piece being tested. Many practical problems must be resolved before such a system can be developed.

1.3. Project 9: Development of Ultrasonic Techniques for Inspecting Vessels in Service

Two methods are proposed for inspecting reactor vessels in service utilising conventional ultrasonic testing techniques. Although both methods seem feasible at the present time, many problems must be resolved before a satisfactory technique can be developed and demonstrated. One technique involves designing and building a complex positioner and recording device for immersion testing from inside the vessel; the other presupposes that inspection of 100 % of the vessel will not be required and that all critical areas can be identified and monitored by ultrasonic transducers permanently affixed to the outside of the vessel.

1.4. Project 10: Evaluation and Development of Advanced Concepts in Nondestructive Testing of Pressure Vessels in Service

Ultrasonic testing, utilising conventional techniques, is being proposed as a promising method for inspecting vessels in service; however, other more sophisticated advanced concepts are in various stages of development. Their applicability will be investigated and appropriate development work will be performed to culminate in a satisfactory system for the evaluation of reactor vessels in service.

2. THE NONDESTRUCTIVE EXAMINATION PROGRAMS

The Industry Cooperative–Pressure Vessel Research Committee Non-destructive Examination programs can be divided into a series of progressive plateaus, each of which will be discussed to some extent. The plateaus can be summarised as follows:

(1) Round robin ultrasonic or radiographic examination of weldments containing natural flaws using the operators own equipment and procedures;

(2)   Ultrasonic or radiographic examinations to one specific set of procedures which forbade certain techniques and limited the type of equipment;

(3)   Ultrasonic examination through weld overlay clad to existing procedures, but with no provisions for internal calibration of weldment;

(4)   Improved ultrasonic examination through weld overlay clad to existing procedures plus provisions for internal calibration;

(5)   Use of advanced techniques (acoustic holography, acoustic spectroscopy) for evaluation of flaws in weldments;

(6)   Statistical evaluation of round robin data using assumed flaw sizes and locations;

(7)   Sectioning of weldments and correlation of actual flaw sizes and locations with values determined by the nondestructive examinations.

Several plates of various thickness were butt welded with measures taken to introduce a spectrum of weld defects (porosity, slag, lack-of-fusion, cracking). Additionally, nozzles were welded into plates with defects introduced into the weldment. These weldments are summarized in Table I. The current status of programs on each weldment studied or under study is given in Table II.

During the period 1967–8 four butt welds and four nozzle welds containing defects were examined, usually by five teams from different organisations. These teams had the option of using their own examination procedures or using those of ASME Section III, Appendix IX. It soon became apparent that some degree of standardisation was required to permit a comparison of the data. Therefore, the reporting level was set at 25 % DAC, the specific angle beam transfer method was recognised, and one couplant, glycerine, was selected. Even with the control of these variables, it was found that there was virtually no agreement amongst the team reports. As a result of this lack of agreement steps were taken to further control or eliminate these parameters:

(1)   Transfer method
(2)   Half or full node technique
(3)   Depth measurement technique
(4)   Instrument and transducer variables
(5)   Gain multiple for scanning sensitivity
(6)   Dual transducer techniques
(7)   Personnel

TABLE I
DESCRIPTION OF PVRC INDUSTRY–COOPERATIVE TEST BLOCKS

Identity	Fabricator	Approx. thickness	Type of weld	Intended flaws
50–52	Babcock & Wilcox	11 in (28 cm)	butt weld electroslag	gross cracks
51–53	Babcock & Wilcox	8 in (20 cm)	butt weld sub arc	gross cracks
155	Babcock & Wilcox	$8\frac{3}{4}$ in (22 cm)	18 in (46 cm) forged nozzle sub arc with cladding	4, all cracks
156	Babcock & Wilcox	5 in (13 cm)	18 in (46 cm) cast nozzle sub arc	3 areas of flaws of varied sizes
201	Chicago Bridge & Iron	8 in (20 cm)	butt weld manual metal arc	10, varied types
202	Chicago Bridge & Iron	8 in (20 cm)	butt weld manual metal with cladding	9, varied types
203	Chicago Bridge & Iron	8 in (20 cm)	21 in (53 cm) forged nozzle manual metal arc	9, varied types
204	Chicago Bridge & Iron	8 in (20 cm)	18 in (46 cm) forged nozzle manual metal arc	9, varied types
251J	Combustion Engr.	11 in (28 cm)	butt weld sub arc	15, varied types
252J	Combustion Engr.	8 in (20 cm)	butt weld electroslag	3 areas of flaws of varied types
253J	Combustion Engr.	11 in (28 cm)	24 in (61 cm) forged nozzle sub arc	20, varied types
254J	Combustion Engr.	10 in (25 cm)	17 in (43 cm) forged nozzle sub arc	25, varied types

TABLE II

ESTIMATES OF PRESENT POSITION ON VARIOUS PVRC PLATE WELD SAMPLES

Weld specimen No.	Size and type	Ultrasonic examination	Analysis of UT	Sectioning
201	$8\frac{1}{2}$ in thick, Butt-welded flat plate	Completed by 5 UT participants +6 radiographic 2 special techniques	Unclad section published, clad section with sub-committee	Completed and reported to sub-committee
251J	11 in thick × 36 in × $50\frac{1}{2}$ in butt-welded flat plate	Completed by 6 UT participants	Completed and published WRC-221	Partially completed; reports to sub-committee
202	$8\frac{5}{16}$ in × 24 × 34·6, butt-welded flat plate	Completed	Interim report to sub-committee 1977	—
155J	$8\frac{5}{8} \times 39\frac{7}{8} \times 10\frac{1}{4}$ curved plate with $18\frac{7}{8}$ OD and $9\frac{13}{16}$ ID nozzle welded in	Completed	—	—
203	$8\frac{5}{16} \times 48 \times 48$ $20\frac{8}{10}$ in O.D. $11\frac{4}{10}$ in ID nozzle welded in	In progress	—	—
204	$8\frac{5}{16} \times 40 \times 40$ 18 in OD × 6 in ID nozzle welded in	Being circulated in Europe for PISC	—	Not before 1979
50–52	$11 \times 36\frac{1}{2} \times 55\frac{1}{4}$ Butt weld flat plate	Being circulated in Europe for PISC	—	Not before 1979
51–53	$8 \times 36 \times 40\frac{3}{4}$ Butt welded flat plate	Being circulated in Europe for PISC	—	Not before 1979

The control of these parameters was obtained through a series of revisions to the so-called 'Old Testing Procedure', with a 'New Procedure' published by the PVRC [2]. The differences are compared below:

| Parameter | PVRC ultrasonic testing procedure | |
	'Old'	'New'
Specifies couplant	No	Yes
Transducer limited to one type and size	No	Yes
Instruments standardised	No	Yes
75% Response of test block for both angled and straight beam	No	Yes
Transfer methods used	Yes	Only 1:1
Scanning gain setting	2 × sensitivity	10 × sensitivity
Records	All 25% DAC	All 10% DAC

Changes have continued since then culminating in Welding Research Bulletin 235 published in 1978 in which Birkes and Lowrie [3] dealt with two subjects; 'Improved Repeatability in Ultrasonic Examination', and 'Ultrasonic Testing System Standardisation Requirements'. Additionally, ASME Section XI [4] developed Mandatory Appendices I and III for ultrasonic examination of pressure vessels and piping. Subsequently these appendices were transferred to ASME Section V [5].

A point of philosophy agreed upon early in the work of the groups was that 'round robin' testing was not to be considered a contest conducted by the 'all-stars' from each organisation, but was intended to be representative of production personnel, equipment, and techniques. Each of the test objects would be examined by as many NDT teams as possible, with results subsequently compared to determine nondestructive testing procedure reliability and repeatability.

The period 1967–68 resulted in what has been defined as the first plateau where virtually no consistency of results was observed from team to team due to a lack of control over procedures. Achievement of better results denoted as higher plateaus will be discussed under the specific PVRC specimens.

2.1. PVRC Specimen 201

Specimen 201 consisted of nominal 8 in (20 cm) plates joined by a manual metal arc butt weld. Ten flaws were introduced. In addition, two laminations adjacent to the weld were included in later studies. The data reported are based on the use of the improved test procedures. Both

L. J. Chockie

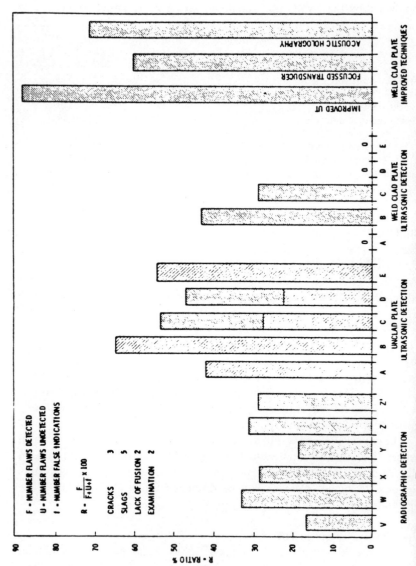

FIG. 1. Non destructive examination of PVRC plate-weld Specimen 201.

radiography and ultrasonic examinations were conducted. The data were analysed in several fashions. The only formal release of information was in an article in the Welding Research Journal in 1971 [2]. However, substantial additional work has been reported to the PVRC NDE Subcommittee. In essence the following chronology has been in effect:

(1) Plateau Two: Radiography and ultrasonics (revised procedures on unclad plate);
(2) Plateau Three: Division of weldment into two sections with one destructively sectioned and the other weld overlay clad; this clad weld was re-examined using Plateau Two procedures;
(3) Plateau Four: The clad plate was examined with conventional UT using more angles and drilled holes for internal calibration of the clad plate;
(4) Plateau Five: Improved techniques such as acoustic holography [6] and focused transducers were used to dimension the flaws.

A variety of analytical tools were used to compare the performance of the various teams as well as examining the detectability of each flaw.

The ratios were utilised; namely:

$$R_{\mathrm{I}} = \frac{F}{F + U} \times 100 \qquad R = \frac{F}{F + U + F} \times 100$$

$$R_{\mathrm{II}} = \frac{F - f}{F + U} \times 100$$

$$R_{\mathrm{III}} = \frac{F}{f + U}$$

where F = number of introduced flaws found, U = number of introduced flaws unfound and f = number of false indications. The data have been assembled and represented in Fig. 1.

It is apparent that a definite need exists for definitive and restrictive ultrasonic examination procedures. Also, cladding seriously perturbs the validity of the ultrasonic examination unless corrective actions are taken for internal calibration to account for the effects of cladding. The ultrasonic data yield nominal locations, but do not give flaw dimensions, on this early, PVRC 201, plate.

2.2. PVRC Specimen 251J

PVRC 251J specimen consisted of two 11 in (28 cm) plates welded together using a submerged-arc single electrode multiple pass technique.

Fifteen welding defects, (slag, transverse cracks, longitudinal cracks) were deliberately introduced.

Sufficient work had been completed on PVRC 201 to highlight potential problem areas. Therefore, the 251J examination was directed toward a re-examination of the problem areas. Specifically, the following programs were carried out:

(1)   Radiography by one team;
(2)   Ultrasonic 45° angle beam, 2·25 MHz using old PVRC procedures, plate unclad;
(3)   Ultrasonic 45° angle beam 2·25 MHz using new PVRC procedures, plate unclad;
(4)   Same as (3), after cladding;
(5)   Ultrasonic straight beam, 2·25 MHz using old PVRC procedures, plate unclad;
(6)   Ultrasonic straight beam, 2·25 MHz using new PVRC procedures, plate unclad;
(7)   Same as (6), after cladding;
(8)   Ultrasonic 60° angle beam, 2·25 MHz using old PVRC procedures, plate unclad;
(9)   Ultrasonic 45° angle beam, 1·0 MHz using new PVRC procedures, plate unclad;
(10) Ultrasonic straight beam, 1·0 MHz using new PVRC procedures, plate unclad;
(11) Ultrasonic 45° angle beam, 1·0 MHz using new PVRC procedures, examination from clad side;
(12) Ultrasonic 45° angle beam, 2·25 MHz using new PVRC procedures, examination from unclad side;
(13) In addition, an acoustic holography examination was conducted from the unclad side of the clad plate.

The raw data were statistically analysed by Buchanan [7] using a defect identification criterion to permit an inter-comparison of the teams. This criterion consisted of adding certain tolerances to the intended defect dimensions. If the dimensions fall within the bounds, the indication was accepted as a correct defect identification. Two criteria were used, one with a 1 in (25 mm) tolerance and the other with a 1·5 in (38 mm) tolerance. This approach tends to assume the flaw size and location is about as stated in the fabrication document and errors are due to examination procedures; however, preliminary and incompletely confirmed sectioning data indicate that neither the flaw sizes nor the flaw locations are precisely as indicated. In some instances, the flaws were much larger than presumed. It should be

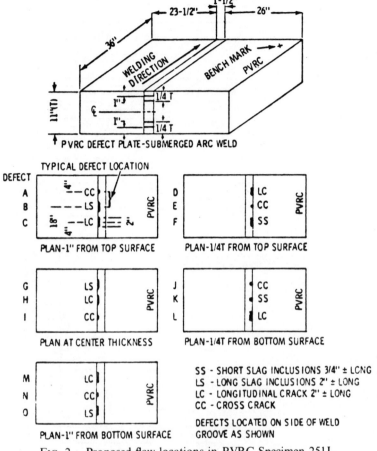

FIG. 2.   Proposed flaw locations in PVRC Specimen 251J.

recognised that the data presented in Buchanan's tables [7] assumed that the predicted sizes and locations were correct. Figure 2 illustrates the presumed size and location of flaws. The data are included as are values for R_{I}, R_{II} and R_{III}. A somewhat different formulation is used for R; namely defining it as

$$R = \frac{F}{F + U + f} \times 100$$

The data using this formula are summarised in Fig. 3.

Sharon and Witek [8] examined the clad plate using acoustic holography. Initial examination indicated poor image quality through the cladding so

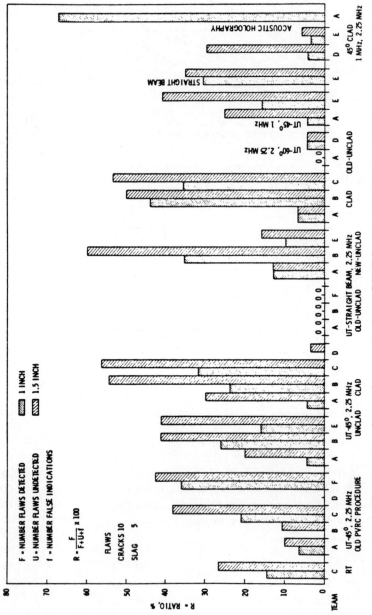

FIG. 3.   Non-destructive examinations of PVRC plate-weld Specimen 251J.

further studies were limited to the unclad side. Examinations were with 2 and 3 MHz longitudinal and 45° shear wave. A significant observation is the lack of imaging from flaws too close to the surface when examination is limited or non-existent from the other surface.

3. STATISTICAL EVALUATION

The significance of actual flaw location versus presumed flaw location is highlighted from a limited and rather cursory study of radiographic and ultrasonic C-scan data after initial sectioning of Specimen 251J. Thirteen data points change from false (f) to flaw (F) which increases the values for the 45°, 2·25 MHz new procedure—from a cumulative R_{II} of 0 to R_{II} of 58%.

The preceding helps clarify some of the apparent discrepancies contained in Table III where the averages and standard deviations from R_I, R_{II} and R_{III} are compared within and between Specimens 201 and 251J. A similar plot will be made for corrected 251J data to establish the actual degree of improvement resulting from the new PVRC procedures when 251J sectioning and analysis are completed.

3.1. Interim Conclusions

Recognising that the final results will depend on the size and location of flaws, the following interim conclusions are believed to be of interest and, probably, not subject to substantial change.

(1) Team F results should be discarded since their participation was limited to one survey;

(2) Operators B and C did better than the others; they were essentially comparable; there was no significant difference in performance with the new angled and straight beam techniques;

(3) The D operator was consistently the least effective, particularly since he did no straight beam examinations;

(4) Operator E appeared slightly better than A but the difference was not significant; generally both did better on angled beam than straight. Both were more effective than D, but generally less effective than B and C;

(5) The new PVRC procedure was substantially better than the old for the same conditions of angle and frequency;

(6) With the new procedure there seemed to be little or no difference in detection reliability for either clad or unclad condition.

TABLE III

COMPARISONS OF EXAMINATION RESULTS FOR PLATES 201 AND 251J: MEANS $\bar{X}$ AND
STANDARD DEVIATIONS σ

Test conditions		Parameter					
		R_I		R_II		R_III	
		1·0	1·5	1·0	1·5	1·0	1·5
Plate 251J							
45°; 2·25 MHz							
Old PVRC	$\bar{X}$	23	32	−41	−23	0·18	0·32
	σ	28	30	30	38	0·24	0·33
New PVRC	$\bar{X}$	31	53	−51	0	0·20	0·54
	σ	27	24	19	10	0·15	0·25
New PVRC	$\bar{X}$	25	47	−47	7	0·21	0·73
(Clad)	σ	26	35	44	55	0·22	0·60
Straight beam							
2·25 MHz							
Old PVRC	$\bar{X}$	0	0	−2	−2	0	0
	σ	0	0	4	4	0	0
New PVRC	$\bar{X}$	22	31	7	22	0·27	0·61
	σ	16	25	24	34	0·24	0·77
New PVRC	$\bar{X}$	31	38	25	36	0·47	0·74
(Clad)	σ	21	27	17	25	0·36	0·58
Radiography	$\bar{X}$	20	33	−20	7	0·17	0·36
Holography	$\bar{X}$	67		67		2·0	
Plate 201							
Old PVRC	$\bar{X}$	54		27		0·92	
	σ	15		27		0·52	
Old PVRC	$\bar{X}$	14		14		0·23	
(Clad)	σ	20		20		0·25	
New PVRC	$\bar{X}$	100		86		7·0	
(Clad)							
Radiography	$\bar{X}$	29		2		0·35	
	σ	10		7		0·12	
Holography	$\bar{X}$	71		71		2·5	

4. RECENT PVRC PROGRAMS

During 1974 a new program was initiated for the examination of PVRC
Specimens 155, 202 and 203. The examination criteria were based on an
evaluation of the results of Specimens 201 and 251J and of the effect of
modified procedures on these results. The procedure decided on for the new
program (155, 202, 203) in essence consisted of an expansion of Appendix I
of ASME Section XI [4]. The specific procedures denoted as the PVRC

Section XI ultrasonic procedure are included as Appendix I to the Buchanan Interim Report to PVRC (August 1977) [9]. This approach was believed to permit a verification of the ASME Code procedure and to establish if a more restrictive procedure would produce more accurate results.

Steps taken to further control the examination included:

(1) All examinations were in one location;
(2) Each team used a matched set of transducers and one of three matched Krautkramer US1P-11 instruments;
(3) Operators were instructed to perform in strict compliance with the procedures;
(4) The same scan paths were to be used;
(5) Data were to be recorded on the same format data sheets;
(6) A modification midway through the testing required increased scanning gain from $2 \times$ to $5 \times$ calibration level and permitted intermediate scan paths to better locate the indication peak (most but not all teams repeated their examination using the new procedure).

Other aspects of the recent PVRC programs bearing on future work included studies of electronic systems variability and variability in the overall test system. These studies culminated in a single document by Birks and Lowrie [3] covering two topics: (1) 'Improved Repeatability in Ultrasonic Examination' which was aimed at limiting the significant variations existing in 'off the shelf' search units; and (2) 'Ultrasonic Testing System Standardisation Requirements' which defines minimum system performance for the system defined as the instrument (pulser–receiver, cathode ray display, gate), coaxial cable and search unit.

Thirteen teams examined the specimens and reported their data. Buchanan [9] initially used the procedure developed for analysis of 251J; namely, tolerances of 0·5, 1·0 and 1·5 in on the x, y, z (R, θ, z) values of the flaws. Results were surprising and discouraging.

A potential source of the very low team rating could be related to the validity of the basic assumption that the intentional flaws are located exactly where intended. Obviously if an indication is judged to be correct only if it matched, within tolerances, the intended location, and if the actual locations differed considerably from the intended locations, large errors could result. A review of available radiographic data indicated that the size, shape and location of the actual flaws differed significantly from the intended values. As an alternative to the tolerance system a two-point

TABLE IV

COMPARISON OF RATING FACTORS ACHIEVED BY DIFFERENT UT EXAMINATION PROCEDURES ON PVRC SPECIMENS

Specimen	Specimen type	Stage of Analysis	UT examination procedure employed	R_{III} (Avg.)
201	plate-weld	metallurgically sectioned	PVRC procedure for ultrasonic examination of welds in plates 201 and 202 for Pressure Vessel Research Committee Program—as published in *Welding Journal*, December, 1971, pp. 529S–538S.	1·52
251J	plate-weld	not as yet metallurgically sectioned	Ultrasonic examination of welds for Pressure Vessel Research Committee Program—February 16, 1968.	0·11
251J	plate-weld	not as yet metallurgically sectioned	Ultrasonic examination of welds in plates 201 and 202 for Pressure Vessel Research Committee Program— March 19, 1970.	0·24
155	nozzle-weld	not as yet metallurgically sectioned	Procedure for manual ultrasonic examination of PVRC welded test blocks—June 27, 1974; Supplement— August 9, 1974; Modification—September 18, 1974.	0·11
202	plate-weld	not as yet metallurgically sectioned	Procedure for manual ultrasonic examination of PVRC welded test blocks—June 27, 1974; Supplement— August 9, 1974; Modification—September 18, 1974.	0·02
203	nozzle-weld	not as yet metallurgically sectioned	Procedure for manual ultrasonic examination of PVRC welded test blocks—June 27, 1974; Supplement— August 9, 1974; Modification—September 18, 1974.	0·07

coincidence method was developed which was to determine if a given ultrasonic indication was correct or not, without assuming actual flaw locations. The two-point coincidence method consists of an analytic division of the specimen into a large number of small essentially cubic elements. If any portion of two or more indications falls within a given element a discontinuity is said to exist and all indications in that element are treated as correct indications.

Three different volume element sizes were used to be somewhat consistent with the previous method of analysis; e.g. the normal edge dimensions were 0·45, 0·90 and 1·35 in respectively, compared to tolerances of ±0·5, ±1·0 and ±1·5 in.

The percentage of reported indications found to be correct with the two-point coincidence method ranged from 74% for the smallest volume element to 80% for the largest.

The analysis was expanded to determine the effect on the percentage rating if the number of points required for coincidence were increased. For the 0·9 in element size (76·8% with two point), the data were analysed using 3, 4, 5, 6, and 7 point coincidence requirements and yielded percentages of 67·9, 62·5, 62·5, 62·5 and 62·5, respectively, a decrease from 2 point to 4 point, then remaining constant to 7 point.

5. COMPARISONS

Tables IV and V permit intercomparisons. The R_{III} values range from 0·02 to 1·52 with the primary reason for the low values being the difference in actual versus presumed flaw locations.

TABLE V

COMPARISONS OF THE TWO METHODS OF ANALYSIS ON PVRC SPECIMENS 155, 202 AND 203

| Specimen | Percentage of reported indications considered correct | | | | | |
| | Standard method (based on intended discontinuity locations) Tolerance level (inch) | | | Two-point coincidence method Nominal volume-element size (inch) | | |
	0·5	1·0	1·5	0·45	0·9	1·35
155	3·6	19·6	57·1	71·4	76·8	80·4
202	0	4·3	7·2	76·8	84·1	81·2
203	2·3	27·3	56·8	54·5	61·4	72·7

Table V compares the standard method, based on tolerance levels and assumed flaw locations versus two-point coincidence.

It will be necessary to await results of sectioning before we can assess these UT results.

REFERENCES

1. Chockie, L. J. and Larson, C. F. (Sept. 1969). 'Industry Cooperative Program on Heavy-Section Steels', Proceedings First International Conference on Pressure Vessel Technology, Delft, The Netherlands, Part II, Paper II-78, pp. 1005–16.
2. PVRC Subcommittee Report, Nondestructive Examination of PVRC Plate Weld Specimen 201, *Welding Research Supp.*, pp. 529S–538S, Dec. 1971.
3. Birks, A. S. and Lowrie, W. E., 'Improved Repeatability in Ultrasonic Examination', and 'Ultrasonic Testing System Standardization Requirements', Welding Research Bulletin No. 235, Feb. 1978.
4. ASME Section XI, 'Rules for Inservice Inspection of Nuclear Power Plant Components', American Society of Mechanical Engineers, New York, 1974 Edition.
5. ASME Section V, 'Nondestructive Examination', American Society of Mechanical Engineers, New York, 1977 Edition.
6. Collins, H. D. and Gribble, R. P., 'PVRC Plate-Weld Specimen 201, Inspection by Acoustical Holography', Holosonics Report to Pressure Vessel Research Committee, Sept. 1972.
7. Buchanan, R. A., 'Analysis of the Nondestructive Examination of PVRC Plate Weld Specimen 251J—Part A', Welding Research Council Bulletin 221, Nov. 1976.
8. Sharon, G. M. and Witek, R. R., 'Acoustic Holography Examination of PVRC Plate-Weld Specimen 251J', NEDO-20735, Dec. 1974.
9. Buchanan, R. A., 'Analysis of the Ultrasonic Examination of PVRC Weld Specimens 155, 202 and 203 by Standard and Two-Point Coincidence Methods', Report to PVRC NDE Subcommittee, Aug. 1977.

10

Plate Inspection Steering Committee (PISC) Reports

FOREWORD

The Plate Inspection Steering Committee (PISC) was set up within the framework of the OECD Committee on the Safety of Nuclear Installations (CSNI), in particular its working group on Safety Aspects of Steel Components in Nuclear Installations, the secretariat of which is provided jointly by the OECD Nuclear Energy Agency and the Commission of the European Communities.

The purpose of PISC was to deal with the offer made by the United States to ship to Europe three plates (containing artificially introduced flaws) from the programme of the US Pressure Vessel Research Committee.

This test series co-ordinated by the Safety and Reliability Directorate of the UKAEA, investigated the ability of the procedure for UT examination, prepared by the US Pressure Vessel Research Committee (in 1974, based on the ASME XI Code) to detect flaws and discontinuities (and to size and locate them) in heavy section steel.

The outcome of the programme, in which more than 30 European testing Institutions participated, including the Joint Research Centre of Ispra, which was responsible for the final destructive examination and analysis, and its relevance to nuclear safety may well influence manufacturing processes and future codes of inspection.

Sincere thanks go firstly to the US Pressure Vessel Research Committee who made this programme possible by offering the plates, and also to all organisations and individuals who participated in the work.

F. Caccia Dominioni

Report No. 1:
A Description of the PISC Project

A. L. ADAMS

UKAEA, SRD, Warrington, UK

and

A. DE STERKE

RTD-BV, Rotterdam, The Netherlands

SUMMARY

This report, written as a historical review of the Plate Inspection Steering Committee Project, records the background of the project and refers in general to the reasons why decisions were made during the five years the project has been running.

Details are given in further reports of which the full list is as follows:

Report No. 1. A Description of the PISC Project
Report No. 2. Ultrasonic Examination of the PVRC Plates
Report No. 3. Destructive Examination of the PVRC Plates
Report No. 4. Method of Evaluation and the Results of the PISC Trials
Report No. 5. Discussion of NDE/DE and Summary Conclusions

A list of all participants is given. Data and results of the test programme are detailed in the other reports above, but to maintain confidentiality of data the individual teams have been allocated a code number known only to the team and the PISC management. Data is only identified against code numbers.

1. INTRODUCTION

The reliability and efficiency of ultrasonic non-destructive examination (NDE) of thick steel sections is one of the remaining uncertainties in understanding the integrity of nuclear reactor pressure vessels. This paper is written as part of a full project report to give the background and historical events of the Plate Inspection Steering Committee (PISC) Project. A list of all committees, committee members and *ex-officio* participants is given in Appendix I.

2.   BACKGROUND OF THE PISC PROJECT

In 1965, in the United States, the Pressure Vessel Research Committee (PVRC) non-destructive examination programme began as part of the industrial co-operative programme on heavy section steels for nuclear reactor pressure vessels (Heavy Section Steel Test Programme (HSST)). The NDE programme was designed to try and produce some quantitative information as to the probability of detection, location and sizing of flaws in reactor pressure vessel steels. Very little data existed on this subject and questions put to experts in NDE were based on personal experience with a wide variety of opinions being expressed.

In 1968 the PVRC had prepared a number of welded thick section test plates for the use of ultrasonic test organisations (12 plates in total). The plates varied between 20 cm (8 in) and 28 cm (11 in) thick and were welded by various methods, submerged arc, electroslag or manual metal arc. Five of the plates contained forged nozzles and one a cast nozzle.

Inspection of these plates was carried out by a number of teams in the USA using their own examination procedures in accordance with ASME Code Section III Appendix 9, the programme calling for five teams to examine each specimen. In 1968, records indicated eight weld specimens had been examined and the outcome of the test results showed a complete lack of agreement amongst several teams. Some tightening up of procedures, equipment and personnel standards was necessary and from 1969 to 1973 examinations were carried out mainly related to evaluating the aspects of the variables discovered in 1968.

A new programme was established early in 1974 for examination of weld specimens, and after a review of the analysis previously carried out the PVRC prepared a procedure related closely to that required by the then current Section XI of the ASME Boiler and Pressure Vessel Code.

Informal exchange of information between members of the PVRC and the Safety and Reliability Directorate (SRD) of the United Kingdom Atomic Energy Authority led to an offer from the PVRC to ship three plates to Europe so that a European programme of non-destructive examination could be carried out. This programme would augment the US programme and hopefully provide further statistics to quantify the probability of detection, location and sizing of flaws using ultrasonic techniques.

The plates were offered to the Commission of the European Communities/Organisation for Economic Co-operation and Development (CEC/OECD), Committee on the Safety of Nuclear Installations (CSNI), Working Group on Safety Aspects of Steel Components in Nuclear Installations, to arrange for these tests to be carried out. SRD were nominated to initiate and generally manage the project under the direction of a multi-national steering committee soon to be named the Plate Inspection Steering Committee (PISC).

3.   PLATE INSPECTION STEERING COMMITTEE

During the second half of 1974, SRD contacted a number of European organisations and found that there was considerable support for a programme of ultrasonic testing. A preliminary meeting of some of the interested parties was held in Cologne, 13th February, 1975. The major decisions taken at this meeting were:

(1)   The organisations invited to perform the tests would initially perform the same tests as the US PVRC to make the European and US tests comparable. Subsequently other procedures could be used.

(2)   All test results would remain confidential within the project and individual team results anonymous.

(3)   Testing of the plates would not be carried out at one site, instead the US procedure of moving the plates to the test organisations would be preferred.

(4)   All costs for testing and transport would be borne by the individual participants but CEC would be asked to give financial assistance for destructive testing. Alternatively each country might be required to share such costs.

(5)   The project was to be managed by SRD on behalf of the Steering Committee; this Committee to be made up of National representatives from all European countries participating. SRD agreed to fund the management costs.

The Plate Inspection Steering Committee was thus to be composed of National representatives from each participating country, chaired by Mr R. O'Neil of SRD with the secretary also provided by SRD. Representatives of CEC and OECD also took part.

The composition of the Committee has inevitably changed over the five year period of the project and in addition has become augmented by representatives of participating organisations who by virtue of their attendance and contribution are considered full members of the Committee. Appendix II gives the dates and venues of all official Committee meetings held.

4.   SUB-COMMITTEES OF THE PISC

From the beginning of the project it was considered expedient to establish sub-committees of the PISC comprising experts in particular fields to advise the PISC in matters relating to the tests. A number of these sub-committees were formed during the project and are listed below.

4.1.   Technical Working Group (Destructive Testing), Chairman Mr A. de Sterke (RTD, Holland)

The group was formed to consider the methods of destructive testing so that problems could be identified in good time. There was also the need to specify the costs of such a programme so that the necessary funding could be provided.

A meeting of this group was held at Eurotest, Brussels on 14th October, 1976, at which most of the points at issue were cleared for PISC approval. Those outstanding were of a long-term nature due to the protracted test programme still to come. Because the actions were long-term no further meetings of this group as such were required.

4.2.   Evaluation Task Force, Chairman Mr P. Caussin (Association Vincotte, Belgium)

Towards the end of the NDE phase of the project it was decided by the PISC that there should be set up a sub-committee to consider all the data and reports received and to make more detailed proposals for the destructive examination, and evaluation and analysis of results. This Task Force was a logical extension of the Technical Working Group on Destructive Examination but with wider terms of reference and became more of a Working Group than a group to discuss principles. This Task Force has met six times and considered and approved 13 working papers listed in Appendix III. Membership of this group was restricted to National representatives or their nominees.

4.3. ETF—Sub-Group

This sub-group of the ETF was set up as a means of giving quick advice during the destructive examination or evaluation and analysis phase of the project, to avoid any hold-up in the programme by waiting for a full ETF committee meeting. It consisted of representatives from France, Germany, Italy, Belgium and the UK and had cause to meet only once in December 1977.

The composition of all sub-committees is given in Appendix I.

5.   TERMS OF REFERENCE OF THE PISC PROJECT

The objectives of the PISC project were first to provide additional test data to augment that available from the US tests; and secondly, to give the European test centres the opportunity to non-destructively examine under controlled conditions heavy section plate and nozzle welds containing deliberately implanted flaws.

The data produced from the trials had to be in a similar form to that used by the US teams to allow comparability and assessment, and therefore it was convenient to initially define the terms of reference of the PISC project to be the same as the American NDE trials terms of reference, i.e. *To determine the capability of the PVRC September 1974 procedure for ultrasonic examination techniques to detect flaws or discontinuities, their size, location and orientation in heavy section steel.* Thereafter tests by alternative procedures could also be made to measure their relative value.

6.   PROGRAMME

A great deal of planning had been completed before the test plates arrived in the UK at the end of October 1975. After cleaning and machining calibration features into the plates they became available for inspection on 5th January, 1976.

Initially it had been proposed that the test plates should reside at one location with the test equipment and manpower from each test house travelling to this location. It was finally decided that it would be better to move the plates to each participating country with local arrangements made for internal movement where relevant. The arrangement followed the US experience in that each test house was responsible for transporting the test plates from the previous test house. In general this worked very well with the greatest problems occurring at Customs. On average it took about two weeks to arrange for Customs clearance for the movement of the plates between countries.

Eight countries initially joined the project and the programme timetable was based on this number. At the end of 1976 Spain joined the programme as did Finland in 1978 who sent a test team to the Joint Research Centre, Ispra, to carry out inspection using Ispra equipment just prior to destructive examination which started in June 1978.

Table I below shows the planned programme of inspection compared with the actual programme achieved.

TABLE I

Country	Completion date	
	Planned	Actual
UK (start 5.1.76)	30.4.76	4.5.76
Holland	30.6.76	30.6.76
Belgium	30.9.76	18.11.76
Sweden & Denmark	31.11.76	20.12.76
FR of Germany	28.2.77	10.5.77
France	30.6.77	7.10.77
Italy	30.10.77	21.1.78
Spain	—	19.5.78
25.5.78 plates to Italy for DE[a]		
Finland	—	5.6.78
		In Italy
Preliminary Report	31.1.78	March 1979

(UK through Italy bracketed as: Initial members)

[a] JRC Ispra of CEC for destructive examination.

This programme should be read in conjunction with Appendix I which gives a complete list of national groups and organisations taking part.

Details of the Destructive Examination programme are given in Report No. 3.

The Preliminary Report will be seen from Table I to be approximately one year later than the original proposal, the main reasons being:

(1) Insufficient allowance was originally made for the problems of Customs clearance and transport.

(2) Insufficient allowance was made for Continental holiday periods (usually one month).

(3) The addition of Spain and Finland to the participants.
(4) The time required for the ultrasonic inspection due to the unexpectedly large number of indications.
(5) The extent of the work necessary to carry out destructive examination for comparison purposes.

The facilities available at Ispra for Destructive Examination (DE) allowed more detailed DE and analysis than had originally been anticipated.

Thirty four organisations participated in the project, of which 28 carried out inspections to the formal PISC procedure. Seven teams carried out inspection to an improved version of the PISC procedure (to 20 % DAC) and 19 teams presented the results on one or more alternative procedures.

7. TEST PLATES

Three test plates were provided by the PVRC for the European test programme, two nominally flat plates (50/52 and 51/53) and a plate incorporating a 45·7 cm (18 in) forged nozzle (204). Each of the weldments in the plates contained flaws deliberately implanted during the welding process. No details are available as to the method of producing these flaws. Fabrication of these plates took place between 1965 and 1968 and they arrived in the UK on 28th November, 1975.

Information regarding the plates is given below. The plates were not specifically selected as being especially good quality, nor were they specifically reject quality and the metallurgical condition as found during the testing will be referred to later in Section 9 (Non-Destructive Examination) of this report. The PVRC has stated that all the test plates had been stress-relief annealed to the standards applicable at the time of manufacture.

7.1. Plate 50/52

This plate was fabricated from two pieces of SA 302 Grade B, Mn–Mo welded together by the butt weld electroslag method with the weld containing gross cracks. Details of the gross cracks were not made available to the project prior to inspection.

The welded plate measured $140·3\,cm \times 92·7\,cm \times 25·4\,cm$ ($55\frac{1}{4}\,in \times 36\frac{1}{2}\,in \times 10\,in$) and weighed 2586 kg (2·54 Imperial tons).

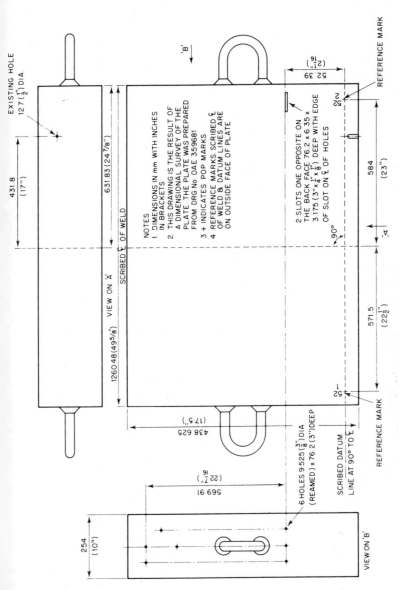

Fig. 1. Dimensions of PVRC test specimen 50/52.

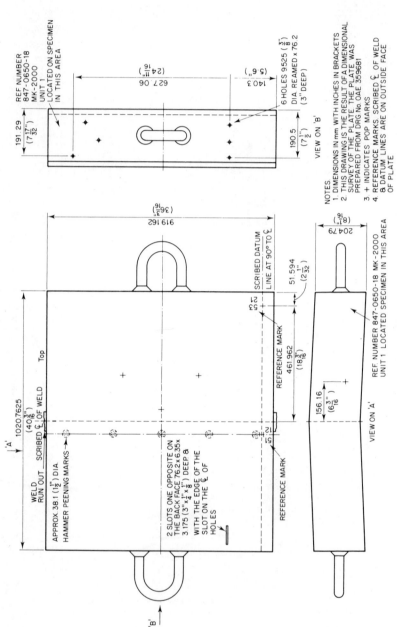

FIG. 2.   Dimensions of PVRC test specimen 51/53.

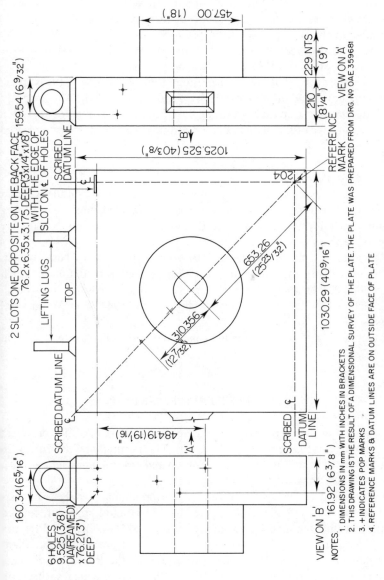

FIG. 3. Dimensions of PVRC test specimen 204.

7.2. Plate 51/53

This plate was fabricated from two pieces of SA-302 Grade B, Mn–Mo welded together by the butt weld submerged arc method with the weld containing gross cracks. Again details of the gross cracks were not made available to the project prior to inspection.

The welded plate measured 104 cm × 91 cm × 20 cm (41 in × 36 in × 8 in) and weighed 1517 kg (1·49 Imperial tons).

A great deal of trouble was encountered during cutting with the plate bending due to residual stresses which trapped the saw blade. The plate had a pronounced bend in it about the weld centre line, the difference between the bottom edge of the plate and the bottom at the centre line being raised 21·4 mm.

7.3. Nozzle Plate 204

This plate was fabricated using a plate section of SA 533 Grade B with a 45·7 cm (18 in) forged nozzle of SA 508 steel welded into place by the manual metal arc method with the weld containing nine discretely implanted flaws.

The nozzle plate measured 102·6 cm × 102·6 cm × 21 cm ($40\frac{3}{8}$ in × $40\frac{3}{8}$ in × $8\frac{1}{4}$ in) and contained a 45·7 cm (18 in) forged nozzle which protruded 22·9 cm (9 in) above the top plate surface, the nozzle bore being un-machined at 15·2 cm diameter (6 in); weight 1944 kg (1·91 Imperial tons).

Figures 1, 2 and 3 show drawings made of the test plates after arrival in the UK.

8. TEST PROCEDURES

As stated in Section 2 of this report the primary object of a European test programme was to augment the US results. This meant that if the European results were to be meaningful the inspection and reporting procedures must closely follow those of the US tests.

Following a review by the PVRC of the preliminary analysis of tests carried out in the US, the PVRC agreed to prepare a test procedure related to the schedule required by Section XI of the ASME Boiler and Pressure Vessel Code (the rules for In-Service Inspection of Nuclear Power Plant Components). The use of this test procedure for the PVRC programme (and hence the European PISC project) would permit practical verification of the Code procedure and demonstrate whether a more restrictive procedure would produce more accurate results.

The PVRC procedure was entitled 'Procedure for Manual Ultrasonic Examination of the PVRC Welded Test Blocks', 27th June, 1974. It was modified on 18th September, 1974 by the changing of scanning level from × 2 to × 5 and recording level to 50 % DAC.

This procedure formed the basis for the inspections carried out by the European participants. Apart from minor changes in wording to make clear the slight differences between terminology used in the US and Europe, the procedures were identical. The European document was issued and approved by the Technical Sub-Committee of PISC in November 1975. The procedure was issued in January 1976 for the commencement of the UK tests.

The procedure described the method for manual ultrasonic examination of the welds and heat-affected zone (HAZ) in compliance with Appendix I of Section XI, ASME Boiler and Pressure Vessel Code as it applies to a vessel in service, accessible only from the outer surface.

The extent of the examination was to measure the through wall dimension and length of flaws with angle beam tests. The full procedure incorporates the other modifications made in November 1976.

These modifications did not change the intent of the inspection exercise, were approved by the Secretary of the PVRC, and were intended to remove ambiguities in the procedure which had caused some confusion and hence loss of time.

Discussions at the beginning of the PISC project had revealed that many of the participating teams commercially used inspection techniques at variance with the laid down procedure of the PVRC/PISC procedures. It was seen to be advantageous to compare the results of these ultrasonic Alternative Techniques with the results of tests carried out to the formal PISC procedure. It was agreed that participating teams could carry out examinations using Alternative Techniques, results to be reported in the same format as the formal PISC examination results such that comparisons could be made. These inspections would be designated second round tests.

Calibration of the test equipment is a very important part of any ultrasonic examination and at the beginning of the programme there were no known calibration blocks available meeting ASME XI requirements available for loan in the UK. Calibration features were therefore machined into the plates. The PISC procedure allowed for the incorporated features in the test blocks to be used for calibration purposes.

9. NON-DESTRUCTIVE EXAMINATION

Although the PVRC procedure and the PISC procedure had laid down a recording level of 50 % DAC, the Technical Sub-Committee of the PISC had recommended that teams also record data down to 20 % DAC. The first inspection teams carried out this instruction which was included in the first part of the September 1974 modification to the PVRC procedure to increase the scan sensitivity from × 2 to × 5. This was not received with enthusiasm since two of the plates contained too many base material and weldment inclusions and/or flaws for this to be carried out in a commercial timescale. Some teams therefore restricted the reporting level to 50 % DAC. There were also complaints about the format of the reporting data sheets.

By October 1976 some 13 teams from Belgium, the Netherlands and UK had inspected the plates and reported to their respective National reporting officer (a total of 35 inspections). A meeting of the reporting officers was held in Brussels on 15th October, 1976 to discuss the presentation of results and to compare experiences with the procedure and consider the complaints as noted above.

It was felt that it would be unproductive to ask the remaining 16 teams (5 teams were still to join the programme) to experience the same problems and pitfalls in the procedure. This led to the issue of the final PISC procedure referred to in Section 8 of this report and to which all further testing was carried out.

All testing to the formal PISC and Alternative Procedures was completed at the beginning of June 1978, representing some $2\frac{1}{2}$ years of testing and $3\frac{1}{4}$ years running period of the programme.

10. DESTRUCTIVE EXAMINATION

To fulfil the terms of reference of the project it was necessary to make a comparison of the actual flaws in the test plates with flaws indicated by the test results. Theoretically, if the implanted flaws had been discrete with known dimensions for location and sizing, then it would have been possible to carry out an analysis without destructive examination. In practice this proves to be impossible. The work of the PVRC had shown that implanted flaws did not, in general, meet these requirements and thus analysis of the type carried out by Buchanan in the US could not be considered.

The method of destructive examination had been considered by the relevant sub-committee and the Steering Committee and the task was put in the hands of the Evaluation Task Force.

The absence of detailed information on the implanted flaws, (although radiographs had been provided by the PVRC) meant that the first task was to acquire information on these flaws and the results of the test teams were drawn out by hand. From these drawings it could be seen that the implanted flaws in the weldment and HAZ were in fact gross flaws, complex in shape and with very little separation. The results were further complicated by flaws in the base material. It was decided therefore that the only way to carry out a destructive examination was to proceed in steps with each step being fully documented and discussed by the ETF before deciding what the next step should be. Three main phases of destructive examination were initially identified with two subsequent stages for selected sections where necessary.

Phase I: Removal of the weldment from plates 50/52 and 51/53 and removal of the nozzle weldment from plate 204. This was followed by intensive ultrasonic inspection and high energy radiography to give more precise indications of the flaws before further sectioning.

Phase II: This phase consisted of systematic transverse sectioning of the plate weldments into slices, with the nozzle weldment being systematically sliced into wedges. Slices of approximately 50 mm thickness at the weld centreline were produced. After cutting each slice was ground, polished and etched on the cut face and macrographs were produced. Each slice was then subjected to radiography, ultrasonic testing, dye penetrant testing, and magnetic particle testing, and it was possible to detect flaws with a resolution of 0·3 mm to 0·5 mm in the 50 mm slices. As previously mentioned, trouble had been encountered with residual stresses in plate 51/53 but as this was unexpected no measurements had been made. It was decided that if residual stresses existed in nozzle plate 204 then an attempt would be made to measure them. The nozzle plate weldment was marked with a matrix on the cylindrical outside surface and following the first cut through the change in matrix position was measured. The results are now being analysed and it is only possible at this stage to say that the first cut reduced in thickness by 20% when the restraints were removed.

Phase III: This phase consisted of further cutting of the slices to within a few millimetres of the heat-affected zone giving in effect a piece of material, approximately 60 mm wide and 50 mm thick. Each piece was then subjected to intensive NDE to give more accurate sizing and location of flaws.

Phase IV: This phase consisted of further sectioning and reduction in size of the Phase III pieces, followed by intensive NDE to isolate individual flaws.

Phase V: This phase consisted of further sectioning when found necessary to resolve uncertainties, e.g. where a flaw diverged.

The destructive examination carried out on the test pieces was in the main carried out at the CEC Joint Research Centre, Ispra Establishment; however the following organisations also carried out controlled destructive examination on portions of the test plates: Association Vincotte, Brussels; the University of Ghent; MPA, Stuttgart; ENEL, Piacenzi; ECAN INDRET, Nantes. All involved organisations followed the same procedure in order to provide a precise map of the defects. Report No. 3 gives full details of the destructive examination.

11. EVALUATION AND ANALYSIS

The method of evaluation and analysis to be used was the subject of a great deal of discussion, both at Committee and informal meetings during the course of the project. It was clear that the main objective was to assess the reliability of a procedure for ultrasonic examination to:

(1)   detect flaws,
(2)   position flaws,
(3)   size flaws, and
(4)   evaluate flaws against the ASME Code, Section XI criteria for acceptance or rejection.

If the implanted flaws had been discrete this would have been a relatively simple task. However, the preliminary assessment of the NDE results prior to destructive examination indicated that both the weldment and the base material contained a large number of flaws. These flaws, ranging in size from large to very small and by virtue of their relative proximity, mostly below reporting level, had an adverse effect on the plan to utilize the number of all flaws as a basis for the statistics. To combat this problem those small flaws in the base material were neglected and small flaws in the weldment and HAZ below 6 mm^2 were rejected as insignificant, thereby eliminating a large number of defects from the analysis. The use of the ASME proximity rules for plate 51/53 for example, indicated that only one 'flaw' existed running the whole length of the weldment and through the whole thickness of the plate! Therefore, in this and other cases the ASME XI proximity rules were modified to enable the analysis to be carried out. Hence for the purposes of the evaluation, only those defects in the weld and the HAZ were considered.

With 34 teams producing results from three plates by both the formal PISC procedure and in many cases the Alternative Procedures, it was found necessary to use computer facilities to handle the data. All results from the tests were entered into a data bank as three-dimensional co-ordinates of the indicated flaw in the X, Y and Z planes. These indicated flaw co-ordinates could then be compared with the co-ordinates of the reference defect as defined following destructive examination.

Full details of the method of evaluation and analysis including the computer programme are given in Report No. 4.

11.1. Comparison Procedure of the Results of all Teams with the DE Results

11.1.1. Simple Statistical Treatment

The available data base was too small to enable a completely comprehensive statistical analysis to be carried out, but sufficiently large for some parameters of importance to be estimated. Consequently, the initial analysis has concentrated on the calculation of these parameters and no complicated statistical ideas have been invoked.

11.1.2. Parameters to be Estimated

The most significant parameters for the evaluation of the procedure were judged to be the following:

(a) *Defect Detection Probability (DDP)*: This is defined as $DDP = n/N$ where n is the number of teams detecting the particular defect and N is the total number of teams participating. Confidence bounds are put to this number in the usual way. DDP is a function of size and position (including orientation) of the defect.

(b) *The Quality and Error of Location, QL and EL*: These are defined in Report No. 4 and give a measure of the accuracy of the procedure for locating each defect. A quality of 1 or an error of 0 indicates perfect positioning.

(c) *The Quality and Error of Sizing, QS and ES*: These are defined in Report No. 4 for all three planes. It is the height of the defect projection in the YZ plane (or in the nozzle in the ϕZ plane) which is the most important for correct sizing. Again a quality of 1 or an error of 0 indicates perfect sizing.

(d) *Quality of Acceptance, QA, or Quality of Rejection, QR:* These are defined relative to the ASME XI rules for accepting or rejecting a defect and are discussed in detail in Report No. 4.

(e) *Correct Rejection Probability (CRP) or Correct Acceptance Probability (CAP):* These are defined as CRP (CAP) = r/N where r is the number of teams correctly rejecting (accepting) a rejectable (acceptable) defect, according to the ASME XI rules.

12. COMPARISON OF NDE/DE RESULTS

Full details of the comparison are given in Report No. 5. All teams presented their results as a Data Sheet 5 which contained the X, Y and Z coordinates within the plates produced from the raw examination data ($R\theta Z$ co-ordinates for the nozzle plate 204). This was used to generate a Data Sheet 6 using the computer and applying the relevant ASME rules.

Teams also produced a Data Sheet 6 of the actual defect again in X, Y and Z or $R\theta Z$ co-ordinates. This Data Sheet 6 involved their interpretation of the raw data as gathered in Data Sheet 5.

Comparisons have therefore been made for each flaw of:

(1)   Data Sheet 6 (team result) against reference flaw,
(2)   Data Sheet 6 (computer) against reference flaw, and
(3)   an average of the alternative techniques co-ordinates against the reference flaw.

The average co-ordinates were used because at this stage no time was allocated for a detailed analysis of alternative procedures.

The flaws in plates 50/52 and 51/53 were numerous, some 500 were discovered during the destructive examination. In addition there were numerous defects in the base material, porosity, inclusions and cracks. Some of these defects clearly had some effect on the inspections but it had not been possible in the timescale to analyse the effect in depth. With such a large number of flaws, many in close proximity and even the gross flaws not being easily separated, it was necessary that comparisons must be made making use of a code of practice, in this case ASME XI. The analysis of possible errors in recording NDE data as described in Appendix 3 of Report

No. 2 by Caussin, showed that location errors as large as 9 cm could be expected, and thus if all individual flaws had to be considered then there would be great difficulty in determining which NDE indicated flaw should be considered against the reference flaw.

The method of comparison has therefore been restricted to flaws which were contained in the weld and HAZ. In doing so, 37 defects and defective zones remained in the evaluation. Among these 37 defects, 31 were acceptable according to the ASME code, Section XI specification, the remainder being unacceptable.

For the nozzle plate 204, all but one of the flaws would, under ASME rules be acceptable but they have been considered because they are discrete and can be evaluated.

Before comparison could be made it was necessary to correct many of the NDE results. These are detailed in Report No. 2. These corrections were mainly associated with teams using incorrect references, i.e. edge of plate, mixing up X and Y co-ordinates, incorrect angular reference on nozzle plate (clockwise/anti-clockwise). Although these errors were correctly resolved, it cost a great deal of time and effort which could have been saved if all teams had worked rigorously to the procedure, and the procedure itself had not contained ambiguities.

13.   FUNDING

The project was not funded in the conventional manner. Each of the participating teams paid for their own examination and for the transport costs to receive the plates, with SRD bearing the overall management costs. Early in the project, it was decided to seek CEC funding for the cost of destructive examination which the Destructive Examination Technical Sub-Group estimated to be approximately 110 000 UA (Units of Account). Tenders were called for and received from some of the participants, but in the event the CEC Joint Research Centre, Ispra Establishment were able to offer to carry out the destructive examination within their existing capability and funding, and the request for CEC external funding was withdrawn. Subsequently, the JRC were also able to offer their services in the overall evaluation of the NDE and DE results.

To help in maintaining the scheduled timescale it was agreed that CEC would make a contribution to the Belgian and French teams to carry out some portion of the more specialised aspects of the DE. 10 000 UA were allocated in each case.

Full details of inspection costs are not available but a global estimate has been made of the total cost of the PISC project as below.

1.	Management costs (SRD)		US$ 120 000
2.	Inspection costs, covered by national teams		US$ 640 000
3.	Destructive examination and		
	evaluation—JRC, Ispra	UA 265 000	
	CEC Contracts	UA 30 000	
		UA 295 000	US$ 370 000
4.	Costs covered by government funding		
	support (FDR)		US$ 500 000
		Total:	US$ 1 630 000

These costs are not fully realistic, as overheads on plant, equipment and machinery have not necessarily been included, particularly in items 2 and 3.

Of this sum approximately half was spent during the year 1978/79.

14.   GENERAL CONCLUSIONS

The PISC project was initially a self-financing long-term project with members comprising a mixture of commercial and national organisations. No financial reward has accrued to the participants and it has been shown to be a remarkable example of international co-operation. The problems that have occurred during the long timescale have been technical and not incompatibility between participants. During the initial inspections the problems were mainly concerned with getting the procedure correct and maintaining the momentum to keep the project on programme. There were also the problems caused by the metallurgical state of two of the plates which extended the destructive examination phase and also complicated the evaluation and analysis requirements.

The amount of data available for investigation is vast (some 1000 sheets of computer data are available).

The effect of flaws extraneous to the weldment has not been evaluated and will be the subject of further investigation and analysis for which discussions are now taking place. In addition a full analysis of the alternative techniques is to be carried out to complement the PISC reports; only average results have been included to date.

ACKNOWLEDGEMENTS

The Plate Inspection Committee wishes to acknowledge the great help and co-operation of all participants in the project as well as the help and advice from many experts in the field.

Acknowledgement is given to the CEC and the OECD for their sponsorship of the project and the CEC funding of the destructive examination and evaluation via the Joint Research Centre, Ispra Establishment. Finally, it should be remembered that the programme would not have begun but for the generous offer of the plates by the US Pressure Vessel Research Committee in the first place, who have subsequently kept the PISC project up to date with information regarding their own programme.

APPENDIX I

Plate Inspection Steering Committee 1979

1.	Mr R. O'Neil (Chairman)	UK	—UKAEA (SRD)
2.	*Mr A. L. Adams (Secretary)**	UK	—UKAEA (SRD)
3.	*Mr P. Caussin	B	—Association Vincotte
4.	*Mr S. Crutzen	CEC	—JRC Ispra
5.	Dr G. Deuster	FRG	—IZFP
6.	*Miss K. Gott	S	—Studsvik Energiteknik AB
7.	*Mr H. D. Harbecke	FRG	—GRS Cologne
8.	*Mr A. Juva	SF	—VVT
9.	*Mr G. V. Maciga	I	—ENEL, Central Laboratory, Piacenza
10.	Mr H. A. Maurer	CEC	—DG-XII, Brussels
11.	*Mr N. Nielsen	DK	—Danish Welding Institute
12.	Mr P. Oliver	OECD	—Nuclear Energy Agency
13.	*Mr A. C. Prot	F	—CEA, Fontenay-aux-Roses
14.	*Dr L. Santoma	E	—Junta de Energia Nuclear
15.	*Mr A. de Sterke	NL	—RTD

Legend

UKAEA (SRD)—United Kingdom Atomic Energy Authority (Safety and Reliability Directorate)

* National representatives.
** Previous secretaries were: Mr G. Lindsay: May 1975–Sept. 1975.
                              Mr H. Crisp: Sept. 1975–Nov. 1977.

CEC   —Commission of the European Communities
JRC   —Joint Research Centre
IZFP   —Institut fur Zerstorungsfreie Prufverfahren, Saarbrucken
GRS   —Gesellschaft fur Reaktor Sicherheit
VVT   —Technical Research Centre of Finland
ENEL   —Ente Nazionale per l'Energia Elettrica
OECD   —Organisation for Economic Co-operation and Development
RTD   —Rontgen Technische Dienst
CEA   —Commissariat a l'Energie Atomique

Plate Inspection Steering Sub-Committees
Technical Sub-Committee

1. Dr R. W. Nichols (Chairman)	UK	—UKAEA (RNPDL)
2. Mr B. Lack	UK	—Clarke Chapman Ltd
3. Mr F. E. Lawrence	UK	—AOTC
4. Dr G. Oates	UK	—CEGB Scientific Services
5. Mr A. V. Scott	UK	—Babcock & Wilcox Ltd
6. Mr J. G. Young	UK	—Welding Institute
7. Mr G. E. Lindsay (Secretary)	UK	—UKAEA (SRD)

Destructive Testing Technical Working Group (DTWG)

1. Mr A. de Sterke (Chairman)	NL	—RTD
2. Mr T. R. Mager	B	—Westinghouse Nuclear Europe
3. Dr H. J. Maier	FRG	—MPA
4. Dr G. Oates	UK	—CEGB Scientific Services
5. Mr A. C. Prot	F	—CEA
6. Dr D. Sturm	FRG	—MPA
7. Mr N. Kirby (Secretary)	UK	—UKAEA (RNPDL)

Evaluation Task Force (ETF)

1. Mr P. Caussin (Chairman)	B	—Association Vincotte
2. Mr A. L. Adams	UK	—UKAEA (SRD)
3. Mr S. J. Crutzen	CEC	—JRC, Ispra
4. Dr G. Deuster	FRG	—IZFP
5. Miss K. E. Gott	S	—Studsvik Energiteknik AB
6. Mr J. F. Gouez	F	—ECAN Indret
7. Mr A. Juva	SF	—VTT
8. Dr G. Maciga	I	—ENEL Piacenza

9. Mr N. Nielsen	DK	—Danish Welding Institute
10. Mr P. Oliver	OECD	—NEA Paris
11. Dr G. W. Parry	UK	—UKAEA (SRD)
12. Mr J. Reynen	CEC	—JRC, Ispra
13. Mr J. B. Perez Prat	E	—Tecnatom
14. Mr A. de Sterke	NL	—RTD
15. Mr E. Higham (Secretary)	UK	—UKAEA (SRD)

Evaluation Task Force Sub-Group

1. Mr A. L. Adams	UK	—UKAEA (SRD)
2. Mr P. Caussin	B	—Association Vincotte
3. Mr S. J. Crutzen	CEC	—JRC, Ispra
4. Dr G. Deuster	FRG	—IZFP
5. Mr J. F. Gouez	F	—ECAN Indiret

PISC Participants (NDT)

No. of participants	Country	National representative	Participating organisation	Participants town
10	United Kingdom	United Kingdom Atomic Energy Authority, Safety and Reliability Directorate (SRD)	Risley Nuclear Power Development Lab. (RNPDL) (REML)	Risley
			Quality Inspection Services Ltd (QIS)	Stockton
			Central Electricity Generating Board (CEGB)	Manchester
			Associated Offices Technical Cttee. (AOTC)	Manchester
			Rolls Royce & Associates Ltd (RR&A)	Derby
			Ministry of Defence (MOD)	Keynsham
			Atomic Energy Research Establishment (AERE)	Harwell
			The Welding Institute	Cambridge
			The Unit Inspection Company	Swansea
			Babcock Inspection	Renfrew
2	The Netherlands	Rontgen Technische Dienst (RTD)	Rontgen Technische Dienst BV (RTD)	Rotterdam
			Dienst voor het Stoomwezen	The Hague

No. of partici-pants	Country	National representative	Participating organisation	Participants town
2	Belgium	Association Vincotte	Association Vincotte	Brussels
			Westinghouse Nuclear Europe	Brussels
1	Denmark	The Danish Welding Institute	The Danish Welding Institute	Glostrup
1	Sweden	Studsvik Energiteknik AB	Tekniska Rontgen centralen AB (TRC)	Stockholm
4	Federal Republic of Germany	Institut fur Reaktorsicherheit (IRS) Koln	Institut fur zerstorungsfreie Prufverfahren (IZFP)	Saarbrucken
			Bundesanstalt fur Materialprufung (BAM)	Berlin
			Kraftwerk Union (KWU)	Erlangen
			Rheinisch-Westfalischer Technischer Uber-wachungs-Verein (RW TUV)	Essen
7	France	Commissariat a l'Energie Atomique (CEA)	Framatome	Courbevoi
			Commissariat a l'Energie Atomique (CEA)	Saclay
			Establissement des Constructions et Armes Navales (ECAN) Indret	La Montagne
			Direction Technique des Constructions Navales (DTCN)	Paris
			Electricite de France	St. Denis
			Centre d'Etudes Techniques des Industries Mecaniques	Senlis
			Institut de Soudure	Paris
2	Italy	ENEL, Central Laboratory	ENEL, Central Laboratory	Piacenza
			JRC	Ispra
4	Spain	Ministerio de Industria Junta de Energia Nuclear	ATISAE SA	Madrid
			Equipos Nucleares SA	Santander
			CIAT Nuclear SA	Madrid
			Tecnatom SA	Madrid
1	Finland	Valtion Teknillinen Tutkimuskeskus (VTT)	VTT Technical Research Centre of Finland	Espoo

Contributors to the Destructive Examination

1. JRC, Ispra Establishment	CEC	Main contractor
2. ECAN–INDRET, La Montagne	France	
3. ENEL, Central Laboratory, Piacenza	Italy	
4. Association Vincotte, Brussels	Belgium	
5. MPA (Materialprufungsanstalt), University of Stuttgart	FRG	
6. University of Ghent, Strength of Materials Laboratory	Belgium	
7. BREDA, Termomeccanica, Milan	Italy	

APPENDIX II

Meetings of the Plate Inspection Steering Committee

Preliminary Meeting	13th February, 1975	Cologne, FRG
1st Meeting	8th May, 1975	London, UK
2nd Meeting	2nd September, 1975	London, UK
3rd Meeting	20th May, 1976	Rotterdam, The Netherlands
4th Meeting	30th November, 1976	Brussels, Belgium
5th Meeting	24th March, 1977	Erlangen, FRG
6th Meeting	12th July, 1977	Saclay, France
7th Meeting	28th November, 1977	Ispra, Italy
8th Meeting	10th April, 1978	Madrid, Spain
9th Meeting	28th September, 1978	Berlin, FRG
10th Meeting	5th February, 1979	Ispra, Italy
11th Meeting	27th March, 1979	Ispra, Italy
12th Meeting	17th May, 1979	Ispra, Italy

APPENDIX III

Paper No.	Title	Author
PISC/ETF(77)P1	Phase I Sectioning Procedure for PISC Weldments 50/52, 51/53 and 204	E. Higham
PISC/ETF(78)P1	PISC ETF Terms of Reference	P. Caussin
PISC/ETF(78)P2	Guidelines for the Analysis of Results of PISC Trials	P. Caussin
PISC/ETF(78)P3	Machining Facilities Available at Ispra for Destructive Examination of the PISC Plates	S. J. Crutzen
PISC/ETF(78)P4	Date Treatment Proposals for the PISC Plates NDE Results Comparison with the Destructive Examination	S. J. Crutzen
PISC/ETF(78)P5	Proposals for the Analysis of the PISC Trials Results	H. Harper
PISC/ETF(78)P6	Proposals for an Analysis Scheme of the PISC Trials Results	S. J. Crutzen and G. Parry
PISC/ETF(78)P7	Evaluation of NDE Results of PISC Trials without 'DE' as Reference	S. J. Crutzen
PISC/ETF(78)P8	Radiographic Examination of Sectional Plate-Weld Specimens	G. V. Maciga
PISC/ETF(78)P9	Ultrasonic testing of the PISC Resulting Blocks after Phase I Cutting of the Three Plates	S. J. Crutzen, C. Vinche and E. Borloo
PISC/ETF(78)P10	Preliminary Sectioning of the PISC Blocks at the JRC, Ispra	L. di Piazza and S. J. Crutzen
PISC/ETF(78)P11	Phase II Sectioning Procedure for PISC Weldments 50/52, 51/53	E. Higham
PISC/ETF(78)P12	Phase II Sectioning Procedure for Nozzle Weldments 204	E. Higham and S. J. Crutzen

Report No. 2:
Ultrasonic Examination of the PVRC Plates

A. C. PROT

CEA, Gif sur Yvette, France

G. DEUSTER

IZFP, Saarbrücken, FRG

and

J. B. PEREZ PRAT

Tecnatom, Madrid, Spain

1. INTRODUCTION

The scope of this second report is a description of the NDE techniques, used by the participants in the PISC exercise to detect and size the defects.

The characterisation and calibration of the equipment used for the PISC procedure is described and discussed.

All the results have been incorporated into a data bank stored on magnetic tape. This data is the input for the analysis of the results and the comparison between the NDE and DE results to be discussed in a later presentation.

1.1. Test Plates

In the frame of the PISC programme three plates for the non-destructive examination were available:

Test specimen 50/52   (electro slag weld)
Test specimen 51/53   (submerged arc weld)
Test specimen 204   (nozzle weld)

2. DESCRIPTION OF THE PISC PROCEDURE

This procedure describes a method for ultrasonic examination of welds and heat-affected zones (HAZ) in compliance with the ASME Boiler and

Pressure Vessel Code, Section XI, Appendix 1, 1974 and Addenda available at the time the PISC Programme was started, as it applies to a vessel in service and accessible from the outer surface only.

This procedure was prepared by the PVRC and later modified in September 1974. Differences between this procedure and the ASME Code, Section XI procedure, as well as the particularities of the plates are described in Part 1 of this chapter.

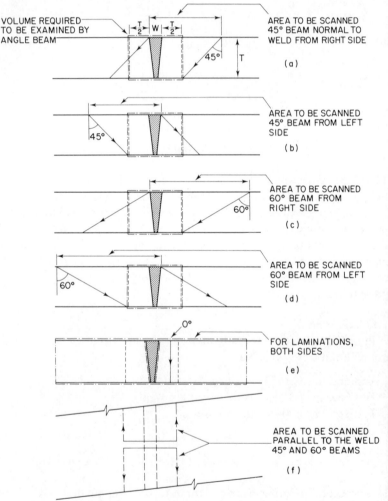

FIG. 1. Examination requirements for plates 50/52 and 51/53.

2.1. Plate Welds

The weld, HAZ and base material adjacent to each side of the weld are examined over a distance from the weld equal to half the weld (plate) thickness, as shown in Fig. 1, using a straight beam and angle beams of 45° and 60°. An extra examination is carried out for the volume of base material through which the angle beams will travel. This examination is performed with a straight beam search unit to detect laminar reflectors.

The examination of the weld with angle beams is performed by directing the beams normal to the weld and from both sides of the weld, as well as by directing the beams parallel to the weld and from each direction, as shown in Fig. 1.

The adjacent base material is examined by the 45° and 60° angle beams from one direction normal to the weld and one direction parallel to the weld, see again Fig. 1.

The examination for transverse defects, where the angle beam is directed in two opposite directions parallel to the weld, is restricted to the area indicated in Fig. 1.

All above examinations are done from the 'outside' surface of the specimens.

2.2. Nozzle Welds

The weld and HAZ, and the adjacent base material are examined as shown in Fig. 2 with a straight beam and 45° and 60° angle beams. The volume of plate base material through which the beam will travel in the angle beam examination is also examined with a straight beam search unit.

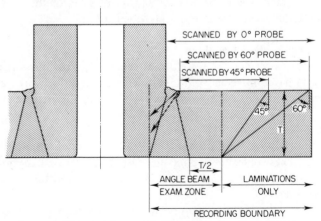

FIG. 2.   Examination requirements for nozzle weld 204.

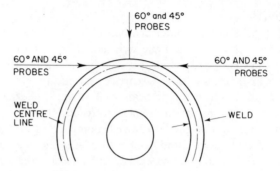

TANGENTIAL TEST OF THE NOZZLE PLATE WELD

Fig. 3.   Scanning requirements for nozzle weld 204.

Laminar reflectors, detected by straight beam tests, are recorded. Only those sections of each scan are omitted where any part of the ultrasonic beam is intercepted by a lamination or area of laminar inclusions.

The angle beam examination is performed normal to the weld in one direction, and tangential to the weld from two directions with 45° and 60° angle beams, as shown in Fig. 3.

2.3. Plate Weldment

Scan overlap: to ensure complete coverage of the material, each successive pass of the search unit must overlap a minimum of 10% of the beam width at the probe.

Nozzle weld: a sound beam overlapping of 10% of the sound beam diameter at the weld centre line is provided for.

2.4. Contact Surface Condition

The surfaces are free from weld spatter and any roughness that would interfere with free movement of the search unit. The surfaces are free of dirt, loose scale, machining or grinding particles or other loose foreign matter.

2.5. Test Block

The calibration reflectors are side-drilled holes and notches in the PVRC specimens. These holes correspond in location and size with the holes in the ASME Code, Section XI test blocks. Surface calibration notches are included (Fig. 4).

Details of the calibration features in the test blocks are incorporated on the drawings, in Figs. 1, 2 and 3 of Part 1 of this chapter.

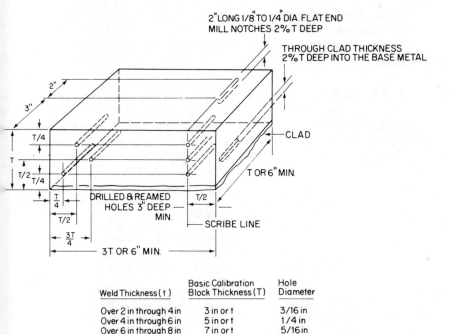

FIG. 4. Calibration block (after ASME Boiler and Pressure Vessel Code, Section XI).

Weld Thickness (t)	Basic Calibration Block Thickness (T)	Hole Diameter
Over 2 in through 4 in	3 in or t	3/16 in
Over 4 in through 6 in	5 in or t	1/4 in
Over 6 in through 8 in	7 in or t	5/16 in
Over 8 in through 10 in	9 in or t	3/8 in
Over 10 in	*	*

*For each increase in thickness of 2 in or fraction thereof the hole diameter shall increase 1/16 in

3. CALIBRATION AND CHARACTERISATION OF THE ULTRASONIC EQUIPMENT

3.1. Equipment

Pulse–echo ultrasonic examination systems in which results are displayed on A-scan CRT (cathode ray tube) screen are used.

3.2. Couplant

The couplant is specified, and recorded on each Calibration Data Sheet and Examination Data Sheet; it may be glycerine, oil, grease, or cellulose paste.

3.3. Amplitude Linearity

The ultrasonic instrument provides a linear (within $\pm 5\%$ of full screen) vertical display for at least 80% of the screen height (sweep line to top of screen).

3.4. Calibrated Gain Control Linearity

The ultrasonic instrument utilises a calibrated gain control, accurate over its useful range to $\pm 20\%$ of the nominal amplitude ratio, which allows measurement of indications beyond the linear range of the amplitude display of the screen.

3.5. Type, Frequency and Size of Transducers

(1) Straight beam examination: transducers of between 2 and 3 MHz and of between 20 and 25 mm diameter, are used.
(2) Angle beam examination: equivalent transducers of 2–3 MHz and 20–25 mm diameter are used, arranged in such a way that they will emit sound at nominal refracted angles of 45° and 60° in steel.

3.6. Search Unit Performance

Search units should have the following performance when operated with the ultrasonic instrumentation:

3.6.1. Spectral Response

The centre frequency has to be $\pm 10\%$ of the specified test frequency, with a bandwidth at the 6 dB points of not more than 25% of the test frequency.

3.6.2. Refracted Angle

The refracted angle, as measured on the IIW block (having a shear wave velocity of $3 \cdot 23 \times 10^3$ m/s in the direction of sound propagation), must be $\pm 3°$ for the 60° refracted angle and $\pm 2°$ for the 45° refracted angle.

3.6.3. Beam Axis and Symmetry

The axis of the sound beam must exit from a point on the contact surface of the search unit:

straight beam: at the centre of the housing,
angle beam: at a point midway across the width of the search unit at the beam exit line. Marks or notches on the wedge indicating the location of the exit line, must be within $\pm 0 \cdot 6$ mm ($\pm 0 \cdot 025$ in) of the measured point.

The beam must be symmetrical, ± 3 mm ($\pm 0 \cdot 125$ in), around the central axis at the Y_0^+ position at the 6 dB points at 90° around the axis, and angle beam units must be checked at the leading and trailing edges of the beam in the vertical plane, and at points 90° from these points in the horizontal plane.

3.7. Sensitivity Check

The combination search unit and instrument, as used to perform the examination, must have a minimum 30 dB gain remaining after adjusting the sensitivity of the instrument for an 80 % amplitude signal from the appropriate calibration reflector of the calibration blocks.

3.8. Calibration Blocks

Calibration holes and notches are in accordance with the ASME Code, Section XI (Fig. 4), except for plate 51/53, on which the positioning of the reference hole is erroneous (see PISC Report No. 1).

3.9. DAC Curve

(1) DAC curves established on calibration holes, must fall within 10 % of the calculated values of the Y_0^- and Y_0^+ points, which represent the last near-field dip and peak along the sound axis.

(2) The distance amplitude correction is established as shown in Fig. 5.

(3) Split DAC. In the event that the indication from the 3/4 T calibration reflector is less than 25 % of the screen amplitude, a second DAC curve must be generated, as shown in Fig. 6.

3.10. Characterisation of Ultrasonic Transducers

Some teams carried out a complete characterisation of transducers with the aim of finding out which transducers to choose for the examination of

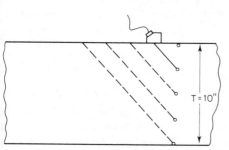
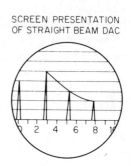

SCREEN PRESENTATION OF STRAIGHT BEAM DAC

T = 10"

FIG. 5.   DAC curve.

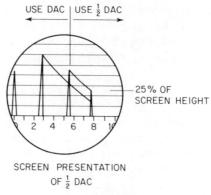

USE DAC | USE $\frac{1}{2}$ DAC

25% OF SCREEN HEIGHT

2 4 6 8 10

SCREEN PRESENTATION
OF $\frac{1}{2}$ DAC

Fig. 6.   Split DAC.

the plates according to the PISC procedure. Only a few of those tested were in accordance with the PISC specifications. From such an examination it appears possible that few teams used transducers which complied with the PISC specifications with regard to the following parameters: frequency, bandwidth, crystal diameter, nominal angle, Y_0^+ distance, beam axis and symmetry, sensitivity, and beam index.

4.   RESULTS DATA

Sheet 5 is the final defect report sheet. It converts the probe position on Data Sheet 4 to actual defect positions as X–Y–Z coordinates with their ranges. These ranges cut off at 50 % DAC. The reference point for Data Sheet 5 is the bench-mark on each test piece.

Sheet 6 is the combination of the indications reported on DS 5. When producing DS 6 teams were expected to use their experience and intuition of the defect to condense as many indications as possible into only one defect. In the case of multiple defects they were to apply proximity rules to assemble defects together.

4.1.   Defect Sizing

The X–Y–Z coordinates have a range to accommodate the length, width and depth of the defects (the reported lengths being related to 50 % DAC cut-off), and since any defect may exist in three dimensions, each X–Y–Z coordinate can have a range. This allows defects of different orientations to be sized with reasonable accuracy.

5. NDT DATA BANK

5.1. Results of NDT

Results of NDT can be divided into two separate categories; (1) defects detected in the welded zone, and (2) defects detected in the base material. The PISC exercise was oriented mainly towards the welded zones (weld + HAZ); therefore defects outside these zones (base material defects) have been treated in a very simple way, or eliminated from the analysis.

5.2.Computerised Image of the Defect

5.2.1. General Description

Using a simple computer program the results submitted by the teams have been listed in the following manner:

(1) List of data submitted by the team
(2) View of the defects projected into the plane $X-Y$ (outside surface)
(3) List of the corrected data.

To gain a clear view of the significant defects and to eliminate insignificant indications and points which arose from using DS5, proximity rules of ASME XI, IWB 3340 and 3350 have been applied.

5.2.2. Data Sheet 5 and Data Sheet 6 Computerised: DS 5 and DS 6 C

The information from DS 5 was used by the computer to produce a Data Sheet 6 Computerised (DS 6 C), to get a precise image of the findings reported by each team applying the PISC procedure and without any corrections included by the teams.

5.2.3. Continuity of the 'Amplitude'

The amplitude of the defect is retained during the operation of condensing the defects using the ASME Code, Section XI proximity rules.

The input data from DS 5 and the corresponding computerised data DS 6 C were listed, the rules for dealing with close-approaching defects given in the ASME Boiler and Pressure Vessel Code, Section XI (the 'proximity' rules) being applied. From these inputs the computer produced diagrammatic representations of the results such as that represented in Fig. 7.

In order to judge the capability for detecting, locating and sizing of the different teams these results were compared with the reference defects after the destructive examination which is explained later on.

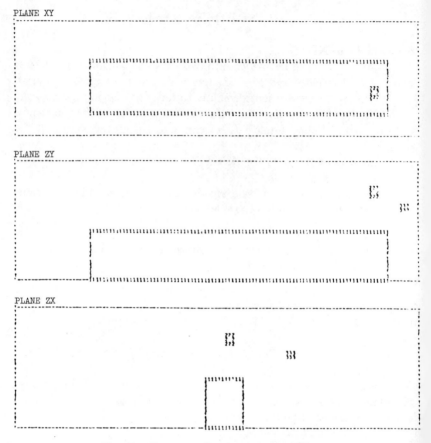

FIG. 7.   Computer drawing based on DS 6 C.

6.   CONCLUSIONS

(1)   For the operators who were not masters of the English language the procedure had to be translated: this sometimes led to a misinterpretation of several paragraphs.

(2)   The definition of the coordinate system for the plates was not completely clear in the first instance: therefore a lot of errors in location occurred and had to be corrected. Some uncertainties also arose when transforming the coordinates of the nozzle plate from a cartesian to a polar coordinate system.

(3) The procedure prescribed an exact pattern for scanning with the probes, that is, it tried to emulate the normal mechanical in-service inspection system; the operator had difficulties as he was not allowed to move the transducer out of the scan line.

(4) The examination conditions of plate 51/53 were disturbed due to a curvature obviously caused by a not optimal heat treatment during welding. For the nozzle plate 204 some areas of interest were not accessible for most of the applied techniques due to geometrical reasons.

(5) Several hundreds of indications were found and had to be handled for evaluation; often it was unavoidable that flaws in the base material, lying on the sound beam, influenced the detection, locating and sizing of the defects in the weld.

(6) It was considered that the size and distribution of defects were not typical of those found in practice. The quality of the plate material was also not typical, containing a large number of defects, and would therefore be unacceptable for nuclear construction.

(7) The NDT results lay in a large scatter band. However the investigation did not consider the quality of the individual results from each team or from the teams collectively.

7. ALTERNATIVE TECHNIQUES

The inspection teams were free to use any alternative ultrasonic procedures to examine the plates, so long as details of the procedure were reported and the results presented in the same manner as the results using the PISC procedure. These procedures fall into two main groups; (1) hand techniques and (2) automatic techniques. Account also has to be taken of whether the examination was performed from the inside and/or outside surfaces of the plates and from the inside of the nozzle.

Data were recorded from the following alternative techniques: (The analysis of these techniques has not yet been fully investigated.)

(1) Focussed probes using immersion technique and contact method,
(2) tandem technique,
(3) acoustic holography,
(4) high frequency back scattering techniques,
(5) amplitude–time locus curves,
(6) delta technique,

(7)   double transducer, longitudinal wave angle probes,
(8)   phased arrays,
(9)   surface waves,
(10) P scan,
(11) other standard probes and surface testing methods.

Some techniques have for certain defects an optimised sensitivity, resolution power and capability of sizing. Their application delivered a larger amount of indications in comparison to the PISC procedure. Some of these techniques are used in the field and are especially developed for application during in-service inspection in order to give a higher detectability and a better analysis of the flaws found.

8.   FINAL COMMENT

The first evaluation of all NDT results seems to indicate a certain inability of the PISC procedure to detect and size correctly, certain types of defects. In opposition most of the alternative procedures especially those using new ultrasonic methods seem to exhibit a better ability to detect as well as to size the flaws to be considered.

Report No. 3
Destructive Examination of the PVRC Plates

S. J. Crutzen

JRC, Ispra, Italy

and

K. Gott

Studsvik Energiteknik AB, Nyköping, Sweden

1.   INTRODUCTION

The destructive examination of the PVRC blocks donated to the PISC was required to obtain the precise and complete description of all the defects the

NDT techniques were supposed to find, locate and size. This precise map of the defects was to be used as the reference for the PISC trial results evaluation. For a complete description the reader is referred to the original PISC document: Report No. 3 issued by the CEC [1].

The destructive examination was carried out under the guidance of a sub-committee of the PISC, the ETF (Evaluation Task Force), at several laboratories involved in the programme, but mainly at the JRC, Ispra.

2. PHILOSOPHY FOR THE DESTRUCTIVE EXAMINATION

Knowledge of the location and size of all the defects in the plates was essential for the complete evaluation of the PISC trials. All defects of 1 mm or less (or groups of smaller defects) had to be considered. Thus the destructive examination was discontinued once NDT, conducted under favourable conditions on small sections of plate, was able to detect all defects larger, or equal to 1 mm in diameter, or when defects could be sized to within 1 mm although only one portion of the defect was visible. Complete destructive examination was therefore only carried out on those sections for which it was necessary, or to give illustrative examples.

In order to avoid any doubt as to the original position of a defect, scrupulous attention was paid to marking the specimen pieces at all stages. Moreover, NDT was also used in the destructive examination: decisions concerning discontinuation were based on the results of high-performance NDT. Decisions to depart from systematic sectioning were based on high-frequency focused probe ultrasonic examination or radiography.

3. PHASE I SECTIONING

In order to be able to identify at all times any portion of any plate, a comprehensive system was adopted for marking the plates [2]. It is illustrated in Fig. 1, and was scrupulously followed at all stages of the destructive examination on each fresh surface which was produced.

Plate 51/53 was curved, and all dimensions and markings were measured from the horizontal plane and not from the curved surface.

In order to be consistent with the original markings, the reference for the destructive examination of the nozzle plate 204, was taken at 135° anticlockwise from the original markings. These were not consistent with the scanning lines laid down on the PISC procedure [3].

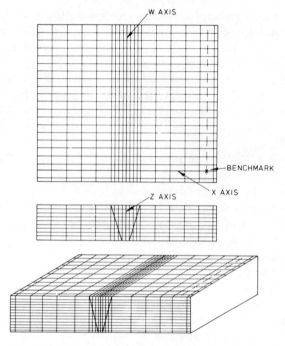

Fig. 1. Plate marked with all axes and scribe lines.

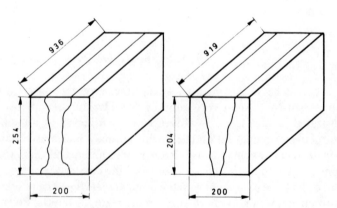

Fig. 2. Weldments of plates 50/52 and 51/53.

In order to keep the effort required within reason, and also to maintain an acceptable time scale, it was agreed to limit detailed examination to the region of the weld and its immediate surroundings [2].

Using all the NDT data available by April 1978 (about 12 teams), rough diagrams of their findings were traced on to transparencies. By simple superposition it was possible to define the minimum portion which could be defined as 'weldment'. This was defined as the regions up to 100 mm on either side of the centre-lines of plates 50/52 and 51/53, Fig. 2, and is shown in Fig. 3 for plate 204.

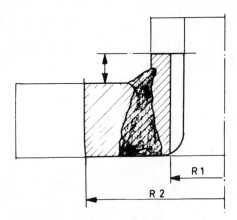

FIG. 3.   Weldment of plate 204.

With plate 51/53, difficulties were encountered in the final phase of cutting. During the last saw passes, a horizontal recess appeared in the piece, resulting in the saw blade becoming jammed, probably because of unanticipatedly large residual stresses in the plate. To complete this phase, the workshop had to use special clamps to retain the plate in position (see Figs. 4 and 5).

In order to preserve as much material as possible and also to retain the external part of plate 204 as a single block, the central core was removed by drilling overlapping holes. The surface was then machined so that the external diameter measured about 710 mm. The internal diameter was enlarged to 360 mm and the nozzle protrusion reduced to 40 mm. No difficulties were experienced during these operations.

Following the cutting of the blocks, high-performance NDT techniques

FIG. 4.   Cutting of the weldment from plate 51/53 at JRC, Ispra.

FIG. 5.   Removal of the weldment from plate 204 at JRC, Ispra.

were used on all the weldments in order to obtain more information concerning the defects to be revealed by further cutting. It was also important that the defects were not destroyed by future operations, and the NDT results were therefore examined very carefully. The main techniques used were ultrasonics at JRC, Ispra and X-rays performed by Breda Termomeccanica, Milan, under the control of ENEL.

The position of each defect was estimated from the radiographs, correcting for the beam divergence which varied between 0·9 and 1·0. Steel plate screens had been placed on the specimen sides to reduce poor definition; even so some difficulties were experienced with plate 51/53 due to its curvature.

Both immersion and contact ultrasonic techniques were used at this stage. Focused transducers were used for verifying some defects. Examinations were performed on the lateral faces of the blocks, and verified through the top and underneath, using an immersion technique for plates 50/52 and 51/53, and a contact technique for plate 204. Flat bottom holes were used for calibration with respect to sizing and sensitivity.

The combined results from both techniques are shown in Fig. 6. Some defects have not been included since they were clearly base material defects which were not to be considered for the destructive examination. From the high-frequency ultrasonic results however, they seemed to be present everywhere!

4. PHASE II SECTIONING OF THE WELDMENTS

In order to retain the welds and their associated HAZs intact, the procedure agreed upon was that of regularly spaced slicing [4, 5]. For blocks 50/52 and 51/53 the slices were nominally 50 mm thick and cuts were made parallel to the X-axis (Fig. 1). For block 204 cuts were made every 15°. The residual stresses were measured during the first of these cuts [6]. The fresh surfaces were ground to remove saw marks, and macrographs were prepared, Figs. 7 and 8.

During the ultrasonic examination of Phase I a reflective zone had been detected in the weld zone of plate 204. Its true extent had not been declared by any of the participating teams. It was therefore agreed that a parallel-sided part should remain intact so that it could be recirculated amongst interested teams [7]. It was cut out around the 165° line.

In accordance with the contracts placed by CEC DG-XII and the JRC,

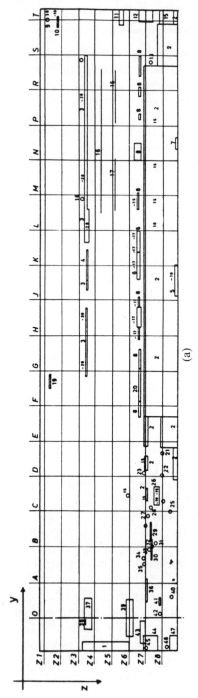

FIG. 6. Results of the radiographic and ultrasonic testing after Phase I cutting (projection on the longitudinal plane of the weld). (a) Plate 51/53. (b) Plate 50/52. (c) Plate 204.

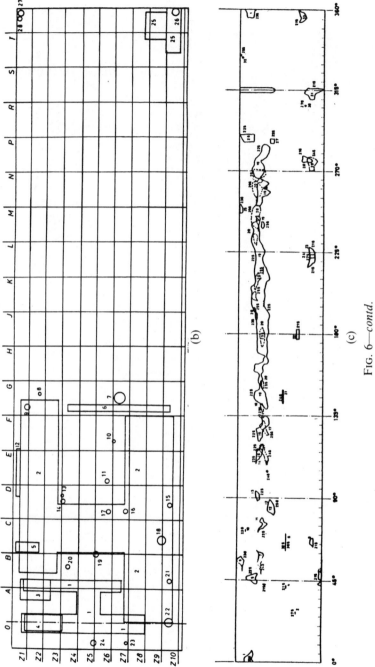

Fig. 6—contd.

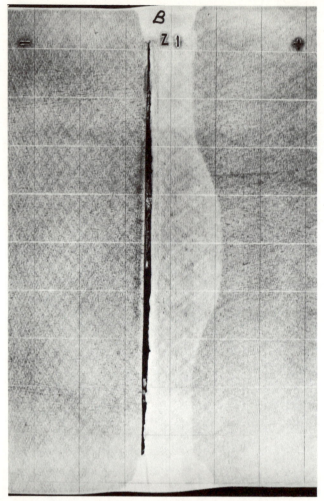

FIG. 7. Macrograph of section B(B → C) from plate 50/52.

and also in response to offers of free help from other organisations, some sections of the weldments were distributed to the following:

(1) Association Vinçotte, Belgium
(2) ECAN Indret, France
(3) MPA Stuttgart, FRG
(4) ENEL Piacenza, Italy.

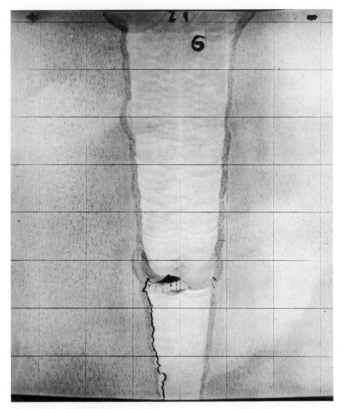

FIG. 8. Macrograph of section G(G → A) from plate 51/53.

JRC, Ispra, kept more than 50 sections for the destructive examination.

All laboratories involved undertook to comply with the cutting procedures as agreed by the PISC in order to furnish a precise map of the defects contained in their sections. MPA Stuttgart have carried out a more detailed metallographic study of their material than that required by the PISC.

After Phase II cutting it was possible to see some of the defects; and as the sections were only about 47 mm thick it was possible to use the following NDT techniques for the second stage in the detection and sizing of defects: radiography, ultrasonic testing, penetrant liquid, and magnetic particle. Not every technique was used on all sections or by all laboratories.

Although NDT and visual examination confirmed the existence, size and location of all the major flaws which had been detected by ultrasonics, both during the round robin test and also after Phase I cutting, some flaws were completely contained within the sections. It was therefore necessary to continue the destructive examination: Phases III and IV.

5.   PHASE III SECTIONING OF THE WELDMENTS

Based on the findings of Phase II, sections were cut 30 to 45 mm on each side of the centre-lines of the welds. The two resulting surfaces were therefore

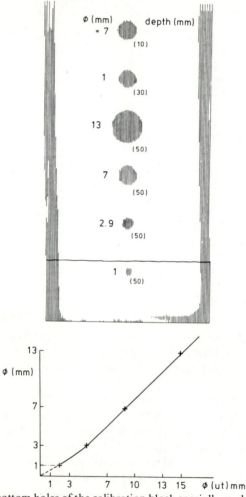

FIG. 9.   Flat bottom holes of the calibration block specially made from plate base material.

very close to the defects to be sized or detected using ultrasonics. The new surfaces were ground after band-sawing, to facilitate high-sensitivity ultrasonic testing. Calibration of the defect sizing was carried out using flat bottom holes, diameter 1, 3, 7, 13 mm at depths of 10, 30 and 50 mm (Fig. 9). The blocks were examined through four and sometimes six faces, making C-scans at different depths. In addition to ultrasonic testing, radiography and magnetic particles were used when necessary.

From these examinations all the necessary information required for evaluating the PISC results was obtained with an equivalent defect dimension of 0·1 mm in the Y–Z plane. Subsequent destruction has shown that the defects were located with a precision of ± 2 mm.

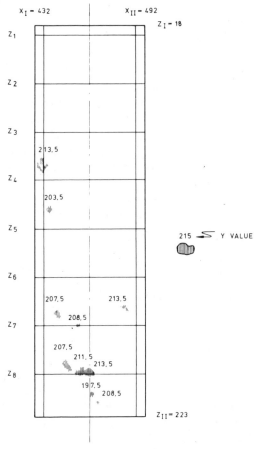

FIG. 10. 'C' scan through face $Y_{II} = 223 \cdot 5$.

Sizing was not possible below an equivalent size of 1 mm, and defects of 0·5 mm or less have often been declared as being 1 mm in diameter. This appeared to be quite sufficient, except in cases such as metallic inclusions at which small cracks or cavities were formed, regions of very small cracks and structural effects. An example is given in Fig. 10.

Mapping the defects a second time confirmed the first results, but indicated nevertheless that some defects existed which were not detectable after Phase I. They were mostly of two types; a) defects found between defect zones previously identified, or b) small individual defects.

6. PHASE IV SECTIONING OF THE WELDMENTS

To resolve those uncertainties remaining after Phase III, as well as to determine the exact nature of other defects not as yet revealed, Phase IV was initiated. It was decided upon in each individual case, as deemed necessary by the laboratory examining a given section. Phase IV was performed on about 80 % of the defects.

Various techniques were used for sectioning: electro-etching, reciprocating saw, band-saw, milling, and grinding, enabling the exact shape, distribution and nature of small defects to be defined. Half of the nozzle was examined in Phase IV because of the small dimensions of many of the defects, and the need to investigate the large defective zone revealed by NDT after Phase I cutting.

Many types of defects were identified and sized by X-rays or sharply focalised ultrasonic transducers: lack of fusion, lack of penetration, cracks, slags, implants, cracks around implants, cavities, porosity, and artificial cavities.

Many of these defects had an equivalent diameter of less than 1 mm and were retained in the final mapping of the defects only if multiple. Ultrasonic echoes were consistently obtained from one region of the nozzle; however no defects of note were found after Phase IV. Further investigation of this region is described below.

7. DETAILED METALLOGRAPHY OF SELECTED DEFECTS

Some defects could not be defined by simple visual examination. Further metallographic investigations were therefore undertaken by ENEL, ECAN and the JRC, Ispra.

7.1. Set of Cracks, Nozzle Plate 204
Artificial defects in the nozzle were introduced by changing the flux during welding, Fig. 11. Microanalysis of the defects demonstrated the presence of sulphur and copper which gave rise to the small cracks.

7.2. Long Inclusion or Artificial Cavity, Plate 51/53
Microanalysis of this defect, Fig. 12, demonstrated the presence of a glass-like substance.

7.3. Major Crack, Plate 51/53 (Fig. 5)
This crack is confined to the fusion zone. Microhardness and chemical analyses are as expected for this steel type. The acicular structure however indicates that the material was subjected to rapid cooling and did not receive a post-weld heat treatment. From microfractographic studies (TEM on replicas) it can be seen that the rupture surface comprises alternating brittle and ductile zones, the former being dominant. The extremity of the crack has been examined and shown to be full of copper.

From this detailed metallographic examination it is possible to make a number of hypotheses:

(1) The cracks may have been initiated from the copper, intentionally introduced during welding to make this region more brittle.

(2) Crack propagation has occurred in the fusion zone due to natural or intentional thermal stresses; the latter could have been produced by the two supplementary welds on the inside surface of the main weld.

(3) The crack could have been caused by fast cooling repeated during welding (e.g. with liquid nitrogen). This could explain the alternating ductile and brittle zones, and also the acicular ferrite structure observed in the deposited metal.

7.4. Further Examination of the Nozzle, Plate 204
After Phase I a large defect zone was evident using ultrasonics on the nozzle block and this was verified using several different frequencies (2·25, 5, 10 MHz), both by echo and tandem techniques. The defect appeared to be somewhat transparent and the extent of the defect zone depended upon the frequency and sensitivity used.

After Phase II sectioning, macrographs revealed very pronounced microstructures in both base material and the nozzle tube. Due to the orientation of the fibre-like weld structure, parallel to that of the base

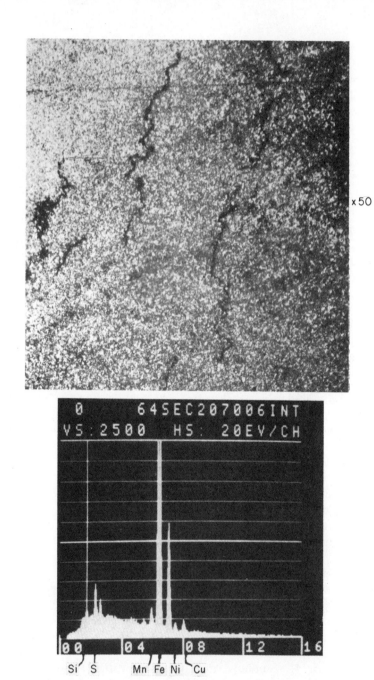

FIG. 11. Set of cracks randomly oriented (plate 204). Microanalysis of cracks (bottom)—Presence of S and Cu indicates probable change of flux during welding causing the defects.

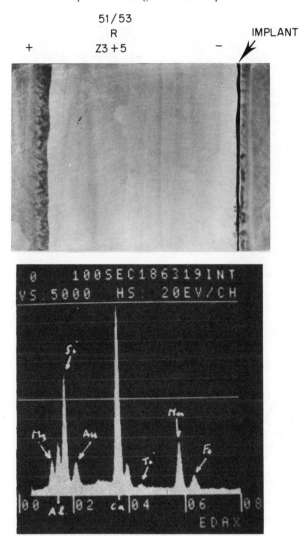

FIG. 12.   Long implant (glass) in section R (at $Z = 60\,mm$) of plate 51/53 and relative microanalysis.

material, the inner HAZ appeared as a thin region of contrast between the two structures. In many cases this type of contrast between orientations can produce a change in the acoustic impedance such as to give an echo (a well-known phenomenon in medicine when examining fibres with different textures).

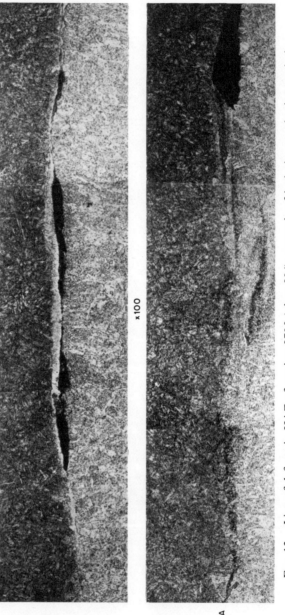

×100

FIG. 13.   Line of defects in HAZ of section 270° (plate 204); example of inclusions and microanalysis.

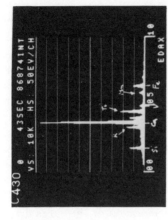

EDAX microanalysis spectrum
(elements: Si, K, Ca, Ti, Mn, Fe)

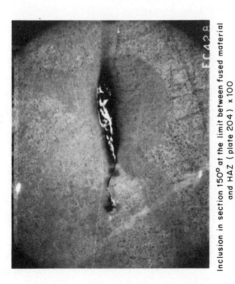

Inclusion in section 150° at the limit between fused material
and HAZ (plate 204) x 100

FIG. 13—*contd.*

Ultrasonic examination after Phase III cutting revealed small reflecting areas over the entire region which in Phase IV were found to correspond to very small defects; pores, pores in conjunction with small cracks, and inclusions. Correct sizing required further cutting and metallography.

Several blocks were systematically sliced after Phase IV in order to obtain surfaces perpendicular to the Z-axis. The samples were made small enough to permit more detailed metallography than just macro-etching. Many defects were found, mainly cavities (porosity), less than 1 mm in diameter, often connected with fine cracks. They are located in the fusion line, Fig. 13. Inclusions are also present. The defect concentration was 1–2 defects per cm³, for which correct sizing was not practicable. Microanalysis indicated that the cavities contained small slags from the welding process, Fig. 13.

Even if defects had been found and sized in all the pieces, the results would not be sufficient to fully explain the observations of Phase I using focused or flat transducers, at both high and low frequencies. It should also be noted that some teams detected parts of this large defect zone using alternative techniques. It is probable that neither of the findings from Phases II or IV are sufficient on their own, but in combination offer an explanation. Very sensitive ultrasonic examination reveals similar defects or effects over the entire HAZ.

7.5. Sectioning at MPA Stuttgart

The procedure used at MPA Stuttgart was not the same as the PISC procedure: instead they systematically cut or ground in 5 mm steps. After each machining operation macro- and micrographs were made, as well as frequent hardness measurements [8].

Detailed reports of the work carried out by the laboratories participating in the destructive examination are to be found in References 8–11, and a complete catalogue of the defects in Reference 12.

8.   BASE MATERIAL DEFECTS AND HAZ

During the round robin test several teams used alternative techniques for sizing defect zones of the base material (high-frequency back-scattering and high-frequency focused probes). Further ultrasonic testing showed that with high sensitivity, the entire blocks could be considered as defects. Some parts nevertheless, demonstrated very high reflectivity. These results were confirmed by Phase II sectioning in which small cracks and inclusions aligned parallel to the plate surface were observed on the macrographs.

The whole central part of the plates (one third of the thickness) is thus reflective to high-sensitivity ultrasonics. Some zones or spots could nevertheless be identified as relevant defects from the macrographs, quite apart from their ease of detection by ultrasonics. They were reported by many teams as defects in the HAZ, and also found by X-rays after Phase I.

It had been agreed that for the PISC programme, efforts would be concentrated on the weld regions of the plates. For the purposes of the present evaluation of the results, defects in the base material have therefore been disregarded. To continue the destructive examination to include all those defects would have been a tremendous task.

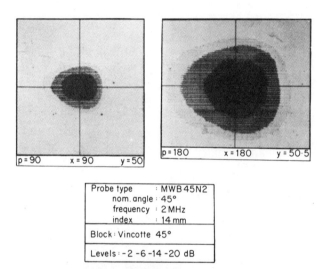

Probe type	: MWB 45N2
nom. angle	: 45°
frequency	: 2 MHz
index	: 14 mm
Block : Vincotte 45°	
Levels : -2 -6 -14 -20 dB	

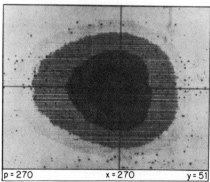

FIG. 14(a). Beam sections in good quality steel.

The effect of the base material segregation on the propagation of ultrasonic waves has been investigated by Association Vinçotte [13]. This was done by comparing propagation through base material from plate 50/52 with a similar block of clean carbon steel. Measurements were made at the wave-paths corresponding to T/4, T/2, and 3T/4. Segregation in the central part of the plate influences the last two beam cross-sections, (see Fig. 14).

From the tests described in Reference 13 it can be concluded that the type of probe specified for the PISC trials has a slightly perturbed cross-section; however the intensity was quite disturbed along the beam axis. These

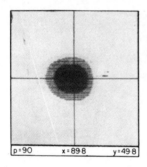 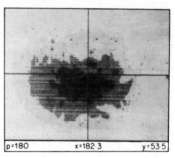

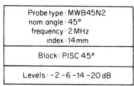

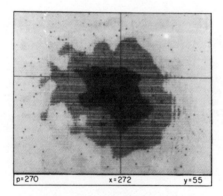

FIG. 14(b).   Beam sections in plate 50/52 steel.

characteristics will probably have more influence on the detectability, which depends on the intensity, than on sizing, which depends on beam geometry.

9. RESIDUAL STRESSES

Residual stresses in block 51/53 complicated the extraction of the weldment. Since it was understood that all the plates had undergone post-weld heat treatments, the presence of such high stresses was not foreseen. It indicates however that the plate did not receive the prescribed post-weld treatment.

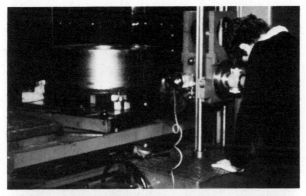

FIG. 15. Network scribed on the nozzle plate weldment and intersection measurement, before and after cutting.

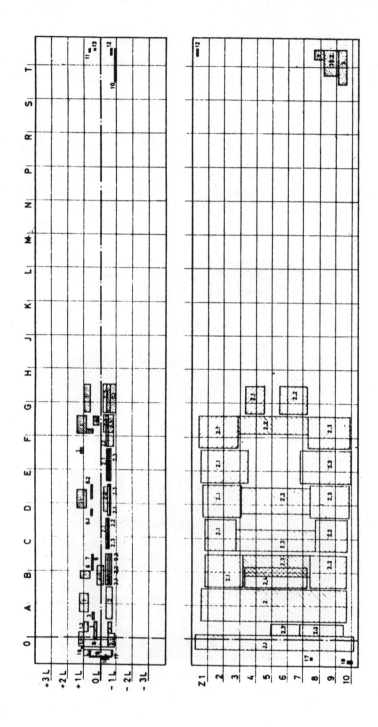

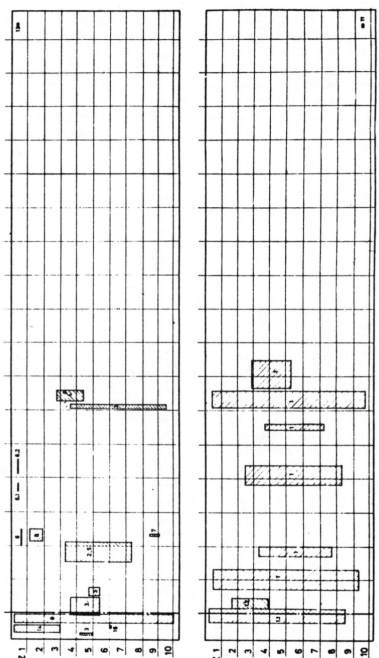

FIG. 16.   Destructive examination results of plate 50/52 (plane X, Y, and section A, B, C).

It was therefore agreed that any residual stresses present in the only remaining block—the nozzle—should be measured.

Before cutting through the weldment (Phase II) of plate 204 a network was traced on the outer cylindrical surface. After cutting through the marked zone, the deformation of the network was measured (see Fig. 15). The cut opening was 20% less than expected, indicating the presence of correspondingly large hoop stresses. The axial stresses in a segment were measured by Studsvik Energiteknik AB, using a double exposure X-ray diffraction technique. There did not appear to be much variation across the weld. All the results were subsequently corrected to compensate for the relaxation of the stresses during dissection. These measurements are all described in detail elsewhere [5, 14, 15].

10.   FINAL MAP OF DEFECTS AND DATA SHEET 6 'REFERENCE'

It has been evident throughout the destructive examination that there were numerous defects of various types (more than 500 sizeable defects). All these defects could be classified into different groups: by their dimensions, by the fact whether they were artificial or natural, and by metallurgical features. As the scope of the destructive examination was the evaluation of NDT results and not a metallurgical study of the defects, a relatively synthetic, or global, attitude was adopted for combining defects regardless of their nature or size. For example, in order to obtain a usable map of defects, it was necessary to combine into one defect all the findings in the lower zone of plate 51/53.

For combining or assembling defects, rules were adopted in accordance with the ASME XI Inspection Procedure (1977 edition), with regard to their proximity, porosities, and multiple defects.

To avoid producing a final map of defects with only one very large defect, some artificial separation has been introduced in cases in which two distinct zones of defects were separated by very small porosities or isolated cavities. Isolated defects with a surface area of less than $6 \, mm^2$ in Y–Z, X–Z and X–Y planes were disregarded. Application of the proximity rules simplified the results, and the results up to Phase IV examination are shown in Figs 16, 17, and 18.

The evaluation of the PISC trial results has to be based on destructive examination and computer work. All NDT results were either received or transformed into Data Sheet 6, in which the coordinates of the

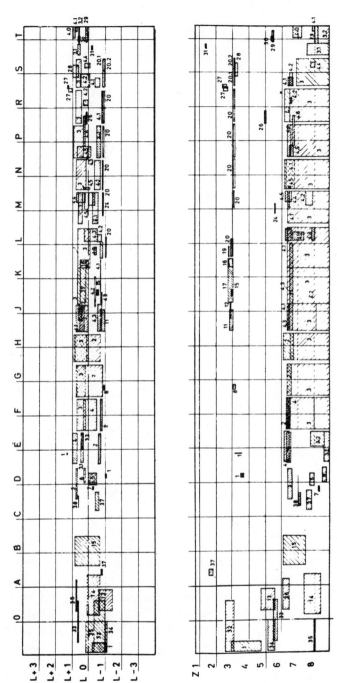

Fig. 17. Destructive examination results of plate 51/53 (planes X, Y and Y, Z).

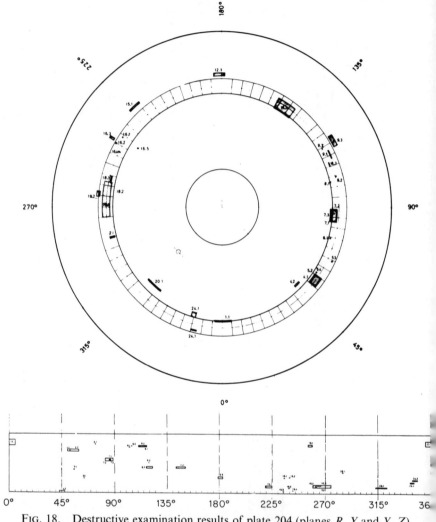

FIG. 18.   Destructive examination results of plate 204 (planes *R, Y* and *Y, Z*).

parallelepiped enclosing the defect and the amplitude are given. The results of the destructive examination were also presented in the various tables of Data Sheet 6 and are illustrated here in Figs 19, 20 and 21. The large defect zone in the HAZ of plate 204 has not been included in the computerised evaluation of results.

A table of defects considered for the evaluation using the ASME XI (1977

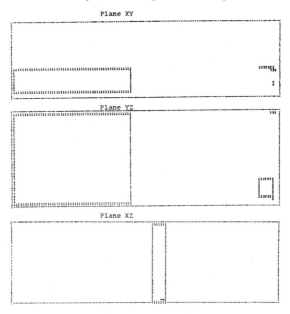

Fig. 19. Computer drawing of plate 50/52 reference defects.

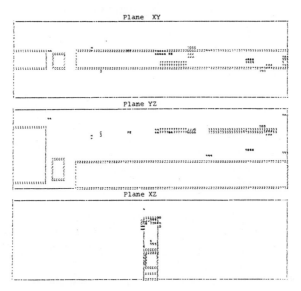

Fig. 20. Computer drawing of plate 51/53 reference defects.

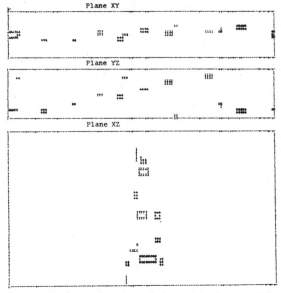

FIG. 21.   Computer drawing of plate 204 reference defects.

edition) acceptance criteria was prepared listing all the defects of the three plates [11]. The results can be summarised as follows:

Plate 50/52:   4 defects—2 unacceptable
Plate 51/53: 19 defects—3 unacceptable
Plate 204:   14 defects—1 unacceptable

11.   CONCLUSIONS

1. The destructive examinations performed at the JRC, Ispra with the collaboration of Association Vinçotte, Belgium, ECAN-Indret, France, MPA Stuttgart, FRG, ENEL, Italy, Breda Termomeccanica, Italy and Ghent University, Belgium, under the guidance of the PISC Evaluation Task Force, proved to be a very time-consuming operation, because of the large quantity and variety of defects.

2. The use of high-performance NDT techniques simplified the destructive examination and enabled Phases IV and V to be restricted to a limited number of sections.

3. All relevant defects, larger than 1 mm, were detected and sized visually and/or using different techniques to obtain consistent correlations.

4. A final map of the defects has been produced for the weldments of all three plates.

5. The quantity of defects was such that this map has been simplified by applying proximity rules, in order to produce a reasonable list of defects for the evaluation of the PISC trials. Small defects (surface area less than 6 mm²) were disregarded for this map.

6. Data Sheet 6 has been produced for the results, which is compatible with the computerised evaluation of the PISC NDT results.

7. Base material defects were detected, illustrated and demonstrated to be present nearly everywhere. A study of their influence on the attenuation of ultrasonic waves has been performed.

8. The particular defect zones detected in the HAZ of the plate 204 have been investigated and explained.

9. Detailed metallographic examinations of several types of defect have in some cases indicated their origin.

10. Residual stresses have been measured on plate 204, but were not considered to have influenced the defect shape or sizes before or after Phase II sectioning.

REFERENCES

1. 'Destructive Examination of the PVRC Plates Nos. 50/52, 51/53 and 204', Plate Inspection Steering Committee (PISC), Report No. 3, EUR 6371/III EN, 1979.
2. Higham, E. 'Phase 1. Sectioning Procedure for PISC Weldments 50/52, 51/53 and 204', PISC/ETF/77/P1, Issue 3, June 1978.
3. 'Procedure for Ultrasonic Examination of PVRC Welded Test Blocks', PISC/UK(76)PL, Revision 2, November 1976.
4. Higham, E. 'Phase II Sectioning Procedure for PISC Weldments 50/52 and 51/53', PISC/ETF/78P11, July 1978.
5. Higham, E. and Crutzen, S. 'Sectioning Procedure for Nozzle Weldment 204', PISC/ETF/78/P12, October 1978.
6. Gott, K. 'Measurement of Residual Stresses in the PVRC Nozzle Specimen 204: 1. Work Carried out at JRC, Ispra, 23–26 Oct.. 1978'. Studsvik Energiteknik AB Internal Report: E1-78/31.
7. Minutes of the fourth meeting (M4) of the Evaluation Task Force (ETF) held at JRC, Ispra on Thursday and Friday, 7th and 8th September, 1978.
8. 'MPA Participation in the Destructive Examination of the PVRC Plates Donated to the PISC', prepared by W. Schellhammer, MPA Stuttgart, FRG, 1979.
9. 'Destructive Examination of the PVRC Plate 51/53, Portion O to B, Donated to the PISC', prepared by P. Caussin, Association Vinçotte and the University of Ghent, Belgium, 1979.

10. 'Destructive Examination of the PVRC 50/52 Plate Portions. Donated to the PISC', prepared by J. F. Gouez, ECAN Indret, 44620 La Montagne, France, 1979.
11. 'ENEL Participation in the Destructive Examination of the PVRC Plates Donated to the PISC', prepared by G. Maciga, ENEL, Laboratorio Centrale DCO, Piacenza, Italy, 1979.
12. 'Catalogue of All Illustrative Material Collected During Destructive Examination at the JRC, Ispra, PISC Programme 1978–79', prepared by S. J. Crutzen, JRC, Ispra.
13. 'Destructive Examination of the PVRC Plates Nos. 50/52, 51/53 and 204', Appendix 2 of Ref. (1), 'Influence of Steel Plate Segregation on the Ultrasonic Shear Wave Propagation: Beam Distortion', P. Caussin, Association Vinçotte, Belgium.
14. Gott, K. 'Measurement of Residual Stresses in the PVRC Nozzle Specimen 204: 2. Work Carried out in Studsvik, December 1978', Studsvik Energiteknik AB Internal Report: EI-79/50.
15. Gott, K. 'Measurement of Residual Stresses in the PVRC Nozzle Specimen 204: 3. Final Report', Studsvik Energiteknik AB Report STUDSVIK EI-79/99.

Report No. 4
Method of Evaluation and the Results of the PISC Trials

S. J. CRUTZEN

JRC, Ispra, Italy

and

G. W. PARRY

UKAEA, SRD, Warrington, UK

SUMMARY

The PISC trials were initiated as part of a scheme to determine the capability of the procedure for ultrasonic examination laid down in the ASME Code, Section XI (1974) for detecting, sizing, orientating and locating flaws in welds in heavy section steel. This report describes the method that was used to analyse the results of the ultrasonic examination using the results of a destructive examination of three test specimens as a reference. The most important results are presented.

1. INTRODUCTION

The aim of the PISC exercise was to determine the capability of the procedure for ultrasonic examination laid down in the ASME Code, Section XI (1974) for detecting, sizing, orientating and locating flaws or discontinuities in welds in heavy section steel. This was to be achieved by a comparison between the results of a non-destructive examination and a destructive examination of three test plates; two with a linear weld (Nos. 50/52 and 51/53) and one plate incorporating a nozzle (No. 204). This paper describes how this comparison was performed.

Since it is primarily the capability of the procedure that was being investigated, the results are presented for each reference defect (i.e. one discovered by destructive examination) in turn and in some sense represent an average team performance.

Teams participating in the exercise were asked to provide their data on the examination using the ASME XI procedure on two separate data sheets:

Data Sheet 5 which gave all indications detected with amplitude above 50% DAC, and
Data Sheet 6 which gave the subjective interpretation of this data in defining the defects.

In addition if they desired teams were allowed to submit a Data Sheet 6 for any alternative ultrasonic procedures used. These Data Sheets are described fully in the PISC Report No. 2.

It was decided to perform the comparison three times, once each with Data Sheet 6 for the PISC and alternative procedures, and once with a Data Sheet 6 derived directly from Data Sheet 5 for the PISC procedure. This last case ought to be free of subjective judgements on the part of the teams.

The results are presented in terms of parameters which are chosen to reflect the probability of detecting a defect, the error in sizing and location of a defect, and the quality of rejection or acceptance of a defect based on the application of the rejection/acceptance criteria of ASME XI, IWB 3500.*

---

* It was decided by the PISC to consider all defects as sub-surface defects and the rejection/acceptance criterion used was that relevant to sub-surface defects. This simplification allows a direct comparison of all defects of all plates from an NDT point of view. The numbers relating to rejection/acceptance are symbolic comparison values only, but the qualitative conclusions are independent of this simplification.

2. DEFINITION OF THE DEFECT AS MEASURED BY THE ULTRASONIC PROCEDURE

Since the PISC trials generated a very large amount of data the comparison procedure had to be carried out by computer. Consequently the definition of the defects had to be such that they could be readily handled by the program written to do the comparison.

2.1. PISC Procedure

2.1.1. Data Sheet 6

This gave the co-ordinates of the cuboid which just encloses the defect (Fig. 1). The faces of the cuboid can be defined as enclosing the ellipses of ASME XI, and the rules of ASME XI (IWB 3300) were applied when considering the separation of multiple or parallel flaws. A maximum amplitude was associated with the defect defined in this way.

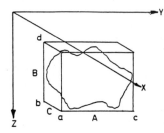

FIG. 1.   The cuboid as defined by Data Sheet 6.

2.1.2. Data Sheet 5

This gave all the indications detected with amplitude above 50 % DAC. This information was used:

(1) as it was for comparison with the results of the destructive examination;
(2) for preparing a 'Computer Data Sheet 6' which should be independent of all subjective judgements of a NDT team.

This 'Computer Data Sheet 6' was constructed using the rules of ASME XI (IWB 3300) as in Section 2.1.1.

2.2. Alternative Procedures

'Data Sheet 6' for alternative procedures gave the co-ordinates of a single, or several adjacent cuboids which just enclosed the indications of defects.

Since the alternative procedures attempt to size the defects better than the PISC procedure, the proximity rules of the ASME XI code were not applied. A maximum amplitude cannot always be associated with a defect when detected with procedures other than that of PISC.

3. PRESENTATION OF THE RESULTS OF THE DESTRUCTIVE EXAMINATION

The results of the destructive examination were presented on data sheets compatible with Data Sheet 6 but there was, of course, no amplitude declaration. For each defect, a precise description and illustration was given, but for the comparison between the ultrasonic examination and destructive examination, which was carried out by computer, only the information given by Data Sheet 6 was used.

The assessment of whether two defects should be considered separately or as a single defect using the rules of ASME XI was carried out by the computer in its preparation of the data bank to be used for the evaluation of the results.

4. THE IMPORTANT FEATURES OF THE ULTRASONIC INSPECTION TO BE EVALUATED

Since the aim of the exercise was to assess the value of the method of detecting defects, the following questions were considered to be the most important:

(1) Was a particular defect detected by the NDE?
(2) Was it correctly localised?
(3) Was it correctly sized?
(4) Taking into account the rejection criterion (ASME XI IWB 3500) for defects, based on fracture mechanics calculations, was the defect correctly accepted or rejected? (See footnote to Section 1.)

This last point is of great importance from both an economic and a safety standpoint. These questions were answered by using the information contained in the co-ordinates of the cuboid given in Data Sheet 6. The answers to these questions were also related to the maximum amplitude (% DAC) recorded.

5. COMPARISON PROCEDURE FOR THE RESULTS OF ALL TEAMS WITH THE RESULTS OF THE DESTRUCTIVE EXAMINATION

Input data for the comparison procedure were given by:

(1) Data Sheets 5 (where applicable) and 6 of each team for the ultrasonic examination;

(2) Data Sheet 6 for the destructive examination.

Figures 19–21 of Part 3 of this chapter show computer drawings of the reference defects of the three plates; Fig. 2 is an example of the results of one team using the PISC procedure on plate 204. These computer drawings were used as a check on the input data and to assist in the actual analysis.

The available data base was too small to enable a comprehensive statistical analysis to be carried out, but sufficiently large for some simple parameters of importance to be estimated. If the results of the present exercise are judged to be encouraging, it may then be in order to attempt a

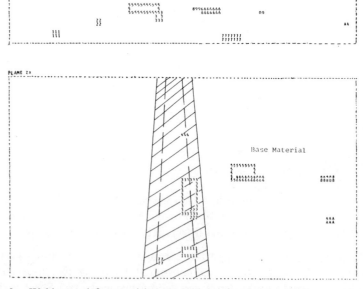

FIG. 2. Weldment defects and base material defect in plate 204 as seen by one team. (Team CN25; procedure = PISC; block = 204; number of defects = 11; DS6 produced by team).

more detailed comparison, and this should be borne in mind for any future exercise of this kind.

The method of comparison is outlined below:

(1) The Defect Detection Probability DDP is the probability that a team following the given procedure detects a particular defect. This was estimated by the ratio of n/N where n is the number of teams who successfully detected the defect and N is the number of teams who participated. Confidence bounds were put on this figure by using the binomial distribution in the usual way. The questions arise as to how it was decided that a team had detected a particular defect and in the case of several nearby reference defects, which one had been detected. If the cuboid containing the reference defect (i.e. that found by the destructive examination) and that containing the defect declared by a team on a Data Sheet 6 had some volume in common, the defect was declared to have been found. If the cuboids were discrete the defect was said to have been detected at a tolerance level t when the maximum separation between two adjacent faces, S (see Fig. 3) was such that $S - t \leq 0.5$ mm. This particular definition

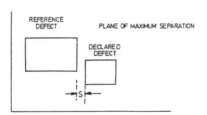

Fig. 3. Definition of '*S*'.

guarantees that for the large defects even a small indication, relatively far removed from the centre of the reference defect but within the reference defect, resulted in a detection. This would not necessarily have been the case for a tolerance defined about the centre of the reference defect. In the case that more than one declaration corresponded to the reference defect, only one was included for the purpose of evaluating n. Similarly, if one declaration corresponded to more than one reference defect, the decision on which reference defect it corresponded to was taken examining the data by hand.

(2) To determine whether the defect had been correctly localised the quantities DX, DY and DZ as defined in Fig. 4 were evaluated for each team. In the event that more than one declaration was judged to correspond to the

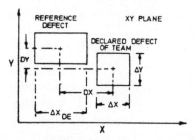

FIG. 4.   Definitions of DX, ΔX, DY, ΔY.

reference defect, the averages of the centre co-ordinates of the indications were used to calculate DX, DY and DZ.

(3) The quality of sizing was assessed by comparing ΔX, ΔY and ΔZ as defined in Fig. 4 to ΔX_{DE} ΔY_{DE} or ΔZ_{DE}. The area of the defect projected on to a plane was defined by the area of the face of the cuboid in that plane. If more than one indication corresponded to one reference defect, then the sum of the areas of the individual indications was taken as being the detected area. Due account was taken of any overlap.

(4) In most cases, it is the projection of the defect on to the plane perpendicular to the plane of maximum stress (the YZ plane in our notation) that is the important area to be considered. The rejection/acceptance criterion of ASME XI for a defect is given in terms of the ratios B/A and B/T where B and A are defined in Fig. 1, and T is the thickness of the plate in the Z direction. Figure 5 is a representation of this rejection/acceptance criterion curve for a typical reactor grade material

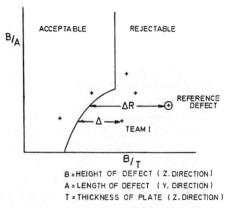

FIG. 5.   Rejection criterion. B = height of defect (Z direction), A = length of defect (Y direction), T = thickness of plate (Z direction).

drawn from the rules of ASME XI (IWB 3500). The acceptable region is well defined. From the positions on this curve of the indications of the teams, relative to that of the real defect, it is possible to estimate the likelihood that an indication will be deemed an acceptable defect when it is not, and vice versa; this varies with the position of the real defect on the plot. As a measure of the accuracy of rejection/acceptance, the distance between the indications and the rejection curve was used (Δ and ΔR of Fig. 5). (See footnote to Section 1.) Two computer programs were written to assist in data handling. The main program performed the comparison between the reference defects and the indications given by the teams, and the subsidiary program was used to implement the rejection criterion.

6. PRESENTATION OF THE RESULTS

The main results of the analysis are presented for each defect in turn in the form of a table. Where it is considered important to do so, a figure showing

TABLE I

Procedure	DDP	Location errors				Size errors			QR	CRP
		ELX	ELY	ELZ	ESX	ESY	ESZ	ES		
PISC DS 5	1	0·07 ±0·4	0·02 ±2	0·37 ±1·3	0·36 ±1·6	−0·03 ±1·3	−0·70 ±0·4	−0·80 ±0·4	0·15	0·95[a]
PISC DS 6	1	0·09 ±0·4	0·10 ±1·1	0·33 ±1·3	0·61 ±2·5	−0·08 ±0·78	−0·71 ±0·32	−0·82 ±0·24	0·11	0·91
ALT	1	0·07 ±0·3	0·04 ±1·3	0·04 ±1·2	−0·15 ±1·8	0·48 ±1·4	0·42 ±2	0·02 ±1·4	0·76	1·0

[a] Corrected value (original: 0·85)

Plate number: 50/52
Defect number: 1

Defect envelope dimensions: $\begin{cases} \Delta X = 57\,\text{mm} \\ \Delta Y = 400\,\text{mm} \\ \Delta Z = 236\,\text{mm} \end{cases}$

ASME XI   IWB-3510: defect unacceptable
Position of the defect in the plane YZ.

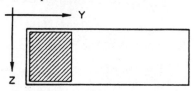

TABLE II

Procedure	DDP	Location errors				Size errors			QA	CAP
		ELX	ELY	ELZ	ESX	ESY	ESZ	ES		
PISC DS 5	0·41	0·02 ±0·30	0·07 ±0·5	0 ±0·18	−0·72 ±0·6	1·37 ±2	−0·5 ±1	0 ±2	0·57	0·36
PISC DS 6	0·6	0·05 ±0·16	0·04 ±0·22	0 ±0·06	−0·71 ±0·6	−0·52 ±1·2	1 ±2	−0·2 ±2·8	1·7	0·45
ALT	0·8	0·04 ±1·8	0 ±0·34	0·02 ±0·16	−0·58 ±0·8	0·31 ±2	1·3 ±4	1·8 ±5	−2	0·4

Plate number: 204
Defect number: 2

Defect envelope dimensions: $\begin{cases} \Delta X = 17\,\text{mm} \\ \Delta Y = 10°/42\cdot4\,\text{mm} \\ \Delta Z = 6\,\text{mm} \end{cases}$

ASME XI   IWB-3510: defect acceptable
Position of the defect in the plane *YZ*.

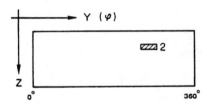

the positions of the reference defect and the team indications on the rejection/acceptance criterion diagram, and a figure giving the DDP as a function of tolerance, as defined in Section 5, are also presented. Examples are given in Tables I and II and Figs 6–8.

The tables list the following parameters:

(1)   DDP: This is defined in Section 5(1) and the value given in the tables is that which is obtained at the maximum tolerance used for the purpose of deciding whether the defect has or has not been detected. This is generally no larger than 50 mm.

(2)   *ELX, ELY, ELZ:* Referring to Fig. 4, *ELX* is defined as

$$ELX = DX/(T/2)$$

where *T* is the thickness of the plate.

$$ELY = DY/(T/2); \qquad ELZ = DZ/(T/2)$$

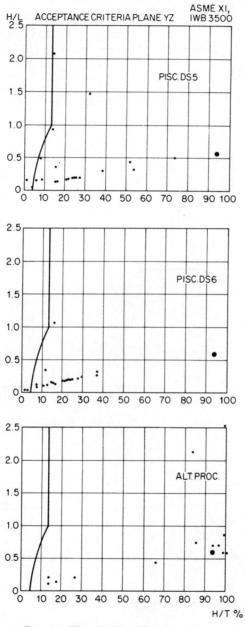

Fɪɢ. 6. Plate 50/52, defect No. 1.

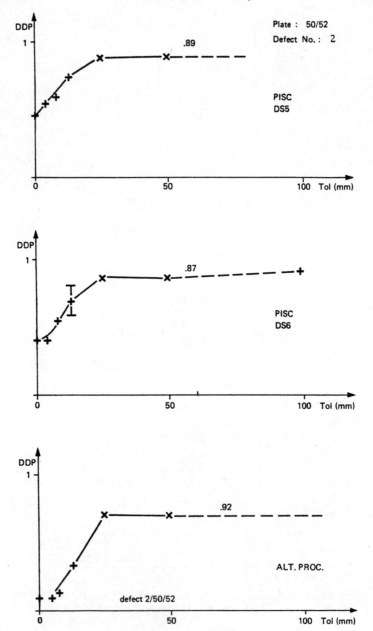

FIG. 7.   Defect Detection Probability as a function of the tolerance in detection

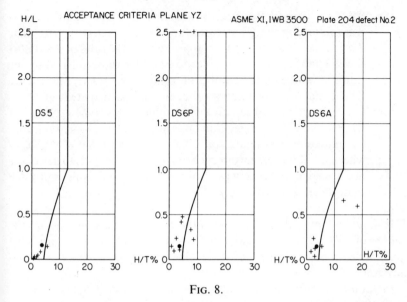

FIG. 8.

Results are presented as the modulus of the average of the team results $\pm$ twice the standard deviation of the results to give 95% confidence bounds for the error of location.

(3) *ESX, ESY, ESZ* and *ES:* Again referring to Fig. 4, *ESX* is defined as

$$ESX = \frac{\Delta X - \Delta X_{DE}}{X_{DE}}$$

and similarly for *ESY* and *ESZ*

$$ES = \frac{\Delta Y \Delta Z - (\Delta Y \Delta Z)_{DE}}{(\Delta Y \Delta Z)_{DE}}$$

Results are presented as the average of all the team results $\pm$ twice the standard deviation of the results.

(4) *QR* or *QA:* Referring to Fig. 5, *QR* is defined as

$$QR = \Delta/\Delta R$$

when the defect is rejectable according to the rules of ASME XI IWB 3500. When the defect is acceptable the ratio $\Delta/\Delta R$ is called *QA*. It is the average value of *QR* or *QA* over all teams which is given in the tables.

(5)   CRP, the Correct Rejection Probability, is the probability that a team following the given procedure correctly rejects a particular defect following the symbolic application of the rules of ASME XI (IWB 3500) (see footnote to Section 1). This was estimated by the ratio r/N where r is the number of teams who correctly rejected the defect and N is the number of teams who participated.

(6)   CAP, the Correct Acceptance Probability: This is the analogue of CRP for acceptable defects and was estimated in a similar fashion. (An alternative estimate for CAP is to take $CAP = \sum_{i=1}^{N} x_i/N$ where $x_i = 1$ if the team either correctly accepts *or* fails to detect the defect and $x_i = 0$ otherwise. This results in higher values of CAP than those reported here.)

It should be stressed that because of the choice of rejection criterion the values of QR, QA, CRP and CAP are only illustrative values. The qualitative trends indicated by the values are considered to be valid however.

In addition to the tables and figures already mentioned, figures are also presented to illustrate correlations that were found between the above mentioned parameters and the size, position and type of defect.

Results are given for three procedures designated as:

PISC DS5—these are the results of the comparison of the reference with Data Sheet 6 constructed by the computer from Data Sheets 5 given by teams following the PISC procedure. PISC DS6—these are the results of the comparison with Data Sheets 6 given by the teams following the PISC procedure. ALT—these are the results of the comparison with Data Sheets 6 given by teams following alternative procedures. These are considered as a group without differentiating between techniques.

7. RESULTS AND CONCLUSIONS

The evaluation programme was carried out first applying the ASME proximity rules (ASME XI, IWB 3300) taking into account; (1) proximity of a defect to the surface (outside or inside) and (2) proximity of multiple defects.

On the basis of these rules Reference Data Sheet 6 obtained from the destructive examination was reduced by the computer to the following results:

Plate 50/52: two large defects
Plate 51/53: one very large defect extending over the entire weldment
Plate 204: since the defects were widely spaced the ASME XI proximity rules had no effect on them.

In order to be able to carry out an effective evaluation of the NDT results a modified method of reduction was applied to the results of the destructive examination. The scope of PISC does not extend to using a fracture mechanics approach to test for defect detection and sizing. In the 'reduced' ASME XI proximity rules the stringency of the rules was relaxed as follows: Defects near the surface retained their detected size. For combination of defects in the YZ plane, Z was not compared to $2A$ but to 13 mm ($\frac{1}{2}$ in) as is prescribed by ASME XI for the X-direction.

These small modifications of the reduction rules allowed the evaluation to take several more defects into account for plate 51/53, thus giving more scope for drawing conclusions on the detection probability of defects.

Reference Data Sheets 6 were prepared for plates 50/52, 51/53 and 204 taking into account these modifications, and the evaluation programme was repeated giving the results summarised below.

7.1. Specific Examples
7.1.1. Defect Number 1 of Plate 50/52

This is a very large unacceptable defect according to the criterion of ASME XI (IWB 3510). Although everyone detected it using the PISC procedure detection was only partial leading to an underestimate of size and a tendency to acceptance as shown by the values of CRP which are less than 1 (Table 1). This is also clearly seen on Fig. 6. Figure 7 shows how DDP varies with the tolerance. Figure 9 shows the detection of the defect as a function of its position in the Z co-ordinate (through thickness). The defect for this purpose has been divided into three parts. The bottom third of the defect is the portion which is detected the best and the central third the worst. This illustrates the important conclusion that the efficiency of detection and sizing of a defect using the PISC procedure is a function of the position of the defect in the YZ plane.

7.1.2. Defect Number 2 of Plate 204

This is an acceptable defect according to the rejection criterion chosen. The DDP is rather low for the PISC procedure and is less than 1 for the

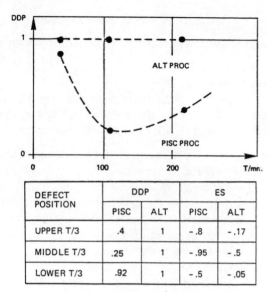

DEFECT	DDP		ES	
POSITION	PISC	ALT	PISC	ALT
UPPER T/3	.4	1	- .8	- .17
MIDDLE T/3	.25	1	- .95	- .5
LOWER T/3	.92	1	- .5	- .05

FIG. 9.   Defect Detection Probability as a function of the defect portion position in the depth of the plate.

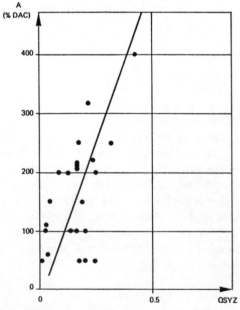

FIG. 10.   Amplitude of detection as a function of the sizing quality; plate 50/52, defect No. 1.

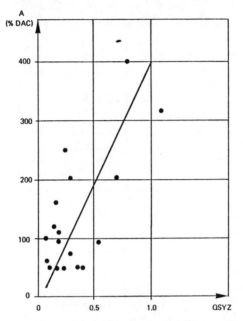

FIG. 11. Amplitude of detection as a function of the sizing quality; plate 50/52, defect No. 2.

alternative procedures (Table II). Figure 8 shows that sizing can be rather random and some teams have rejected the defect.

7.2. Global Results

When the set of results for all defects is considered it is possible to make the following conclusions:

7.2.1. Amplitude Correlation

The amplitude A (% DAC)–size correlation is highly dependent on the defect type and its position in the plate. No general rule can be drawn as can be seen in Figs 10–13 which give examples of the correlations found.

7.2.2. Size Correlation

As shown in Fig. 14 it is only for the alternative procedures that a correlation seems to exist between the real defect size and the average estimated size.

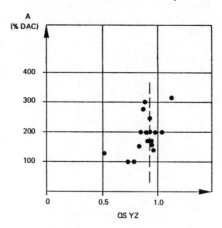

FIG. 12.   Amplitude of detection as a function of the sizing quality; plate 51/53,
defect No. 2.

Oversizing can be significant for small defects (acceptable defects). Most
of the defects for which ΔZ is less than 6 mm are not reported on the
diagram to avoid confusion.

7.2.3. Correlation between DDP and Defect Size
The size of the defect is represented by its height. When plotting DDP

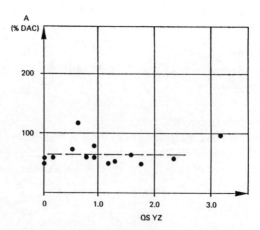

FIG. 13.   Amplitude of detection as a function of the sizing quality; plate 204,
defect No. 6.

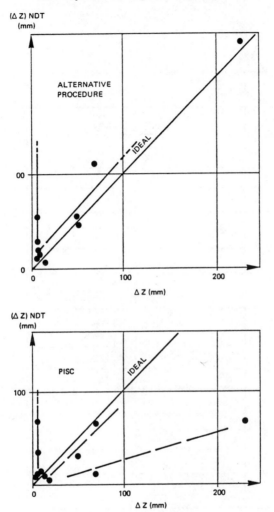

FIG. 14. Estimated size as a function of the defect size.

(Defect Detection Probability) as a function of size ($\Delta Z = 2a$ mm), three groups of defects clearly appear:

(1) acceptable defects,
(2) rejectable defects (cracks in the through-thickness direction) and
(3) sets of defects (porosities or cracks).

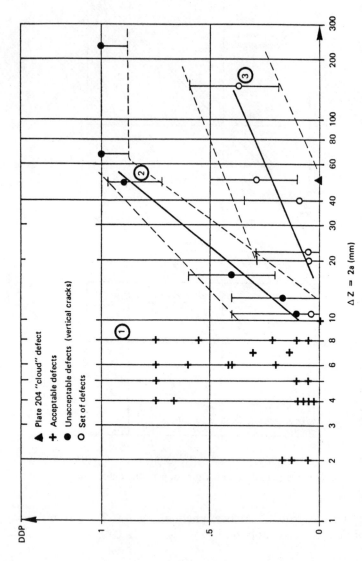

FIG. 15. Defect Detection Probability as a function of the defect size; PISC procedure. (The solid and broken lines are drawn to guide the eye through the best estimate and upper and lower 95% confidence bounds; these bounds are derived from the binomial distribution.)

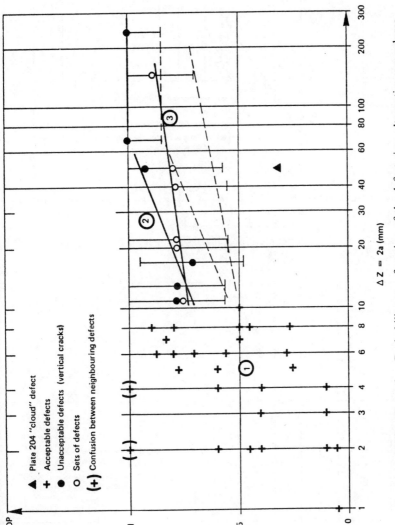

Fig. 16. Defect Detection Probability as a function of the defect size; alternative procedures.

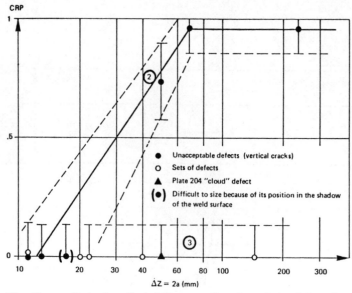

FIG. 17.   Correct Rejection Probability as a function of the defect size; PISC procedure.

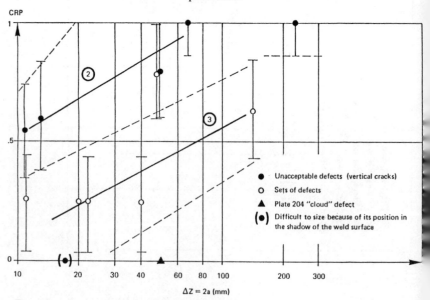

FIG. 18.   Correct Rejection Probability as a function of the defect size; alternative procedures.

Figure 15 shows that for the small defects (acceptable defects, ASME XI (IWB 3500)) no correlation exists between DDP and defect size.

For larger defects such a correlation seems to exist. No safe detection appears to be provided for sets of small defects (unacceptable global defect as defined by ASME XI proximity rules).

In Fig. 16 the same plot is given for the alternative procedures. It can be seen that the values of DDP are generally higher.

From these figures it seems that the most optimistic statement that can be

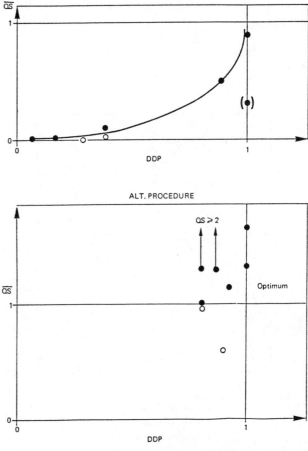

FIG. 19. Correlation between quality of sizing and Defect Detection Probability (only unacceptable defects are considered).

made is that for through-thickness orientated cracks DDP will only become large (∼ 0·95) when ΔZ is ≥ 55 mm. For the sets of small defects no such statement can be made.

7.2.4. Correlation between CRP and Defect Size

The defect size is represented by its height $\Delta Z = 2a$ mm. Plotting CRP against ΔZ again suggests that there are three groups of defects:

(1)   acceptable defects (not represented),
(2)   single defects (cracks perpendicular to the outside surface of the plate) and
(3)   sets of defects.

Figures 17 and 18 show CRP as a function of ΔZ for the PISC and alternative procedures.

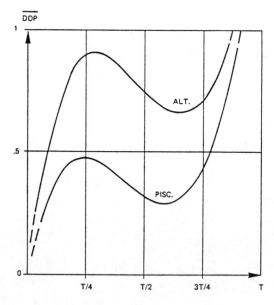

FIG. 20.   Average Defect Detection Probability as a function of the defect position in depth.

7.2.5. Correlation between Quality of Sizing and DDP

Figure 19 shows the link that exists between the average value of QS ($= 1 + ESZ$) taken over all teams and DDP, for the PISC and alternative procedures.

7.2.6. Correlation between Defect Position (in Depth) and DDP

The average value of DDP seems to be a function of the defect position in depth in the plate (Fig. 20). High values of DDP result when the defect is near the inside surface where double reflection helps detection. Low values in the central region are evident when using the echo technique, particularly for through-thickness orientated cracks. A low value of DDP appears also when considering the upper surface of the plate, which is generally in the transducer dead zone.

8. CONCLUSION

In this paper the method of analysis that was adopted for the results of the PISC trials has been described. The most important results of the analysis have been summarised.

Report No. 5
Discussion of NDE/DE and Summary Conclusions

R. O'NEIL

UKAEA, SRD, Warrington, UK

and

P. CAUSSIN

Association Vinçotte, Belgium

SUMMARY

The information presented in Reports 1 to 4 has given details of the background to the PISC project, the method of non-destructive examination, the method of destructive examination and the results and evaluation carried out. This paper deals exclusively with a discussion of the results and the conclusions which can be drawn from the results, having regard to the constraints placed upon the PISC project.

1. INTRODUCTION

Previous reports have given details of the PISC project and specifically Report No. 1 stated in the introduction that the reliability and efficiency of ultrasonic non-destructive examination (NDE) of thick steel sections is one of the remaining uncertainties in understanding the integrity of nuclear reactor pressure vessels. This paper can not set out to remove this uncertainty but rather goes some way towards further understanding of the problems that remain in the use of ultrasonic examination to underwrite the integrity of reactor pressure vessels.

2. CODES OF PRACTICE AND PROCEDURES

The state of the art in ultrasonic examination of thick steel is very well advanced. It is clear that with freedom to select equipment, the right conditions, freedom to select procedures and adequate time, workers in the field can detect, localise and size flaws correctly and with great accuracy. In reality, these freedoms are not all readily available and some compromise has to be agreed between safety, practicability, and economics. This compromise is achieved by producing codes of practice acceptable to the plant operator, the regulatory bodies and the inspectors and users of ultrasonic equipment. This compromise in the case of nuclear energy is heavily and correctly biased towards safety with the lower level being determined by acceptable risk.

The American HSST programme embodied under the supervision of the PVRC initiated an investigation into the reliability and efficiency of ultrasonic examination of thick steel plates and it was the PVRC who offered to the OECD/CEC the three plates on which to carry out the tests reported here. The results were meant not only to stand in their own right but to augment the American inspection programme and the procedure adopted for the PISC project was virtually identical to the PVRC procedure which itself was based on the 1974 ASME XI code. The reader should understand that it was largely the *procedure* that was being tested, rather than the ultrasonic equipment or the ability of such equipment to detect, locate and size flaws.

In addition, a number of teams carried out inspection by what have been called alternative procedures. No restriction was placed on the procedures or the equipment used. These results are still to be analysed and evaluated individually and it is not possible to say at this time, if at all, whether one kind of alternative inspection is better or worse than another or how the individual results may compare with the PISC procedure results. A global evaluation using an average of all the alternative results has been carried out and reported.

3. LIMITATIONS ON THE PROJECT

3.1. The Plates and Calibration Holes

Plates were not specifically selected as being especially good quality, nor were they specifically reject quality; however they were characterised by a large number of defect zones in the base material (segregations and small cavities) which disturbed the clear sizing of the major defects. Attenuation of the ultrasonic beam intensity due to these base material defects was not too high, but beam symmetry was substantially affected. However this influenced the sizing of the defects, rather than their detection.

No computer evaluation of the base material defects has yet been made, and analysis was initially concentrated on the weld and heat affected zone. Very few reports of base material defects were submitted by the participating teams.

For the purposes of equipment calibration, a number of holes following the ASME XI procedure, I-3131, edition 1974 or T-434.1, edition 1977 were drilled in the plates themselves. In plate 51/53, the holes were displaced to a deeper position which made time-base calibration of the equipment difficult and required slightly higher amplification.

3.2. Inspection Procedure

As the 204 nozzle plate was not large enough, inspection of the weld foot with the 60° angle probe was possible only in front of the four corners of the plate. Also, since the weld surface was not smooth, inspection of the weld top was not possible with either 45° or 60° angle probes using contact techniques.

The procedure required transducers to be moved across the plates following the scan lines; even slight skewing to optimise echo amplitude was forbidden. Because of squint angle, this rule lowered the reproducibility of response amplitude between teams. Because the inspection procedure was so rigidly prescribed, the detection rate might be expected to be slightly lower than that obtained when the operator is allowed to orientate the probe to find the highest response, but it is probably more characteristic of automatic scanning procedures.

3.3. Destructive Examination

Since the destructive examination of the plates was based upon intensive NDE techniques, the map of reference defects can be considered to be reliable. However, since the great majority of defects were finally sized by NDE techniques applied to small cut-outs and not visual examination of the actual flaw, the envelopes of the reference defects are subject to the following uncertainties:

± 1.5 mm on each dimension

$\pm 0.5°$ on the ϕ dimension for the 204 nozzle plate (equivalent to 2·1 mm on the weld centre line)

± 3 mm on its location in the plate

Some defects (five in total) are in fact material variations and were therefore not included in the evaluation; they were retained in the final defect map because they were detected by certain alternative techniques of high sensitivity. All of them are 'acceptable' defects within the ASME code.

No fracture mechanics evaluation of the real severity of defects had been done but may be the subject of future work on the remnants of the PISC plates.

3.4. Proximity Rules for Assembling the Defects

Owing to the enormous quantity of data collected (the average total number of indications per team was about 200) and the difficulty of separating indications when equipment tolerances had to be taken into account, it was necessary to apply the ASME XI proximity rules for assembling indications. Using the full ASME IWA-3300 (1974) assembly rules reduced the effective number of defect indications such that, for example on plate 51/53, the entire weld area could be regarded as one defect. Because of this effect, modified assembly rules were applied to the data in order to enable a more complete evaluation of the NDE performance to be made. These modifications involved:

(1)   ASME XI IWA-3300 (1977) assembly rules;
(2)   disregarding surface proximity rules;
(3)   Defects considered as separate when the through-thickness separation distance is greater than 13 mm;
(4)   for plate 204, the cloud defect was omitted.

3.5. Tolerance in Defect Detection

The prescribed specifications for the equipment would suggest that location error for some defects could reach 90 mm. It was decided that a defect should be declared detected if the indicated and reference defects have some volume in common or if the minimum distance between two adjacent faces is less than a specified tolerance. However, owing to the large number of defects, their proximity and the existence of base material defects, this tolerance was generally reduced to 25 or 50 mm. Diagrams of detection probability as a function of tolerance show that using a tolerance larger than 25 mm does not improve the detectability significantly.

3.6. Rejection Criteria (ASME XI, IWB-3500)

The rejection/acceptance quality parameters, QR/QA, and the probability of correct acceptance/rejection parameters, CAP/CRP have been evaluated using the modified form of the ASME defect assembly rules mentioned above, so as to separate defects for the purposes of NDE evaluation without considering fracture mechanics analysis. The values given to these parameters are correct only for planar sub-surface indications.

3.7. Alternative Procedures

As already stated, the results of all alternative procedures were evaluated together, although a separate evaluation of each procedure is to be carried out in the future. The results given for these procedures should therefore be regarded as no more than an indication of trends or possibilities.

No formal proximity rules for assembling defects were used in evaluating results of the alternative procedures; teams were requested to present their results on Data Sheet 6 which considers only the envelope of defects and thus represents the team interpretation.

3.8. Corrections to Team Reports

For a number of reasons, a number of teams were unable to follow the instructions for the presentation of results. For example, reference marks on the plates became indistinct during the round-robin test, leading to some confusion.

To enable the evaluation to be made, it was necessary for such results to be corrected. The corrections made were of four types:

(1) Change of co-ordinates (cylindrical co-ordinates instead of cartesian co-ordinates).

(2)   Inversion of co-ordinates

$$(Y = K - Y' \text{ or } X = Y', Y = X')$$

(3)   Rotation of co-ordinates

$$(\phi = \phi - 90° \text{ or } 45° \text{ or } 135°)$$

(4)   Giving a dimension to defects declared as a point

(only one Z, Y or X co-ordinate).

Despite the procedural errors necessitating these corrections, all data, except those supplied by one team, were usable.

3.9. Estimation of the Value of Parameters

The Defect Detection Probability (DDP) was estimated for all defects. However, when the DDP was low (i.e. few teams detected the defect) not all parameters (QL, QS, QR/QA, CAP/CRP) were calculated. This occurred only for certain 'acceptable' defects.

3.10. Human Factors and Qualification of Operators

Generally speaking the plates were inspected in ideal conditions. In real conditions, human factors could well reduce the performance values found here. Because of the size, number and dispersion of the defects in the plates, it is possible that operators did not record all data. Even more important is the human tendency to underestimate or ignore low level indications because of the relatively very large and numerous indications found elsewhere.

It is to be noted that the many operators involved in the programme had a variety of qualifications, related to a number of different codes. Nevertheless the participants were all practising inspection organisations.

3.11. Nature of Flaws

Most of the flaws in the PISC plates that were amenable to evaluation were artificial and had been deliberately implanted during fabrication, hence they were only approximations to the type of weld defects that could exist in practice. Although a total of some 3 m of weld was inspected, the reflectors available did not necessarily represent the whole range of defects, type, size, orientation and location that could be found during the inspection of a heavy section pressure vessel.

4. RESULTS

The results have been reproduced in Report No. 4 but it is worthwhile reiterating the most important parameters considered and these are as follows.

4.1. Defect Detection Probability (DDP)

This is defined as n/N where n is the number of teams recording an indication of a defect and N is the total number of teams carrying out the inspection. Clearly this is a most important parameter because unless a defect is detected then no sizing is possible and no analysis of the importance of the flaw can be produced. However *any* indication within the actual defect size is a success and it is necessary to consider how well the procedure allowed correct sizing.

4.2. Correct Rejection Probability (CRP)

Having found the defect it is essential to size it. In accordance with the ASME XI code the size of the defect is compared with a table consisting of the flaw aspect ratio against height to plate thickness ratio and the use of this table determines whether or not further investigation such as more detailed sizing on fracture mechanics evaluation is carried out. Other codes can be more stringent. The ASME XI acceptance table has been plotted and the results of each team for each flaw have been placed on this graph, the object being to give some symbolic representation of the way the teams tended to acceptance or rejection of the flaws. It must be emphasised that the points whilst correct in position on the diagram are only related to the curve drawn for sub-surface flaws; a different curve would be drawn for flaws which under the ASME code would be considered surface breaking and as has already been explained all flaws were considered as sub-surface for NDE comparison purposes.

Correct rejection probability is conditional upon the defect having been detected. The ratio used is r/R where r is the number of teams correctly rejecting the defect and R the number of teams detecting the defect. When this ratio is multiplied by the DDP this gives the correct rejection probability (CRP = DDP $\times$ r/R).

4.3. Other Parameters

Other parameters such as Error of Sizing (ES), Error of Location (EL) etc. are detailed in Report No. 4 and the results are used to determine 4.1 and 4.2 above.

5. CONCLUSIONS

Report No. 4 in this series gives the main conclusions that can be drawn from the results and these are augmented by the presentation of a series of tables and diagrams drawn up from these tables. A summary of the conclusions is given below and the most important diagrams have been produced as Figs. 15–18 and 20 of Part 4 of this chapter.

5.1. Conclusions Drawn from the Inspection of the Plates Using the PISC (ASME XI) Procedure

Analysis of the results shows that the defects fall naturally into three main groups:

(1)   Small defects having a general volumetric character (sometimes consisting of many small cracks),

(2)   discrete cracks oriented in the plane perpendicular to the maximum stress (through-thickness oriented),

(3)   large sets of defects which on application of the ASME proximity rules are to be considered as one unacceptable defect.

Separate conclusions can be drawn in respect of each group, as follows:

(1)   For small defects having a general volumetric shape the defect detection probability showed a large amount of scatter. Thus any extrapolation based on this type of defect could be optimistic.

(2)   Defects perpendicular to the surface were not consistently detected except when close to the bottom wall. From the results of the PISC exercise, probably the most optimistic statement that can be made is that cracks which have a depth greater than about $\Delta Z = 2a = 50\,mm$, have a probability of ≥ 0.95 of being detected. This conclusion is based on a linear fit to the logarithmic plot of DDP versus ΔZ (Fig. 15 of Part 4). It is important to note that data are missing in the region between $\Delta Z = 20\,mm$ and $\Delta Z = 50\,mm$. Nevertheless this result does suggest that vertical cracks of less than 50 mm in depth have a probability of detection which at best is of the order of 0·95 (the results of CRP are similar although the fall off of the optimistic limit with decreasing ΔZ is faster (Fig. 16 of Part 4)).

(3)   For sets of defects which have been combined using the ASME XI proximity rules, the teams generally underestimate size.

The average location error of detected defects was about 9 mm or $T/20$. In general the 'acceptable' defects were oversized whereas the 'rejectable' defects were undersized. Although oversized, the 'acceptable' defects were generally accepted.

Composite 'rejectable' defects were never rejected.

The curves on Fig. 20 of Part 4 indicate low values of DDP in the central zone of the plate.

5.2. Conclusions Regarding the Alternative Inspection Procedures

The results of all the alternative procedures were considered together. Some of the procedures were very close to the PISC method, differing only as to the calibration technique, or scanning surface used; others are in fact the PISC procedure with a 20% DAC cut-off instead of 50% DAC.

It should be noted that all these procedures satisfy the requirements of the ASME Code, Section XI and some are currently used for quality control and in-service inspection.

From the analysis carried out so far, there are strong indications that certain alternative procedures, when considered on their own merits, could give comparatively reliable detection, sizing and rejection of all 'rejectable' defects regardless of their size, location and nature.

This observation is subject to confirmation by further detailed analysis which will be carried out in due course. Similar diagrams to those for the PISC have been drawn up (Figs. 17 and 18 of Part 4) and although the points are average values of all alternative techniques, they tend to show the improvement mentioned above.

6. DISCUSSION

Because of the limitations noted in Section 3 the conclusions reached are also somewhat limited. A vast amount of data has been produced and still awaits analysis. Subject to these limitations, the results have indicated definite trends, e.g. inspection to the procedure tends to oversize flaws which are small (of the order of 40%) and tends to undersize flaws which are large (of the order of 60%).

Of the 500 flaws found in the weld and HAZ only 45 were above the 6 mm² limit chosen for analysis, and of these only six were discrete. Figure 15 of Part 4 shows that these 45 flaws were in three groups. The first group consists of flaws (32) which under ASME rules would be acceptable and the diagram indicates that there is no correlation between size and DDP. The second group are unacceptable planar defects (6) perpendicular to the surface with sizes ranging from 11 to 236 mm in height. For those defects less than about 70 mm in height, DDP and size are fairly well correlated, however the statistical sample is small and there is a large gap between 20 and 50 mm which could increase or decrease the slope of the line considerably. The third group consists of seven unacceptable (ASME proximity rules) zones made up of a number of flaws such as porosities, small cracks and inclusions. One of these seven was not used (cloud defect of plate 204) and there is reasonable correlation between DDP and size. The difference between the DDP for discrete flaws and composite flaws is quite marked and even more so when CRP is used for comparison purposes. The CRP for composite flaws is always zero. This difference needs further investigation before definitive conclusions can be drawn but gives rise to some concern at the inability of the pulse echo technique used in the procedure to find and size potentially large flaws. Figure 20 of Part 4 shows the DDP as a function of plate through thickness and the implications of this variation again gives rise to the need for further investigation.

Whilst the PISC project had clear terms of reference, i.e. to investigate the reliability of the given procedure to detect, locate and size defects, it should not be forgotten that the underlying need is to provide evidence of ultrasonic inspection methods to underwrite the integrity of reactor pressure vessels both by pre- and in-service inspection. The PISC project has gone some way towards indicating some of the shortcomings and clearly the results imply the need for further investigation. The effect of cloud defects in the base material has yet to be analysed, as has the metallurgical state of the material and this is already underway. The analysis of alternative techniques individually has commenced and will be reported towards the end of the year.

It is considered that there is a need for a further programme of testing carefully prepared to consider:

(1)   surface defects,
(2)   defects near to the acceptance limit,
(3)   fatigue type defects,
(4)   defect distribution in through-thickness,
(5)   the effect of stainless steel cladding,
(6)   more investigation into alternative techniques,
(7)   improvement of procedures,
(8)   multiple or composite defects, and
(9)   effect of instrument characterisation.

The means by which such a programme of testing could be carried out is now being investigated by the members of the committee. It may again be in collaboration with other investigators to avoid overlapping or where necessary to improve statistics by working in parallel.

11

Non-Destructive Inspection of Thick Section Materials Using Advanced Non-Destructive Examination Techniques

A. E. Holt and J. W. Brophy

Babcock & Wilcox Co., Virginia, USA

SUMMARY

The need for advanced fieldworthy ultrasonic techniques to improve the repeatability and reliability of defect detection and characterisation has been recognised by experts in the field of non-destructive examination (NDE) for several years. This recognition has come primarily from disagreement between ultrasonic NDE results and the results of destructive examination. Attempts to verify ultrasonic findings using complementary NDE methods have proved unsuccessful. Acoustic holography (AH) was the first advanced ultrasonic NDE technique to provide improved repeatability and reliability in defect characterisation as verified by agreement with destructive test results. Based on AH results and findings, many investigators are now developing advanced techniques to improve ultrasonic inspection capabilities.

The Electric Power Research Institute (EPRI) has sponsored a program with Babcock and Wilcox (B&W) USA to compare defect sizes obtained using both conventional ASME Section XI ultrasonic techniques and AH results with those obtained by destructive tests (DT). Results from selected phases of this program are reported in this paper. One phase was B&W's participation in the HSST thermal shock program conducted at Oak Ridge National Laboratories (ORNL). Babcock & Wilcox's contribution was to measure crack growth that was induced in two vessels. Acoustic holography was used to characterise an induced crack in the vessel before and after thermal shock. The results were in excellent agreement with DT results of these vessels. Details are also given of a second phase in which the results of AH, conventional ultrasonic testing (UT), and radiography are compared to the DT results of a cluster of indications detected in a thick section pressure vessel (PV).

233

A brief outline is also given in this paper of advanced United States and European techniques applied to a test block. A large test block containing induced weld flaws was fabricated by B&W. This block was examined using advanced NDE techniques and conventional Section XI inspection by both US and European teams. The block will be destructively examined to obtain verification data of all NDE techniques.

1. INTRODUCTION

This paper presents information obtained by Babcock & Wilcox (B&W) from an ultrasonic holography program jointly funded by the Electric Power Research Institute (EPRI) and B&W. The purpose of this program is to acquire empirical data to demonstrate that acoustic (ultrasonic) holography is capable of accurately characterising naturally occurring defects. The results reported here constitute only a very small portion of the activities planned and carried out on this program.

The purpose of this paper is to report results showing that acoustical holography has accurately measured crack growth and sized small imperfections in thick section materials. Acoustic holography was used on two heavy section steel technology (HSST) test vessels in which cracks were produced by thermal shock. Holographic 'base line' images were made of reflectors in the vessels prior to thermal shock, and images of the cracks were made after thermal shocking. Crack growth was determined through comparison of the images before and after growth. Comparisons of the holographic results to the destructive test results were excellent. Details of the AH evaluation and results are discussed.

Several previous papers have shown the ability of AH to characterise isolated defects of various sizes [1–6]. The AH results obtained on a cluster of 'small' imperfections are briefly discussed. These results are compared to the results obtained using conventional ultrasonic examination techniques, radiography, and destructive tests.

Acoustic holography is only one of several evolving ultrasonic techniques which can be used to more precisely characterise defects. Many of these other newly advanced techniques, as well as AH, have been applied to the evaluation of defects in a large test block for part of the EPRI/B&W program. Participation of organisations in the United Kingdom, France, and Germany, and within the US has made this possible. When the test block is destructively tested, data from many advanced ultrasonic techniques will be available for comparison.

2. ACOUSTIC HOLOGRAPHY IMAGING OF THERMAL SHOCK CRACKS

Descriptions of the thermal shock vessels and AH examination procedure are presented below.

2.1. Test Vessels Description and Examination Procedure

Two HSST pressure vessel thermal shock specimens were examined by acoustic holography. The vessels were 21 in (533 mm) in diameter, 36 in (914 mm) in length, with 5·75 in (146 mm) wall thickness and an electron beam (EB) weld running the length of each vessel on the inner surface. In addition, test specimen HSST 1 had a machined 3/8 in (9·5 mm) wide, 0·2 in (5 mm) deep notch that ran the length of the inner surface with the EB weld area coincident with the notch. Figure 1 is an end view of the HSST 1 vessel showing the flaw initiators, crack plane, and energy field of the inspection aperture used in the AH test.

The examination procedure used to map the crack was to obtain holograms of the test vessel before and after crack creation by thermal shocking. Overlapping scans were made along the length of the vessel prior to shocking and holograms were obtained from approximately the same

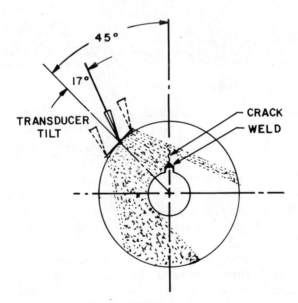

FIG. 1.   HSST 1 end view.

areas along the length of the vessels after crack creation. Figure 2 shows the planar view of the vessel surface and base line scan for HSST vessel 2. Base line and after shock images were obtained from both sides of the weld line. All holographic examinations were done using 45° shear waves. In the case of HSST 1, the after shock holograms include areas not covered by the base line scan. The images obtained from the optical reconstruction of the holograms were used to establish the line configuration and magnitude of the cracks produced.

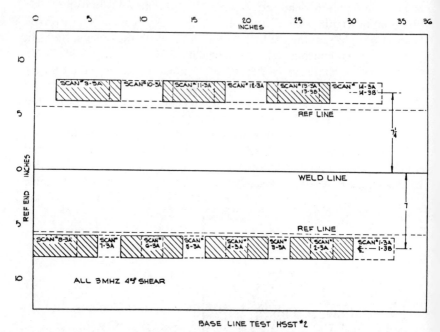

FIG. 2.   Scan areas for HSST 2, (each scan area is overlapped at the ends).

Vessel HSST 1 was thermal shocked twice to initiate a crack. The strain gauge data on the first attempt gave no indication of crack formation and it was after the first thermal shock attempt that the base line examination was performed. The base line examination on HSST 2 was done prior to any thermal shock treatment.

The depth of the flaw, which is required for proper image reconstruction, was determined by the transit time observed on the monitoring oscilloscope when the transducer was in the normalised position. This did not provide the absolute optical bench setting but it did enable a first estimate. The final optical bench setting was obtained by visually monitoring the flaw image while focusing the optical system. Final image focusing is a matter of operator judgement based on image clarity. This operator judgement has since been improved by digital decision techniques.

Determination of crack dimensions is based on the multiplication of an image dimension by a magnification factor. The flaw depth is one factor that is needed to compute the magnification factor. In most cases variations in the flaw depths determined from oscilloscope transit time were sufficiently small that the magnification factor varied by 15 % at most. If the optical reconstruction setting for optimum focus agrees with the transit time estimate of depth, accurate flaw sizing is obtained. For example, a typical transit time reading on the EB weld area of HSST 1 was 116 to 120 μs which equates to a one-way transit time band of 58 to 60 μs. This corresponds to a depth range of 7·2 to 7·5 in (183 to 190 mm) and also corresponds to a magnification factor change of only 0·525 to 0·510.

The relative positions of the flaw line and scanned regions were essentially the same for both vessels. The after shock examinations of HSST 1 and HSST 2 were performed on both sides of the anticipated flaw line. HSST 1 was examined from only one side of the flaw line in the base line test because of the physical constraints of the immersion tank. These constraints were eliminated later to enable examinations from both sides of the flaw line for all subsequent examinations.

After completion of the holography examinations of both vessels, conventional ultrasonic inspections of the crack were made and core samples (trepans) were removed for examination. Finally, destructive analysis by sectioning the vessels was performed. The purpose of this section of the report is to compare the holography results with the destructive analysis findings.

2.2. Equipment

The holographic unit used in this study is a Holosonics 200 system consisting of a mechanical scanner and controller, data acquisition and signal processor electronics, and an optical processor for reconstruction of the holograms into a viewable image. The system is generally used in a pulse–echo mode with the hologram data being acquired from a time-gated volume within the scan aperture.

The test specimen must be immersed in a medium or a coupling system supplied that will propagate ultrasonic energy from the transducer face to the specimen efficiently. For all tests conducted by B&W, the vessels were immersed in water. Figure 3 shows one of the HSST vessels in the water tank

A. E. Holt and J. W. Brophy

Fig. 3.   HSST 1 in the test tank with temporary scanner mounting.

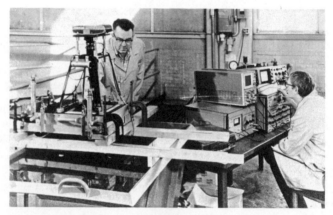

Fig. 4.   Holographic system and operators at Oak Ridge National Laboratory
(ORNL).

during the AH examination. Figure 4 shows the holographic system, electronic processor and temporary scanner mounting system over the immersion tank.

The scribing on the surface of the vessel is for determining relative coordinates of the scanner with respect to the crack initiation line.

The system has been modified to make it more versatile in a field environment. The major modification was an addition to the scanner assembly to make it possible to mount the scanner and normalise the ultrasonic beam when mounted over non-ideal geometries.

2.3. Results
2.3.1. Holography

Figures 5 and 6 summarise the examinations performed. The figures are side view projections showing only the inside to outside diameter portion of the radial plane containing the crack. Thus, the crack extent as mapped by holography can be determined directly as a through-wall dimension.

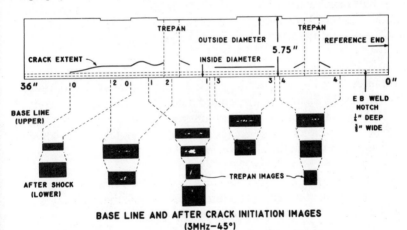

BASE LINE AND AFTER CRACK INITIATION IMAGES (3MHz−45°)

FIG. 5. HSST vessel 1, holographic determination of through wall crack.

Figures 5 and 6 also include the reconstructed images for the base line and after shock states of the test vessels. The cracks in both vessels ran along the length of the vessel along the same line as the EB weld, and both cracks had an average through-wall dimension of approximately 0·5 in (1·25 cm).

Figure 5, for HSST 1, does not show the entire length of the crack because of inaccessible regions on the vessel. The crack in HSST 2 was fairly uniform in extent, showing significant deviation only at the ends of the

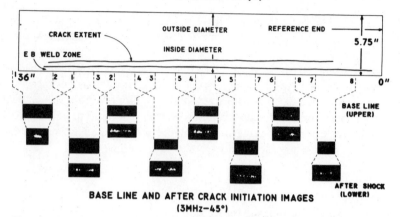

BASE LINE AND AFTER CRACK INITIATION IMAGES
(3MHz–45°)

FIG. 6.   HSST vessel 2, holographic determination of through wall crack.

vessel, whereas the crack in HSST 1 showed more fluctuation in size, especially near the two trepan areas that existed prior to the severe thermal shock. The crack dimension was obtained from the difference in the nominal size of the EB weld (base line) image and after shock image.

2.3.2. Destructive

Figures 7 and 8 indicate the crack extent for HSST 1 and HSST 2, respectively. In Figure 7, the machined notch and EB weld zone are clearly visible as well as the crack. Figure 8 consists of three separate core samples extracted from HSST 2 showing the EB weld zone and the crack, which are quite uniform in size for all three core samples.

2.3.3. Comparison of Holography and Destructive Tests

A comparison of prominent features in each vessel, found by holography and destructive analysis, is shown in Table I.

FIG. 7.   Section of HSST 1 showing machined notch, EB weld and crack.

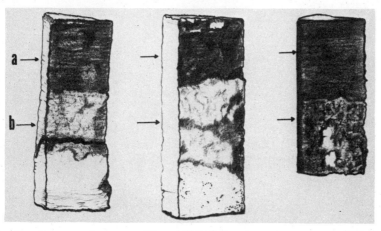

FIG. 8.   Core samples removed from HSST 2, (arrows point to extent of EB weld area (a) and extent of crack area (b)).

The agreement between the destructive testing done by ORNL on HSST 1 shows good qualitative agreement as to the locations of minima and maxima in the through-wall extent of the crack. Of particular significance was the prediction by holography and the later verification by destructive analysis that the crack extent increased at the trepan repairs. HSST 1 had two trepans removed after the first attempt to produce a crack by thermal shocking the vessel (see Fig. 9). These areas were repaired by putting an insert into the trepan and welding it at the outer surface of the vessel. The AH images of these inserts provided additional data for correlation of AH and destructive test results. The size of the insert diameter as imaged by holography was within 5% of the actual size (see Table I) and the average depth of the EB weld and notch as seen by holography corresponded very well to the depth determined destructively.

TABLE I

COMPARISON OF HOLOGRAPHIC AND DESTRUCTIVE ANALYSIS FEATURES

	Feature	Holography	Destructive
HSST 1	EB weld zone	0·5 in (1·25 cm)	0·5 in (1·25 cm)
	Trepan diameter	0·9 in (2·25 cm)	1·0 in (2·54 cm)
	Maximum crack extent	1·55 in (3·9 cm)	1·7 in (4·3 cm)
HSST 2	EB weld zone	0·5 in (1·25 cm)	0·5 in (1·25 cm)
	Average crack extent	0·5 in (1·25 cm)	0·5 in (1·25 cm)

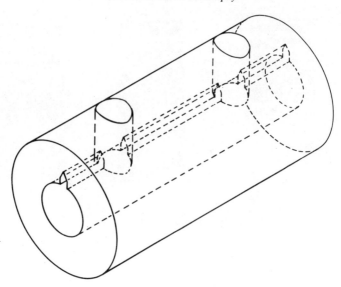

FIG. 9.   Artist's drawing of HSST 1 showing EB weld, notch, and trepan areas.

The quantitative agreement with the destructive test results for the maximum through-wall crack dimension is within 10%, the holography result was 1·5 in (39 mm) and the destructive test indicated a maximum of 1·7 in (45 mm). Part of the quantitative disagreement between the two tests, results from the crack closure reducing ultrasonic reflectivity at the crack extremities. However, there is no way of estimating the magnitude of this effort at this time.

Quantitative agreement between HSST 2 holographic and DT results are also quite good, as can be seen in Table I. Due to the lack of any prominent features, such as the trepan inserts in HSST 1, only average values are reported. The EB weld zone did provide one good test. The intent was to have a 0·5 in (12·5 mm) deep weld zone and both the holography and DT results confirm that this was accomplished.

3.   CURVED SURFACE CORRECTION

The information on the hologram and reconstructed image is affected by the geometric relations of the transducer focal plane as it is scanned over the specimen surface. In this case the equipment constraints imposed are a flat planar scan over a convex curved surface. Figures 10 and 11 show the general geometry used in this study. There are two basic effects that require a correction factor. The first is the change in the refracted ultrasonic beam angle as a function of scan position, and the second is a combinatory effect of change in path length and change of focal zone with respect to the specimen surface. It can be shown that for the HSST study, the second effect

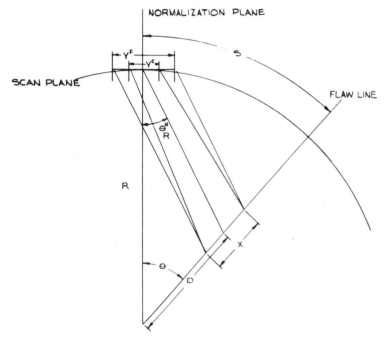

FIG. 10. Scanner geometry for shear wave hologram over a curved surface. $\theta = (S/R)(180/\pi)$; $X = (Y^F \cos \theta_R^N)/(\sin(\theta + \theta_R^N))$; $D = (R \sin \theta_R^N)/(\sin(180 - \theta - \theta_R^N))$; S, R, Y^F, θ_R^N are given.

is negligible, because in the worst case the path difference at the extremity of the scan was less than 3λ, which is near the practical resolution limit for time-gated pulse–echo holography. The length of 3λ is also less than the length of the focal region for the focused transducer used in this study.

The effect of the change in refracted angle when entering the curved surface is treated by considering the equivalent flat surface scan relation, see Fig. 10. The assumption is made that if the area of the scan plane over the

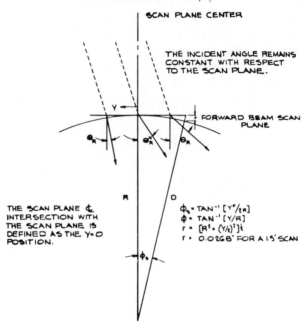

FIG. 11.   Test geometry showing change in refracted angle as a function of scan
position.

curved surface is small compared to the area of a flat scan and encompasses
the same volume of material as the flat scan, then the correction to the image
size is small. This also assumes that the equivalent flat scan area is not
aperture-limited with respect to the flaw. Based on these assumptions, a 'ray
optics' type of calculation was done on the equivalent scan areas for the
scanner position with respect to the flaw line for each hologram. An
iterative technique was used to step the scanner position from the
normalisation line, which was always the scan plane centre, calculate the
refracted angle and from the refracted angle at the surface, calculate the
amount of the flaw line intersected, (see Fig. 10). This value was compared
to the equivalent flat scan area and the scan position stepped again if the
value of the curved area was less than that of the equivalent flat scan. A
program was written for an HP-65 programmable calculator to perform
this calculation. The inputs needed for the calculation are: R, radius of the
vessel; S, centre of scan to flaw line arc length; θ_R^N, refracted ultrasonic beam
angle at the normalisation point; Y^F, the scan length; and X, flat scan
intersect distance on the flaw line. Figure 12 shows in more detail the

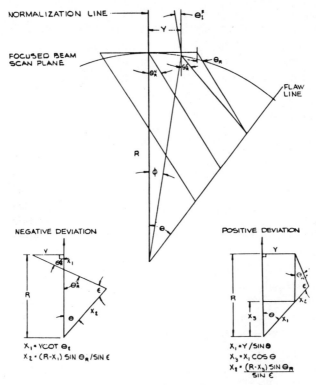

FIG. 12. Geometry for calculating equivalent scan apertures.

geometric relations used to calculate the equivalent scans. The calculation of the refracted angle, θ_R^C, is given by

$$\theta_R^C = \sin^{-1}\left[\frac{v}{v_w}\sin\theta_i\right]$$

$$\theta_i| = 19\cdot22^\circ - \phi \qquad \phi_i^F = 19\cdot22^\circ \tag{1}$$

$$\theta = \tan^{-1}(Y/R)$$

where v_w and v are the ultrasonic velocities in water and the material respectively, θ_i is the incident angle and ϕ is the relative change of the incident angle as a function of the scanner position with respect to the centre of the vessel, (see Fig. 12).

The result of the calculations showed that for a typical scan aperture of 1·5 in (38 mm) by 6 in (150 mm) at an arc length of 8 in (200 mm) from the flaw line, the equivalent flat scan aperture versus the curved scan was approximately 25 %. In other words, the curved scan equivalent for 1·5 in (38 mm) was covered in 0·375 in (9·5 mm). Based on this result, the curvature effect was considered not important for this particular study. This approximation was borne out as shown by the sizing accuracies obtained on the crack, EB weld, and trepan area in the HSST vessels.

4. CLUSTER OF DEFECTS

Most of the defects characterised by holography were isolated defects. However, one sample was evaluated in which clusters of small reflectors were found rather than a single isolated defect. These ultrasonic indications were detected in a thick wall pressure vessel section during fabrication. The indications were located at a depth range of 2·5 in to 4 in (64 mm to 100 mm) from the surface of an 8 in (200 mm) thick component. Over a surface area of 5 in by 5 in (125 mm × 125 mm), four indications were detected by conventional pulse–echo ultrasonics.

In an effort to further characterise these indications, several transducers with different frequencies and crystal element diameters were used. The variation in the results obtained with the use of the different transducers created several questions. The primary question which arose was why different amplitude responses were obtained at different frequencies from the same reflector when calibrated on the same reference block. This was satisfactorily explained by application of diffraction theory. However, the

TABLE II

CLUSTER RESULTS SHOWING NDE AND DESTRUCTIVE SIZES (ALL DIMENSIONS IN INCHES)

Indication	UT	X-ray[a]	AH		DT		Depth
			L	W	L	W	
1	0·19	0·562	0·80	0·08	0·76	0·09	3·625
2	0·44	0·625	0·45	0·20	0·40	0·10	2·875
3	NS	0·156	NS	NS	0·55	0·03	2·875
4	NS	NS	0·44	0·09	0·50	0·07	3·625
5	0·19	0·312	0·24	0·15	0·25	0·18	2·875

[a] The size of each indication as determined by the radiographic area total after the flaws were removed from the vessel in a small 5 in × 5 in × 6 in section (125 × 125 × 150 mm) of material. All other NDE results were obtained while the indications were in the vessel.

next question was not an easy one to answer; which frequency gives highest reliability?

Acoustic holography was used to show that at different frequencies the AH image characterisation would yield consistent results. Also, the AH results were compared to the destructive results to show not only consistency but accuracy. Table II shows the accumulative results of this study by comparing AH, UT, X-ray, and DT sizing of this cluster of indications.

5. CONTINUING PROGRAM EFFORTS

A second phase of the ultrasonic holography contact is to evaluate flaw characterisation through cladding and compare AH capability with DT results and with the results obtained from base metal (weld material and base metal) only. A large test block was fabricated of the following dimensions: 5 ft × 5 ft × 5·75 in (1525 × 1525 × 145 mm) from two blocks $2\frac{1}{2}$ ft × 5 ft × 5·75 in (762 × 1525 × 145 mm). These blocks were welded together with flaws intentionally introduced into the weld. One-third of one side of the block was then clad. The block was originally scheduled to be tested by current ASME Section XI ISI techniques and acoustic holography prior to destructive tests. Through the efforts of EPRI, research organisations which had work underway in the development of advanced NDE ultrasonic techniques, both in Europe and the US agreed to test this block using their newly developed techniques. An enormous amount of data will be obtained from this block using the advanced techniques which will then be compared and verified by destructive evaluation. A partial list of the techniques that were applied is given along with the organisations participating:

(1) Conventional ASME Section XI Ultrasonic Testing
   B&W Construction Company
   Southwest Research Institute
(2) Acoustic Holography
   B&W Lynchburg Research Center
   1. Optical reconstruction
   2. Computer reconstruction
   Battelle Northwest
   BAM—Linear holography
   Saarbrucken IZFP
   Harwell UK

(3)   B-Scan
      Risley, UK
(4)   Radiographic—X-ray (conventional)
      B&W USA
      Risley, UK
(5)   Focused Probe Ultrasonics
      CEA France
      BAM
(6)   Time-domain Analysis
      Harwell, UK
      Saarbrucken, IZFP

Other ultrasonic techniques which have been used on the block will be reported at a later date when the testing has been completed. The goal of this program is not to determine the 'best' technique, but to find the most applicable for the specific test being conducted. Each of these techniques exhibit advantages and disadvantages. All techniques are advanced in the sense that much more of the information is used in the interpretation than used by conventional pulse–echo techniques.

6.   CONCLUSION

Acoustic holography has been successful in accurately characterising crack growth in thick section thermal shock vessels. This accurate monitoring of crack growth was achieved even in the presence of inspection geometry limitations.

Holographic inspection is undergoing rapid development and will be applied in a much different manner to that used in this program. The principle will remain the same but small computer systems will be used to acquire, process, and display the holographic data. The use of computers is required to make holography and other advanced ultrasonic testing techniques which use more information than amplitude, usable by shop inspectors.

Holography has proven to be repeatable and consistent in the characterisation of indications even when different frequencies and transducers are used. This is in contrast to the widely varying amplitude obtained in conventional pulse–echo examination.

A number of advancing ultrasonic techniques are being developed and the authors believe that acoustic holography has shown the need for more reliable data and verified that this data can be obtained. The basic physical principle of holography will be the building block of future 'imaging' systems which employ signal processing, adaptive learning, and a more comprehensive understanding of basic ultrasonic wave propagation phenomena.

ACKNOWLEDGEMENTS

The authors wish to thank Dr Gary Dau, the EPRI program monitor, and Dr Karl Stahlkopf of EPRI for coordinating B&W's participation in the HSST program. We are grateful to the following people at Oak Ridge National Laboratory for their assistance—Grady Whitman, Dick Cheverton, Sam Bolt, Jim McCracken, Bob Smith, and Jack Smith. The authors also acknowledge the assistance of C. A. Shields of B&W for his help in the field data acquisition.

REFERENCES

1. 'Acoustical Holographic Imaging—A Method for Evaluating Defects in Thick-walled Pressure Vessels', presented at the Conference on Periodic Inspection of Pressurized Components, London, June 4–6, 1974.
2. 'Characterization of Defects in Thick-walled Pressure Vessels Using Acoustical Holography', Third Conference on Periodic Inspection of Pressurized Components, London, September 20–22, 1976.
3. 'Acoustical Holographic Characterization of Defects in Pressure Vessel Materials', Third International Conference on Pressure Vessel Technology, Part 1—Analysis, Design and Inspection, Tokyo, 1977.
4. 'The Role of Acoustical Holography in the Characterization of Defects in Thick Section Components', Nondestructive Examination Conference, Washington DC, November 18, 1976, Sponsored by B&W/TUV Rheinland.
5. 'Ultrasonic Characterization of Defects', in *Seventh International Conference on Acoustical Holography: Recent Advances in Ultrasonic Visualization*, August 31–September 2, 1976. Vol. 7, Plenum Press, Chicago, Illinois.
6. 'Quantitative Ultrasonic Holographic Defect Characterization', B&W/TUV Conference, Cologne, Germany, September 1978.

12

Size Measurement and Characterisation of Weld Defects by Ultrasonic Testing

T. J. Jessop and P. J. Mudge

The Welding Institute, Abington, UK

SUMMARY

The application of ultrasonic testing to many different types of high integrity welded fabrication has resulted in indications being misinterpreted. The present collaborative programme of work is aimed at quantifying ultrasonic testing capability by providing detailed information on the application of both conventional and more specialised ultrasonic techniques to a large sample of known defects and features in ferritic steel weldments in the 38 to 95 mm thickness range. This paper describes the various phases of the programme and particular reference is made to the first phase, dealing with non-planar defects, which has been completed and reported in full [1]. The results so far obtained on subsequent phases dealing with planar defects and metallurgical features respectively are also discussed. The results emphasise the problems with conventional techniques and recommendations are made on the use of more specialised techniques, where appropriate, to improve the results.

1. INTRODUCTION

Reports from the fabrication industry on the misinterpretation of defects with conventional manual ultrasonic testing have been widespread [2]. Over-estimation of defects has resulted in unnecessary, expensive and time-consuming repair and under-estimation may have led to significant defects being allowed into service.

251

The object of this programme is first to define the problem by studying the interaction of ultrasound with weld defects using conventional equipment and assessment techniques, and secondly to establish how the more recently developed and sophisticated techniques can be used to advantage. In the first phase of the work, volumetric in-process weld defects such as porosity, slag inclusions and lack of penetration have been studied extensively in ferritic steel butt welds. Similar investigations are now being carried out on planar defects (such as cracks and lack of fusion) and metallurgical features (defined as sources of response which are not readily identified as defects, e.g. coarse grain structure). The so-called 'spurious indication' would come into the latter category. Studies on more complex weld geometries will be included at a later date.

The ultrasonic testing programme is being conducted in collaboration with the NDT Centre, Atomic Energy Research Establishment, Harwell and the NDT Applications Centre of the Central Electricity Generating Board (CEGB), North West Region, Scientific Services Division, Wythenshawe, Manchester.

2. WORK PROGRAMME

The format for each phase is as follows:

(1)   manufacture specimens with the required weld defects or features,
(2)   ultrasonically test the specimens using conventional equipment, specialised equipment, and recently developed sizing techniques,
(3)   destructively test the specimens to determine exact size, character, etc., of the defect or feature under study,
(4)   correlate the results of parts (2) and (3).

2.1. Research Specimens

Defects have been included in various shapes, sizes, orientations and positions in 38, 65 and 95 mm thick butt welds using $0.2\%C:1.4\%Mn$ ferritic steel plate. Both double and single sided joint preparations were used with both manual metal arc (MMA) and submerged arc (SA) welding processes. All test surfaces were machined flat. The procedures used to incorporate the defects have been developed during previous work at the Welding Institute and every effort was made to make them as realistic as possible [1, 3].

2.2. Ultrasonic Tests

The ultrasonic testing programme is divided into several parts. More details on each technique can be obtained from the quoted references.

(1) Conventional equipment—laboratory test [1]: Control is exercised over scanning variables (i.e. *X–Y* only) and methods of recording the results are employed.

(2) Conventional equipment—'shop-floor' test [1]: A certificated operator was asked to test each specimen as if it were part of a complete production welded structure. The results could then be used as a reference level for other tests.

(3) B-scan tests [1, 4]: Conventional flaw detection equipment is used and the results are displayed in the form of a trace on a bi-stable storage oscilloscope.

(4) C-Scan tests [1] (work conducted by CEGB): Again conventional flaw detection equipment is employed. The received echo amplitudes are displayed in the form of coloured contour maps.

(5) Ultrasonic holography [1, 5] (work conducted at Harwell): Complex laboratory based equipment was employed.

(6) Time domain analysis [1, 6] (work conducted at Harwell): This involves a time-of-flight approach to defect sizing which was originally developed for surface breaking cracks.

2.3. Destructive Tests

Full destructive tests have only been carried out on the specimens containing non-planar defects. The object is to obtain data on the actual size, type, position and orientation of the defects. This has been accomplished using both brittle fracture techniques, and detailed radiography with progressive sectioning.

3.   RESULTS AND DISCUSSION

3.1. Non-Planar Defects

The results can be conveniently divided into sizing and positioning accuracy and characterisation capability.

3.1.1. Sizing and Positioning

In general terms positioning was within 1·5 mm for all techniques and length sizing accuracy was within 10% in most cases. Table I shows the accuracy of through-thickness sizing for each technique. It can be seen that

TABLE I

ANALYSIS OF DEFECT THROUGH-THICKNESS SIZE MEASUREMENTS FOR NON-PLANAR
DEFECTS (RANGE OF SIZES STUDIED WAS 1·5 TO 7·0 mm)

		Mean error (mm)	Standard deviation (mm)	Sample population
	4 MHz (20 dB and Max. Amp.)	−2·2	2·2	89
Conventional	2 MHz (Max. Amp.)	−2·6	2·4	28
Tests	DGS	−1·8	1·6	113
	Manual operator	−0·8	1·4	25
B-Scan		−1·3	2·2	30
C-Scan		No through-thickness information		
Ultrasonic holography		Small sample—very inaccurate		
Time domain analysis		−0·3	1·0	24

all the conventional methods tend to undersize the through-thickness dimension by about 2 mm and with a large spread of results. The B-scan shows some improvement, but since, effectively, conventional sizing methods are employed (although without manual plotting) the similar spread of results is not surprising.

The inaccuracy of these results highlights the limitations of conventional ultrasonic testing. The fact that only one small facet of a non-planar defect may be sufficiently well orientated with respect to the beam to be sized by probe movement goes some way to explain the results but they do emphasise the unreliability of probe movement methods generally even when scanning and/or display techniques are more sophisticated. Whether changes in flaw detector and/or probe characteristics would influence the accuracy of the results is open to question. It may be argued that narrower or focused sound fields would improve sizing accuracy or that short pulse/broad band transducers would be better than the rather long pulse/narrow band transducers used in the present work. Efforts should be made to assess these variables in future work.

Better results were achieved by the manual operator and, since conventional probe movement sizing techniques were used, this is difficult to understand. However, there are two points which should be borne in mind. First, unlike the laboratory tests, no negative values were recorded*

* Negative values for 20 dB drop sizing have been reported previously by de Sterke [7].

and it is reasonable to assume that any negative readings found by a shop floor operator would not be recorded as such; and secondly, the manual operator is not confined to strict $X-Y$ scanning.

The best results were achieved by the time domain analysis technique which showed little tendency to undersize and a much smaller spread of results (see Table I). The sample is small (24 readings) because the equipment was not always capable of resolving the upper and lower extremities of a small defect. Work is currently underway at Harwell to improve resolution by using shorter pulse probes and providing this is successful, the technique should be applied more widely.

Despite excellent lateral resolution which gave accurate estimates of defect plan position and size, the interpretation of the holography results grossly over-estimated defect through-thickness (e.g. by up to 300%). This has been attributed to the generally low level of experience with shear waves (which were widely used in this exercise specifically to provide through-thickness information) as opposed to normal compression waves. Efforts are being concentrated on feeding back detailed destructive test information to assist in the interpretation procedures and better scanning and display techniques for assessing through-thickness size are being investigated.

3.1.2. Characterisation of Defects

All but the time domain analysis work has contributed some information on defect character although the information from ultrasonic holography was limited to predictions of defect shape. Again the latter was accurate in the plan view but distortion occurred in the through-thickness direction owing to the over-estimation of size. A detailed assessment of the C-scan technique is not included here as it is felt that a more meaningful comparison will be possible when work on planar defects is complete.

In the conventional tests, records of echo envelopes have been compared qualitatively with defect structure and some correlation has been noted. However distinction between the different defects under study can not be guaranteed because the echo envelopes are dominated by the resolution power which is in turn dependent on beam characteristics. This subject has been dealt with by Coffey [8].

The B-Scan displays provided the most information on defect character because this technique has already been extensively evaluated for specific applications in the power generation industry and interpretation procedures have been defined. In the present work, reasonably accurate information on defect shape and structure has been produced for all types

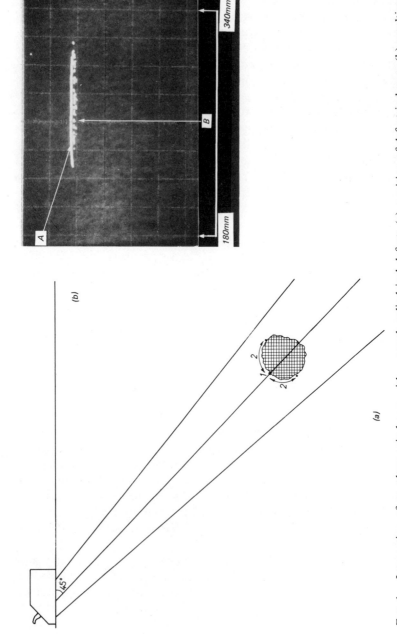

Fig. 1. Interaction of an ultrasonic beam with a rough cylindrical defect; (a) position of defect in beam, (b) resulting B-Scan (4 MHz).

of non-planar defect from interpretation rules based on fundamental ultrasonic interaction considerations with some reliance on past experience. An example of B-scan characterisation is shown in Fig. 1. Here, an angled probe is scanned along a rough cylindrical defect (lateral scan) and the resulting trace shows an oblique longitudinal cross-section of the defect responses. The continuous trace A is produced by specular reflection of the sound from point 1. The region B contains many indications which correspond to reflections from facets of the defect surface (the zones marked 2 on Fig. 1). A cylindrical cluster of small reflectors may produce a similar result if they are sufficiently tightly packed but complementary information from other scans (e.g. transverse scans) and different angles might reduce the uncertainty.

3.2. Planar Defects

Since, at the time of writing, sectioning has not begun, the results are limited to radiographic evidence and a knowledge of the defects intended. A selection of defects have been examined to indicate the results so far. Only tests carried out at the Welding Institute are considered.

There is a problem in detecting planar defects when the plane of the defect is not perpendicular to the ultrasonic beam, even if the defect is faceted. This is demonstrated by the set of B-Scans from a large vertical jagged crack (~ 15 mm in through thickness) shown in Fig. 2. The display is dominated by diffracted echoes from the upper and lower extremities of the defect. (The 'shop-floor' tests on the same defect resulted in two separate reflectors being plotted.) With smaller cracks and incomplete fusion defects the extremity echoes may not be resolved, resulting in a single peaked echo envelope.

If a specularly reflected signal can be obtained either by virtue of an orthogonal beam, a corner echo (i.e. surface breaking defect) or by using two probes in tandem (for vertical, embedded defects) detection capability is greatly increased. Compared with the single probe diffracted wave response from a crack tip, the specular reflection response can be as much as 36 dB greater. Where crack tip echoes can be resolved, accurate size determination from the time domain analysis technique would be expected.

On the limited evidence so far, the B-Scan technique may prove useful in assessing whether a defect is continuous or composed of small reflectors since a continuous defect casts a shadow area behind the main response.

3.3. Metallurgical Features

This work is divided into several parts and the aims and qualitative results to date of each are dealt with individually.

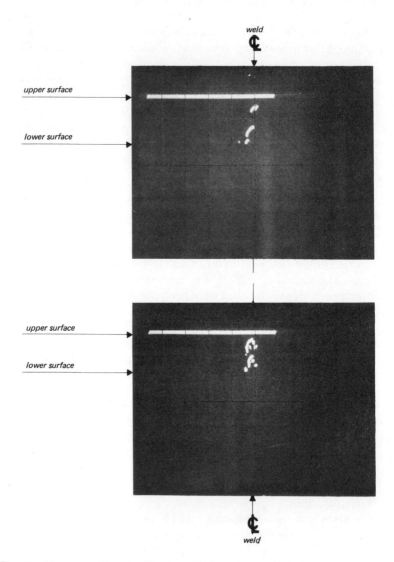

FIG. 2. Transverse B-scans of large vertical crack showing indications from defect extremities; (a) 45° 4 MHz, (b) 60° 4 MHz.

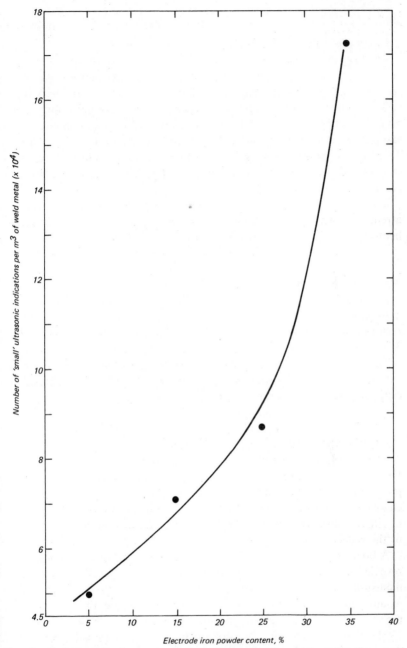

FIG. 3. Relationship between density of 'small' ultrasonic indications and electrode iron powder content (ignoring responses coincident with defects found radiographically).

3.3.1. Weld Zone Characteristics

In this series of tests the effect of various features on ultrasonic attenuation and scatter characteristics is being assessed. In particular, grain size (84·5 μm to 894 μm average diameter, equiaxed), weld heat input (1·3 KJ/mm to 6·9 KJ/mm), transformed microstructure, and fusion boundary effects are being studied. This has been done by machining a sample containing the required feature into a 30 mm diameter cylinder. This is then placed in a jig which allows the disturbance effects on a transmitted beam to be examined at a range of angles with a receiver probe.

The work is still in progress but the expected trend of increased attenuation with increase in grain size has been quantified and little effect of heat input and transformed microstructure has been noted.

3.3.2. Effect of Electrode Composition

Reports from industry have claimed that the iron powder content of manual metal arc (MMA) electrodes affects the ultrasonic response of the resulting weld metal. This has been tested and the results are shown in Fig. 3. A large increase in the number of 'small' indications (defined as those arising from discontinuities which may be difficult to confirm by sectioning) with increase in iron powder content is evident. Efforts are being made to establish the source of the responses.

3.3.3. Heat Affected Zone (HAZ) Reflectors

These types of reflector have occurred in specimens from two sources. One was a laboratory specimen produced for Phase 1 of the current programme and the other was from a circumferential butt weld in a chemical reactor vessel. In the latter case, the indications were characterised by site operators to be severe HAZ cracking. Figure 4 is typical of the form of the reflectors in a B-Scan display.

A boat sample extracted from one of the positions recorded as cracked revealed only inclusions in the HAZ, see Fig. 5. Detailed study of these inclusions showed decohesion of the inclusion/matrix interface which would cause an increase in the acoustic mismatch at the interface and therefore increase ultrasonic reflection.

Methods of ultrasonically distinguishing between these reflectors and true cracks are being investigated, particularly the shadow technique mentioned in Section 3.2.

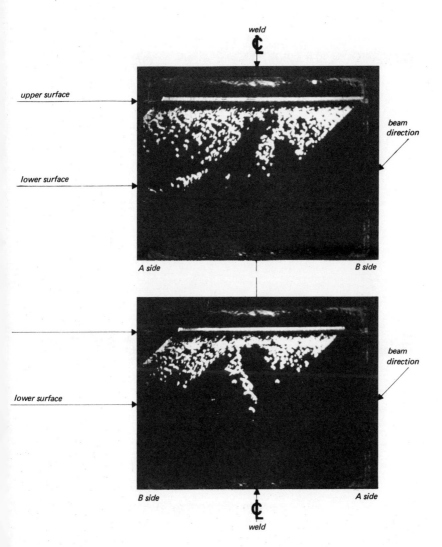

FIG. 4. Transverse B-Scans at high sensivity showing indications on 'B' side wall
(45° 4 MHz).

Line of fusion boundary

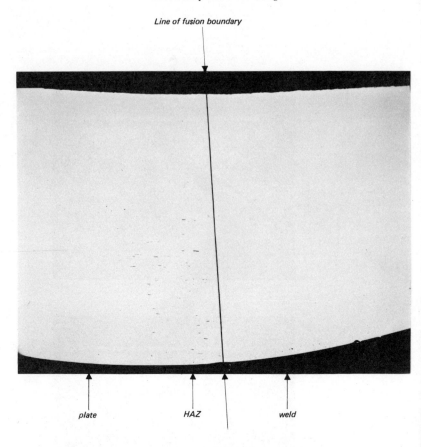

plate   HAZ   weld

Neg. no. OM 3601 x 4.5

FIG. 5.   Example of HAZ inclusions found in boat sample.

4.   CONCLUDING REMARKS

The work completed so far has enabled the accuracy and characterisation capability of all the ultrasonic techniques when applied to non-planar defects to be quantified. The results highlight the inaccuracy of conventional methods for defect through-thickness determination but the time domain analysis technique offered a distinct improvement.

The B-Scan proved a useful aid to characterisation of non-planar defects.

The current work on planar defects is quantifying the effect of beam angle on detection and sizing capability. Specular reflection is essential for reliable detection whereas diffraction at the defect extremities may prove useful for sizing.

Systematic study of metallurgical features (defined as those which are not readily identified as defects) is solving some of the mysteries of the so-called 'spurious indications'. In particular, electrode iron powder content and HAZ inclusions have been shown to influence such responses.

ACKNOWLEDGEMENTS

The work at the Welding Institute and Harwell is being funded by the Mechanical Engineering and Machine Tools Requirements Board of the UK Department of Industry. The freely given support of the CEGB is also acknowledged. The authors are particularly grateful to Dr M. G. Silk, Dr J. P. Charlesworth and Mr A. B. Clare of Harwell; Dr K. J. Bowker and Dr K. A. Short of the CEGB; and Mr D. Holland of the National Coal Board.

REFERENCES

1. Jessop, T. J., *et al.*, 'Size Measurement and Characterisation of Weld Defects by Ultrasonic Testing,' Part 1. Non-planar Defects', Welding Institute Report Series Publication.
2. Anon. (Nov. 1975). Major areas for research, *Metal Construction*, 7(11).
3. Gregory, E. N. (July 1974). Making defective welds, *The Welding Institute Research Bulletin*, 15(7), 199–205.
4. Harper, H. (Nov. 1974). Improved displays for ultrasonic testing, *CEGB Digest*.
5. Aldridge, E. E. (Dec. 1972). Ultrasonic holography and non-destructive testing, *Materials Research and Standards*, 12(12), 13–22.
6. Silk, M. G. and Lidington, B. H. (Feb. 1975). Defect sizing using an ultrasonic time delay approach, *British Journal of NDT*, 17(2).
7. de Sterke, A. (1976). 'Flaw Tip Reflection as a Help in Ultrasonic Flaw Size Determination', British Institute of NDT Conference, London.
8. Coffey, J. M. (1978). 'Quantitative Assessment of the Reliability of Ultrasonics for Detecting and Measuring Defects in Thick Section Welds', I. Mech. E. Conference. Tolerance of Flaws in Pressurised Components, 16–18 May, Paper C85/78.

Discussion of Requirements for Non-Destructive Examination

DISCUSSION ON 'NON-DESTRUCTIVE TESTING FOR FIELD WELDS' (CHAPTER 1), PRESENTED BY MR KEARNEY

C. Serpan (US Nuclear Regulatory Comm., Washington, DC, USA): I can make a comment based on work that has been sponsored by NRC for about five years which tends to do the same thing, which is to detect flaws as they are being produced during the welding process, but which used a different technique from yours. This system put an acoustic emission transducer on the plate, so placed as to get a signal if it cracks. We have been able in fact to determine the presence of porosity of cracks and so forth. Where we hear one crack, we go in and find it and repair it. We also get information that way on why and what kind of crack it is.

Author's reply: Thank you for that comment on the NRC sponsored work. We are working concurrently with acoustic emission and I believe that the combination of acoustic emission and optical electronic evaluation methods may well provide the real answer.

R. W. Nichols, Chairman (UKAEA, Risley, Warrington, UK): May I add that there is work in the Marchwood Engineering Laboratories of CEGB where they have been using assemblies of optically activated temperature measuring devices to measure the temperature at the back of the weld on the far side of the welding, the nozzle weldment. Their procedure is to feed this back on to the welding controls and attempt to produce something which monitors the weld and feeds it back on to the control of welding conditions.

G. J. Posakony (Battelle Pacific Northwest Labs., Richland, Washington, USA): Does the method described in Mr Kearney's paper have application to both manual and automatic welding fabrication?

Author's reply: Yes it does. The manual arc welding presents a particular problem in speed measurement. We are working on some optical electronic techniques for measuring speed on manual welding that I am not at liberty to discuss now. In fact I have already—in some of my previous discussions —overstepped the constraints on patent which the Attorneys have put on me but I think that for the sake of welding technology and NDE we can ignore some Attorneys occasionally.

G. Oestberg (Lunds Tekniska Logskala, Lund, Sweden): I am quite surprised about what you said about the difficulties of reproducing defects. If I understood what you said, you had a theoretical model for the formation of defects, so I guess that you should be able to use that model to create defects. Could you comment on this please?

Author's reply: Yes, there are difficulties and know-how problems in the matter of putting in controlled defects for experimental process. For instance, we can make some defects with very simple methods of varying the gas flow rate for a gas metal arc. On the other hand there are certain things in the chemistry of the metallurgy of the base metal that we cannot control. Ideally we would like to be able to choose the conditions to control the reproducibility and the length of the flaw, but even though we have been working for nearly 10 years on reproducible flaw development, this is quite an onerous problem, and I was glad to see that Risley also has that problem too, when I was there last week.

A. E. Holt (Babcock & Wilcox Co., Lynchburg, Virginia, USA): We have also developed an acoustic emission weld monitor and we have found that in the automatic process we require about two or three passes over a slag entrapment, before we can verify the validity of the formation of a flaw due to weld washout. Could you comment on a single pass or a double pass—I mean how many passes do you need to verify that you have an imperfection?

Author's reply: I cannot give too much on our experience on that off the top of my head but I know that we do have that problem in a similar way when cracks are welded over.

B. Watkins (UKAEA, Risley, Warrington, UK): First of all I would just like to say how much I commend you for the type of work that you are doing. I think that this work is extremely important because I am somewhat of a cynic and I feel that ultrasonic or non-destructive testing may sometimes miss defects. I would like to ask you two questions. I believe that as you stand with your techniques you will have problems with the detection of delayed hydrogen cracking of ferritic steels. Have you any experience of this aspect or of using the technique for hot cracking in stainless steels? Secondly many of the practical applications which I am interested in involve submerged arc welding and I foresee some practical problems in applying the details of the apparatus you have described to such techniques. Can you hold out any hope that the principles you described can be used in this context?

Author's reply: Our work on stainless steels is only just beginning now so I am not able to comment at present although preliminary results have often been good. On submerged arc weldments we have looked at a couple of techniques and the one thing that we are hoping to do with the University of Illinois is to try and come up with some appropriate sensor configurations. There is some hope for using the technique on the submerged arc weldments but once again it is too premature to answer firmly.

DISCUSSION ON APPLICATION OF ACOUSTIC EMISSION AS A MONITORING SYSTEM (CHAPTER 2) PRESENTED BY DR VOTAVA

K. E. Stahlkopf (EPRI, Palo Alto, California, USA): One of the things about acoustic emission that has always bothered me is not what it finds but what it does not find and so my question to you is—was any subsequent ultrasonic inspection made of the vessel on which you made the acoustic emission inspection and, if so, was there a correlation between what was found and what was not found by subsequent methods?

Author's reply: Well first of all I think that the methods of acoustic emission and ultrasonics techniques are physically completely different. With ultrasonics technique you find from a certain level on, that is from a certain size on, defects if the defects are great enough. On the other hand, acoustic emission will only recognise flaws which are growing so it is a different method. Another difference is that, as I have shown you, acoustic emission will show very small defects in a large structure. Such defects were 2–3 mm thick and approximately 0·2–0·3 mm deep. I do not think we can find such defects with ultrasonic techniques so the physical basis is different, and you have to look at acoustic emission—you have to think completely differently, as you do with ultrasonic techniques or with any other method. For example, we cannot understand why such defects have been later detected with the magnetic particle method and why the dye penetrant method did not find this particle so I think we have to think of acoustic emission in a completely different way. We must not transfer knowledge of non-destructive or other methods to this technique.

B. Watkins: I think your paper makes the basis for a case for acoustic emission during hydro tests but I want to ask you two questions relating to the large number of indications reported in some of your cases. My first question is—did you have any acoustic emission indications from positions where you subsequently were unable to find any source for the indication?

The second question is—did you ever find one defect or more than one defect which was above the ultrasonic acceptance level?

Author's reply: We did some work in collaboration with the MPA in Stuttgart which involved a large assembly 1300 mm long, 700 mm large, and 200 mm thick. A ring section was cut out and it was stretched at 65 °C in the machine at Stuttgart. We got clear emissions from cracks which have been identified by ultrasonic techniques before and after. I think there is evidence that a crack which has been tested from ultrasound can also be confirmed by acoustic emission test. Does this answer your question?

B. Watkins: Not really—the question I was really trying to get the answer to was—have you found by acoustic emission a defect which ultrasonics missed and should have picked up?

K. E. Stahlkopf: I believe there is an answer to this question in a paper presented by myself and people from Acoustic Emission Technology at last year's Salt Lake City Conference which presented the results of both an acoustic emission and an ultrasonic inspection of a very large boiling water reactor pressure vessel at which in fact we found very little correlation between the ultrasonic inspection and the acoustic emission inspections results using normal Section XI techniques. However, we later went in with improved ultrasonic techniques and then at the position of every one of our acoustic emission sources we ultimately were able to find something—often only something very small. Our initial attempt was to try and see if the most acoustic emission active sites in fact were the largest sites from ultrasonic flaw size and we found absolutely no correlation.

Author's reply: I think we have to consider the implications of comparing different NDT methods. Maybe acoustic emission is much more sensitive than any other non-destructive testing method.

Chairman: The present situation appears to be that acoustic emission can detect very small defects but on the other hand we have got some evidence that acoustic emission can miss very large defects. There are reports of a vessel in which a crack was growing from both ends of an artificial flaw but the acoustic emission sensor only showed it as growing from one end. It was not seeing the growth from the other end.

Author's reply: You say that the fatigue crack was produced by first putting the notch inside. I think we should be careful. There is I think a good distinction between a real defect and an artificial defect. What I have shown here on this large sample is a natural defect and if you put a notch in and produce a defect I do not think that this is a natural defect. We should concentrate on natural defects and I think then that acoustic emission as a great chance.

Chairman: In fact it was not a notch, it was a fatigue crack which had already grown to a crack.

Author's reply: Yes, but you had put the notch inside previously and were now growing a fatigue crack. If you analyse most of the pressure vessels that have been tested in America and England you usually find a condition of plasticity before the crack develops.

Chairman: Are you saying that for effective acoustic emission detection you must not have plasticity?

Author's reply: Yes, but we have also been successful with samples which were perfectly ductile in pressure vessels at 300 °C where we have obtained signals from the growing crack.

DISCUSSION ON ACOUSTIC EMISSION TESTING OF PRESSURE VESSELS MADE FROM $2\frac{1}{4}$Cr—1Mo STEEL (CHAPTER 3), PRESENTED BY DR YAMAMOTO

Dr G. Engl (KWU, Erlangen, FRG): Would the author please confirm that the sizing of the defect and the acceptance or non-acceptance followed the methods etc. of ASME XI and also that the inspection techniques and sentencing complied with the requirements of ASME XI?

Author's reply: Yes, that is right.

G. Engl: I raise this point because of the question which has been discussed considerably following the two previous contributions concerning the possibility of comparing the results of acoustic emission tests with those from other inspection techniques such as ultrasonics. I regard this as a slightly misleading question especially if you are taking as a standard of comparison the results of whatever inspection technique by ultrasonics has been used in any particular case. I would rather see the successful detection you expect from acoustic emission stated in absolute terms and the expected results of ultrasonics to be also stated as absolute terms. It is necessary to remember that from the basic facts of physics by the use of ultrasonics one is not measuring any size of defect but one is merely measuring the potential of each defect to reflect ultrasound. If we want to have real information of the absolute size of the defect, we must do more studies by ultrasonics than simply those described in ASME XI. About acceptance and non-acceptance, we must also be aware that there are 'factors of safety' included in the codes to allow; for example, the possibility and extent of future growth of a defect. So one must not under-estimate the potential of acoustic emission techniques by always making the comparison with the results of ultrasonic examination—neither of them are absolute.

Author's reply: I think a most significant point for increasing the reliability of acoustic emission testing in practice must be to relate the acoustic emissions to fracture mechanics.

D. G. H. Latzko (Delft University of Technology, Delft, The Netherlands): In my laboratory, we did indeed try to establish a relationship between acoustic emission count rate and the stress intensity K_I in a simple three point bend bar which is very easy to do in the laboratory. I think the work was done very carefully using specimens of mild steel and we failed to establish any kind of meaningful relationship of the kind you have shown, so I wonder whether and how far this is material dependent.

Author's reply: Our presentation is limited to $2\frac{1}{4}$Cr1Mo steel and it is likely that the fracture mechanics relationship is highly dependent on the material. However this relationship is important in determining the relevance of a particular magnitude of acoustic emission in relation to flaw size. To use an analogy, if people are studying an earthquake motion they can now provide information on where the earthquake has happened and what its magnitude is. The present state of acoustic emission technology is less advanced and we can only estimate the location of the source. However, in future we are going to try to obtain the magnitude of the source energy release which we believe to be highly dependent to the materials fracture toughness.

A. E. Holt: You reported in your conclusions that in the ultrasonic examination carried out after hydro test there was some evidence of increased echo heights from 3 to 5 discontinuities that had emitted acoustic signals. Did you perform a destructive examination of these five areas and in fact did the ones which showed an increased ultrasonics response show any evidence of actual crack propagation? In other words, did you have any direct evidence of whether there was any real crack growth at the positions which showed increased ultrasonic response?

Author's reply: We have not direct evidence for the growth of a crack.

However when I asked the UT inspector after the pressurising if the crack was increasing in size, and that inspector knew that the vessel had been subjected to a programme of pressurising and acoustic emission testing, his reply was 'yes, increasing'. However, other people were less definite. We did not examine destructively because we wished to use the vessel after.

A. E. Holt: Can you tell me how you had the transducers arranged on the vessel? How many transducers you used during the examination?

Author's reply: Twenty-four transducers were used for the coincident detection location method and two others for counting energy, making a total of 26.

G. Engl: I have a question relating to your statement that your CDL system can distinguish acoustic emission signals from the background noise. Does this mean that you can find signals which are lying within the background? In other words where there is a level of background noise, do the signals which you record only have an amplitude bigger than the background noise or did you also make notes of any signals which lay within the amplitude of the background noise?

Author's reply: We measured all kinds of signals including the noise so later on the CDL detection method eliminates the background noise; where we have got a specific noise even if the amplitude is less than the grass we will record it.

D.-H. Njo (Swiss Nuclear Safety Div., Würenlingen, Switzerland): You used waveguides instead of putting the detectors directly on the vessel. Which is the better method?

Author's reply: We always use a waveguide because we are going to use inservice inspection in future and we wished to have a technique that would be suitable for that purpose; the choice of the waveguide is thus not to improve the technique but to make it more general.

P. Caussin (Association Vinçotte, Rhode Saint Genese, Belgium): In your evaluation of the acoustic emission signals you are using energy-level. Does this mean that to compare results from different cracks you have to calibrate your system? If so, how do you calibrate your system and how do you take into account the attenuation of the signals as they travel between the source and the sensors?

Author's reply: In our testing we had two kinds of apparatus which were compared with each other and another for attenuation of the wave propagation. Before making the test we studied the nature of the propagation of the wave in the inner vessel and determined the attenuation factor so that we could compensate for attenuation.

DISCUSSION ON PRESSURE VESSEL NOZZLE INSPECTION USING ADAPTIVE LEARNING TECHNIQUES (CHAPTER 5), PRESENTED BY DR COOKE

G. Engl: If I understood correctly you have concentrated your efforts on cracks starting at the cladding surface itself. Have you also collected some experiences with cracks starting at the interface—not opening to the surface?

Presenter's reply: Not that I am aware of.

T. Currie (HM Nuclear Installations Inspectorate, London, UK): How much improvement in total were you able to achieve and how much of this was due to the filtering techniques?

Presenter's reply: There was a total improvement of about 20 dB of which about 5·1 dB came from the band pass filtering and match filtering. Most of the improvement has come from the non-linear signal averaging adaptive learning.

D.-H. Njo: You calibrate your technique with a saw-cut. I wonder whether this represents a real fatigue crack that is not opening—is that functioning also if you calibrate it with a saw-cut to find a fatigue crack?

Presenter's reply: If the calibrations are done with a saw-cut then obviously the best performance will be given for detecting saw-cuts—how well that performs when you take networks trained on saw-cuts and try to detect real cracks with them is yet to be determined.

B. Watkins: I was very impressed by its sizing capability on the nozzle inspection system. To achieve this, do you have to do any dressing of the radius on the outside of the nozzle or is the as-made nozzle adequate for the results you presented?

Presenter's reply: Yes—if I understand the question the outside blending radius does not change.

G. Engl: I understand that your work was done using a given inspection technique and so developed only the processing of the signals. However, does adaptive learning teach you how to improve your ultrasonics? Can you draw a conclusion on the choice of inspection frequency? For instance, you already said that the ability to size flaws is improved by the use of 1 MHz. If you also take into account other types of defects with slightly random orientations then you might end up doing better with a lower frequency which had a higher potential of detection.

Presenter's reply: The adaptive learning technique does not teach you any more than what is in the data basis you use so that if the data base you use to train on contains information from two different types of frequencies, it is possible to get some information on this aspect. What I have not shown, and I do not have the data with me, is that the network can act as its own differentiator so you can perform a sensitivity analysis. The methodology for answering your question is there but I do not have the numerical answer to your question.

DISCUSSION OF ULTRASONIC TESTING APPLIED TO AUSTENITIC STEELS (CHAPTER 7), PRESENTED BY MR CAUSSIN

B. Watkins: I think that this question of stainless steel inspection is a very difficult one, it being very difficult to isolate the purely inspection problems from other aspects. For example, you have got to take into account the fabrication processes both of the as-fabricated material and of the weldments. It could well be that the question of ultrasonics inspection of stainless steels is one that we may not be able to answer as well as we would like unless we are prepared to put some limitations on the fabrication processes, as for example was indicated in the elegant work which John Whittle and his colleagues did in CEGB where they controlled the fabrication processes in such a way that they have a constant grain orientation. Under those conditions I think that you may be able to achieve a solution. However we must remember that stainless steel is a ductile material and can tolerate large defects on a 'fitness for purpose' basis. My plea is that more effort be concentrated on the kind of work that will be discussed in the PISC papers (Chapter 10), all looking at the fabrication process to eliminate defects and the use of acoustic emission during welding and I believe that in these two areas as far as stainless steel is concerned the benefits could be quite considerable.

Author's reply: I would like to come in on that. I think that in the inspection world you have two problems, as you know better the physics of the phenomenon you could influence the technique of the future but you will not have enough information from the past to influence the inspection of old pipes or welds and these kind of things, so I think that the physics should help us both to design components with better inspectability and also to tell us how to become able to inspect old items.

Chairman: I have a mental blockage on this particular approach which arises from the following argument. You can choose the orientation of the structure by controlling the fabrication processes but you cannot choose the direction in which the defects are going to form. If you have random defects then you have a random orientation of reflected waves and these too must come through the structure in some way. How do you cover this point? Do you mean that the only worry is about defects in particular orientations? Maybe this again is true in many applications.

J. Whittle (CEGB NDT Applications Centre, Wythenshawe, UK): There are two points that need to be made regarding orientations. First, I think that on inspections—ferritic and austenitic—we make assumptions about the orientations in which we expect to find defects. I know of very few inspections—in fact I do not know of any—in which you make an assumption about random orientations. The second point is that among the best of the various techniques that have been used to look at austenitic welds, appear to be those which rely on obscuration of a standing beam either by using two probes and collecting the beam off the bore of the components or by using a back-wall echo and in that situation the technique is somewhat insensitive to defect orientation so long as it intercepts the beam with cross section.

DISCUSSION ON PROBLEMS ASSOCIATED WITH
REPETITIVE INSPECTIONS OF REACTOR PRESSURE VESSELS
(CHAPTER 8), PRESENTED BY DR MEREDITH (SOUTHWEST
RESEARCH INSTITUTE, TEXAS, USA)

P. Caussin: I should like to know if you know if the equipment which was used for all those inspections was the same. In particular were the transducers the same in each inspection? Also I should like to know if there was crack characterisation of all the equipment.

Presenter's reply: The equipment was exactly the same. In fact the transducers and search equipment are being kept safely locked away between examinations back home and we intend to use it again on a programme in Spring 1980. I am sure that the characteristics of that equipment—which means the transducers—are checked. Our transducers are recertified every six months and in particular they are checked carefully.

H. Wurstenberg (BAM Berlin (West), Germany): I am afraid that the kind of defects we must expect during inservice inspection will not be those that would give good image by radiographic presentations. You will find perhaps inclusions but I do not think you can really have a high probability for cracks to be detected by such techniques.

P. Hernalsteen (Traction & Electricité, Brussels, Belgium): In your paper you have correlated increasing amplitudes with increased reflectivity of the flaws, and considered that the size remained the same. Do you now have some evidence? Do you have an opinion about the opposite situation; in other words is it possible for the amplitude to diminish as a result of a reduction of the reflectivity of the flaw which is always a constant size?

Presenter's reply: I have no information on these points although such effects can be expected.

Chairman: Another possibility is that in service the residual stresses could be gradually disappearing and the stress across the defect will also affect the reflectivity.

N. Haines (CEGB Berkeley Nuclear Labs., Berkeley, UK): There is some work in the CEGB at Manchester which experimentally has been looking at transmission through surfaces under compressive forces which shows this effect. Recently we also at Berkeley Nuclear Laboratories at CEGB have been worrying about the mechanism of transmission of ultrasonic energy through surfaces under compressions of this type and we now have a basis of a physical model which can quantitatively explain the transmission through service of this type in terms of things like the frequency of the waves you are using, the yield stress of the material, Young's modulus and the acoustic impedance of the metal. I will not perhaps go into details at this point but there is a model and it is fitting in extremely well with the Manchester experimental work.

J. Whittle: This was actually a point I was going to raise in the general discussion but I would like to say at this stage that the change of reflectivity of fatigue cracks that we have seen as a function of compressive stress is entirely consistent with the explanation put forward by SWRI for this change of reflectivity. You can get quite a large change of a factor of 2, or even 3, with very small changes in the stress across the crack. There are regions in the plot of reflectivity as a function of stress in which the reflectivity is extremely sensitive to changes in stress.

P. Caussin: It seems to me that the question of influence of stresses on reflectivity must depend upon what kind of reflection is used—are they using a specular reflection or only tip reflections? It seems to me that tip reflections will be very strongly influenced by the stresses. Therefore I am afraid to generalise this problem since we must differentiate between different types of reflected energy.

A. de Sterke (RTD, Rotterdam, The Netherlands): Just a little observation to add to the confusion. In the first place I would like to observe that this phenomena of transmission across the faces of a flaw in compression has been known for many, many years. It is an effect used to advantage to examine shrunk-fitted joints but we have experienced the effect also in welding work, as a result of regions in compression due to welding stresses. My considered observation is this, that wherever the signal amplitude is increasing or decreasing, it both may be a signal of an increase or fall because of changes in the reflection of a flaw and of the changes in the size of the flaw. Indeed the changes in reflectivity can override the other effect, producing an inference in the wrong direction.

A. E. Holt: If I understand what has just been said this tells me that you cannot measure size of flaw by amplitude.

Chairman: That is my understanding too.

DISCUSSION OF 'PLATE INSPECTION STEERING COMMITTEE REPORTS' (CHAPTER 10)

D. L. Marriott (Atomic Energy Board, Pretoria, South Africa): I would like to know whether there are any plans in the PISC programme or perhaps even in the PVRC work to try and evaluate the real significance of defects that have been found in terms of safety. After all some of these great big clouds are of very great concern because they are so large—but are they really worriesome in terms of the degradation of the structural integrity.

R. O' Neil: Part of our continuing CSNI programme is to look at the significance of the defects and in particular the defects which are joined by the proximity rule. With regard to the cloud defect it is perhaps worth reminding you that it ran about half-way round (say an arc of 150°) and it was about 2 or 3 cm in depth. We do not know anything about the severity of it as a flaw or whether it would matter or not and we are considering programmes to investigate the significance of such defects.

L. J. Chockie (*General Electricity Co., Nuclear Energy Group, San Jose, California, USA*): I would comment that that particular type of defect was to simulate as closely as we could the type of defect that we had later in the Hatch vessel and in the Pilgrim vessel. In the Hatch vessel, because it was prior to a service, a repair was required. In the Pilgrim vessel the analysis shows that it is in a neutral stress region and there would be no possibility of crack growth, and as such that flaw would be perfectly acceptable. However, it does cause a lot of concern and consternation on the part of the people who do the examination.

Chairman: On the other hand I presume that everyone here would agree that there were a large number of the defects reported which without further study would have a strong *prima facie* case that they would be significant. Take for example the 140 mm deep defect going almost through the thickness. That is one which unless your stress intensity is very, very low, even with the advice we had yesterday, we could have a job to get down to a stress intensity which would tolerate that size of defect.

D. L. Marriott: It was specifically these clouds which I referred to.

Chairman: There was only one cloud defect—I think we must be careful to distinguish between the cloud defect and the clusters of sizeable cracks covered by the proximity rule—these are different things. The single case of the cloud defect was a series of many, very small micro fissures—if I understand aright, whilst the clusters covered by the proximity rule could behave, I believe, as a big crack-like defect. I think the presentation did allow the audience perhaps to be a little confused into thinking that the cluster and the cloud were the same sort of thing whilst these were quite different.

R. O'Neil: I just wanted to respond to the question from Mr Marriott relating to the 'cloud' defect with one comment. The work that Dr Kussmaul did at Stuttgart tended to show that where you get heat affected zone cracking of the sort associated with such cloud-type defects, then if you are careful enough to put the notch of a Charpy specimen into the HAZ at that point you got a very reduced Charpy value for that HAZ. Now, I am not going to start an argument, I hope, about whether or not Charpy values measure fracture toughness but if you get a very low Charpy value I think you are entitled to assume that you are going to have pretty low toughness associated with this crack material.

S. J. Crutzen: A further comment on this cloud defect in the nozzle is that the decision was taken at the last meeting of the PISC to make a special investigation to find what is exactly the significance of that cloud. The problem is not to evaluate indications or report indications which could not be a relevant problem. The problem is that the cloud was not revealed by many examinations so we have to know if it is important or not to find such clouds and to assess the importance of failing to detect such cases even in careful applications. So we do intend to make an investigation using fracture mechanics and an actual test to see if effectively there is a need.

Chairman: I would like to change the subject away from this one cloud defect as I think it is clouding the issue. Supposing that we decide to forget about the cloud defect and to take it off the diagram, you will have still got a very significant set of results to think about, with many cases of poor detection and sentencing.

A. de Sterke: The only observation I would like to make is that Mr O'Neil and Mr Crutzen referred to the cloud defect as one that was worrying as it was missed by the alternative techniques. I think it is necessary to make the point that this defect could not be revealed in this particular case by the alternative techniques because of the restricted size of the plate. If the questions related to the cloud defect come from the worry whether this defect has been undetected I think it is worthwhile to remember that such defects can in real applications be detected with available alternative methods and that this has been actually proved.

Chairman: Thank you for that comment. May I return for the time being to any questions that do not relate to the cloud defect and do not relate to the alternative procedures?

P. J. Mudge (Research Laboratory, The Welding Institute, Abington, Cambridge, UK): I was just wanting to ask whether or not any estimation was made by the teams performing the inspection on the nature of the defect they found. It is one thing to be able to detect something in a weld and to specify its size within a certain cuboid which you can then section but there is no evidence presented beyond the three discreet groups given in the final analysis from a destructive testing as to what the actual groups had found. Now it is one thing to find something and another to say that I think that is a significant crack—could we have some explanation on that please?

Chairman: I understand that the groups were asked to say whether this was a reportable defect or not by ASME XI which implies some judgement on whether it is innocuous or not.

S. J. Crutzen: It is a good remark because effectively what people were giving were only data sheets in which they were giving what they thought the dimensions were or locations without giving very important remarks or decisions about the defect they thought to be rejected or not. Nevertheless, when you have a defect which is covering the entire depth of your plate, if you do not give this dimension which is the one at the limit of rejection, it means that you considered it was not important. So that for the major defects which are giving us concern because of the high frequency of the cases where they were not rejected, people when giving these dimensions were really making the decision. For certain other defects that I did not give as a request for a decision could have perhaps changed something, but many of those were acceptable and there really we see that the statistical sample we had was not really the right one. We were missing defects in a region where a decision was very important.

K. E. Stahlkopf: A question for both Mr Chockie and perhaps Mr O'Neil or Dr Nichols—one of the most profound things that the PISC programme has demonstrated is something that we have known for a long time and that is that amplitude is a very poor correlation of sizing. If we look at the ASME Code accept/reject criteria we in fact see that it is based on amplitude although I have no detailed knowledge of the British accept/reject criteria, I assume that it is based on the same and I expect that the German code is also based on amplitude, so my question then becomes —now that we know that the criteria which we have previously been using is perhaps no longer the best, what should we do, what necessary steps should be taken next, and what time-frame do we see them take in?

L. J. Chockie: It may well be that in my position on the PVRC as well as the ASME Code I really do not make the judgemental decisions, I merely try to manage these committees so that they do the right thing and we have to sometimes provide ourselves with data before we are really convinced that we should do something. As I have said before, I think it is my personal opinion that we pushed the amplitude time-dependency on ultrasonics about as far as we can and I do not think much more push will give much more results. We do need to draw up other techniques, other procedures and the goal that I would expect to see is the improvement in both the detectability and the sizing and as soon as we can see evidence that there is not a definite improvement in detectability and sizing from anyone of the combinations of the alternative procedures then we can revise the Code to take out some of the conservatism that is there. Right now the conservatism is there to take care of the problem that we have poor detectability and poor sizing. There is too much conservatism, like factors of 50—much too much —but we cannot take anything out until we have some evidence that we can improve the sizing and the detectability. You ask about time-framing, I would estimate it is probably at least four years away before we can change the Code even though you may see results on alternative procedures come along much faster.

Chairman: I think that I must remind myself, however interesting this discussion, that we still have two papers to present and if we drift into a general discussion then those two poor gentlemen who have come all this way to present those papers will have a difficult task, so I would like to restrict questions to the specific papers on the PISC programme.

G. Engl: Two remarks in a question to Mr Crutzen—I think the diagrams, showing the Correct Rejection Probability as a function of the defect size which gives a band of scattering boundary by the two dotted lines, is misleading people. Could you explain this case because also one could draw the conclusions from the presentation of Mr O'Neil that the band of scattering which is drawn in does not mean the average which depends very much upon the technique which was used.

R. O'Neil: I thought I explained this point but obviously I said it too quickly; whereas the PISC results are genuine statistical spread the alternative procedures represent a series of discreet measurements and you cannot read them as a statistic—the text explains that in the paragraphs following the diagram.

Chairman: The alternative procedures should not really be in this section of the discussion at all since the alternative procedures tell us nothing about the reliability of NDT because they are not a statistical trial.

G. Engl: But the question applies also to the PISC procedure because that is also a band width and I should like to see the results.

R. O'Neil: I think it is alright for the PISC ones to use the band width because there you have one population, you have all the teams doing the same thing and it is quite right to combine them statistically, but in the case of alternative procedures you are adding apples and oranges and you really have to just take them as a scatter of possibilities.

S. J. Crutzen: I would like to add something on the work, which is still underway and which will be finished this year, on alternative procedures. Please treat the following comments with caution as being just to show you present trends. I agree that in the present diagram on alternative procedures the scatters there have not a lot of significance. What we are doing now is to try to evaluate in a better way the alternative techniques—trying to find out which are the ones which can be put into meaningful results. We do not have a final result, only an indication but this is giving a good idea of what can happen. Let us restrict the alternative procedure population to those six teams using effectively different techniques, for example different transducers, or different techniques in the sense of equipment, or tandem or focus probes, or things of that kind. In this case we find that the detection probability for the 'rejectable' defect was almost unity. Similarly if you limit this population to those teams that are effectively doing long inservice inspection all day with these alternative techniques, then you have this successful result. This work is going on.

P. J. Mudge: From some of these diagrams you see that if we have a probability of 1 what it really means is that every team has reported that defect. Something that would worry me possibly more than that was that for one of these large defects every team had only recorded shall we say 60 % DAC because that would imply that our margin over the 50 % threshold level was very, very small and that does not seem to be possibly reflected in the results.

S. J. Crutzen: I should like to answer in a very strange way—because I do not have a real answer. We made a lot of diagrams at the trials to take the amplitude into account but at the end we withdrew everything concerning the amplitude of these documents because it did not reach a conclusion; we still have to work to understand, because if you want to take this amplitude into account you have to be very careful and this work is not finished. Exploration work which is still going on is not only on the alternative technique but also on all the correlations we can have on the basis of the amplitude of detection.

R. O'Neil: I wish that everyone could see the number of different attempts we made to present the results, we plotted everything against anything—from the colour of the milkman's eyes to whether it was raining or not—and it is very hard on a single piece of paper to convey it. What you have to do is go back to the source data and for people who are seriously interested in the field we hope eventually to find some way of making the raw data available and people can go away and try playing their own things but it is going to be some time yet.

Chairman: Is the amplitude in the raw data?

S. J. Crutzen: All data is either on computer cards or magnetic tape and of course all data can be given as a computer list. It is in existence at Ispra but it will take time before it is available.

DISCUSSION ON NON-DESTRUCTIVE INSPECTION OF THICK SECTION MATERIALS (CHAPTER 11), PRESENTED BY MR HOLT

Unidentified questioner: You have shown some very nice holograms concerning the crack propagating from a V-shaped notch but do you have some experiences with actual cracked specimens with real cracks growing from a planar surface and forming inside of the right angle with the surface.

Author's reply: In our case the defect came from the id surface; even though it was a rough flaw on the second vessel it was smooth in the first case. No there was no V-notch in there. It was an EB (electron beam) weld defect and all that was done was to make a pass through there to create a poor penetration, so it was very, very narrow. In answer to your other question the cracks were already perpendicular to the weld direction and they were considered to be transverse oriented mini-cracks. They were real cracks—I can use the word cracks—but they ran the length of the weld for a good distance. We were able to discern that they were about 0·04 in and were transverse to the weld direction. Sometimes they would run about 0·2 in through the wall dimensions and none of them were running straight up and down, they were at a peculiar angle.

DISCUSSION ON SIZE MEASUREMENT AND CHARACTERISATION OF WELD DEFECTS BY UT (CHAPTER 12), PRESENTED BY MR MUDGE

A. E. Holt: I have two questions on the use of acoustic holography, specifically 'What frequency did you use and at what angle of incidence'?

Author's reply: I believe the frequency was 3 MHz and that the angle of incidence was 45°. The work was actually done by Dr Aldridge at UKAEA (Harwell).

PANELLISTS' COMMENTS

Chairman: I think we have been through the various questions as far as time allows. Thank you all for presenting and for providing the papers. In the short time remaining I believe that there are two or three things which we must do and some things which we should not do. I think that we should not go on with the idea that we had originally for a panel discussion because the time has got rather late. I would however like to give each of the people who were on that panel the opportunity if there is something they want to say. If they have come along with any slides or something prepared please do not go without giving us the benefit.

L. J. Chockie: There was one point. I was reminded today by someone who made the remark that you should put a lot of attention to getting a high quality in your original welded construction. I think that we have put a lot of attention over the years in trying to inspect after the fact. I am reminded of one vessel that was manufactured, the first vessel for a nuclear power plant, where they used not the sophisticated ultrasonic techniques, just ordinary practice, but they followed each welders pass and they did not argue whether the indication was acceptable or unacceptable, that was the time to fix it and they did. That vessel today upon final radiography had absolutely no rejects, its ultrasonic base line had no indications, and none have developed yet and that plant has been in operation for ten years. I think that is the only message I would like to give to you—you really do not need all these fine techniques after the fact if you do some real work before the fact.

K. E. Stahlkopf: I think that the results of PISC have given us cause to stop and look at ultrasonics as it is practised and hopefully as it will be practised. I will not dwell on PISC but simply say that I think that now is not too early to start planning for son of PISC because it is very clear that there are a variety of competing techniques, some of which are good, some of which perhaps are better, and some of which perhaps are not good at all and the only way that we can absolutely sort out which of these techniques would be most productive to pursue into full commercialisation in later years is by going through such a blind exercise as we have done with PISC. Therefore I would call only for planning now for a rerun in both the US and Europe in a 3–4 year time period.

Professor J. R. Frederick (University of Michigan, Ann Arbor, Michigan, USA): Out of this conference has come an inspiration to carry forward the work at the University of Michigan on our synthetic aperture technique and also to try doing all we can to get the operator out of the loop and replace him with computer techniques which you could do with the use of colour for identifying flaws, characterising them and more accurately locating them and their orientation. Right now also we use phase information which I think is in the right direction in order to do a better job of characterising the flaw and I think we need a lot more communication across the oceans between the US and Germany. I got this from following the conversations across the meeting.

D. L. Marriott: I wanted to say something rather from the point of view of the reliability analysts than the NDE experts. One thing which people have been looking for for a long time is whether the ability to detect defects is going to be the big factor to improve the reliability figures being calculated for pressure vessels and so on. It will be seen that if one were to blindly take the results of what has been presented today, that this factor is rather small, a generous figure of the reliability is perhaps 90%, and if you put that into the calculation you say that in fact it does not make a very significant improvement on the reliability of the pressure vessel. You could take this to its apparently logical conclusion by saying that all this effort does not seem to be contributing much to pressure vessel reliability. Now I do not believe that, because I am pretty sure that it must be making a very big difference to pressure vessel reliability but what it is sending me off thinking about is maybe the way, the sympathetic way, that we have been trying to factor the effect of these NDE's into reliability calculations, is not doing it in the right way and perhaps what Mr Chockie mentioned, what the influence of NDE has been is in guiding the way in which people are putting the vessel together right from the first place.

J. Whittle: In a time when we are still going to have a panel discussion I prepared a brief talk which has been twice amended as plans have changed during the day, but this time I am going to stick to it. What I really wanted to do perhaps to promote discussion was to do a quick review, as I saw it, of the major development needs in ultrasonic testing as seen from the point of view of a major user of ultrasonics in the UK, CEGB, and also as a development laboratory. I think perhaps one of the most important needs that I see in ultrasonic testing is the need to get to grips rather more with the physics of the ultrasonic process. A lot of work we have heard about today has been very useful work, very interesting work, but it is largely empirical. There is a need I think to try and understand a lot better the physics of the interaction of ultrasonics with defects, to understand better how the roughness of the reflecting surface of a defect, its orientation and so on, influence the way in which sound reflects from it and probably a better understanding of that process, as it has got very strong implications for determining probabilities of detection of welds and does provide I think a complementary approach to the ones which we have been hearing about which has been using test blocks. Test block work is extremely useful, it is realistic but it is limited, and the defects we are looking at are not representative and we are often in doubt as to how the results we obtain on test blocks can be extended in a more general sense. Now the sort of work I have in mind is in progress at the NDT Applications Centre and at Berkeley Nuclear Laboratories of the CEGB. We have made calculations of how the RMS surface finish of a reflecting surface can influence the reflected signal strength and as we expected the amplitude falls as the roughness increases. Because the surface is statistically rough then we get a statistical variation of echo reflection. We have studied this for both normal incident beams and for beams of different angles of incidence and one of the interesting points about these results is the way that the curves tend to level off as the roughness increases. We have looked at this for two sensitivity levels corresponding to the 20% and the 50% DAC levels on the ASME definition, so we can see how the reflections as a function of angle incidence, relate to those two particular sensivity settings. The results from the test block are showing that although there is not a direct relation between the amplitude of reflection from a defect and the size of the defect it may well be possible to set a sensitivity value such that one may have sufficient confidence that the reflection from a significant defect will rise above the 'reporting' value. I think that this may well be a possible thing to do so that, having increased our detection probability by appropriate choice of sensitivity (this being based on the results of this type of work and the test block work), we may then develop sizing techniques which can be applied to the defects we have found.

Another aspect that requires further attention is a concentration on our ability to detect *growth* in defects. It often occurs that our ability to detect small amounts of growth may be more important than our ability to measure its absolute size to maybe 1 or 2 mm. As an example I refer to some results we obtained on a defect which was found on a nozzle weld at one of our fossil fuel stations. We went in there with a simple jig and measured the amplitude of ultrasonic response as a function of the distance along the nozzle and we obtained a plot of ultrasonics response and repeat inspection at 6 months and 14 months. An analysis of those curves showed that if growth had occurred in that particular defect it was certainly less than 1/2 mm. I think that there are grounds for believing that development in this area could yield a performance significantly better even than that. So it may be that even though we might not be able to make absolute size measurements to better than a few mm we may be able to detect growth to considerably finer limits than that.

I think another improvement in testing that will follow from a better understanding of the physics of the process relates to standardisation. First of all we must do much more related to the standardisation of equipment. If we understand better what will happen as the parameters of the test, such as frequency and beam shape, change then it will be possible to specify acceptable values for those parameters and certainly if we are going to be able to detect small amounts of defect growth then we need to be rather certain either that the equipment performance is reproducible from test to test or that if it varies we know how to allow for the effects of the variation. That leads on to standardisation of the test itself, for example covering such aspects as sensitivity, the sizing technique to be used, and so on. All these points need specification in the light of a better understanding although it may well be necessary to strike a balance between standardising in detail to promote a uniform test on the one hand, and on the other hand avoiding the danger of over-standardising which can lead to a rather uncritical application of non-optimised techniques.

I will just close on the work I mentioned earlier relating to the effects of compressive stress of ultrasonic reflection. We found the reflection from a fatigue crack varies as a function of compressive stress, although the results showed rather peculiar and unexpected behaviour whereby the amplitude falls and then rises again before it finally falls down to an asymptotic value. Such work really bears out the point I was making earlier that in certain regions quite small changes in compressive stress can have quite a dramatic effect on the amplitude of response. This effect has been found in several cases, in some of which we have seen rather larger drops before the thing rises and then falls again. Talking in terms of reflections from the crack face, the maximum change that we have observed has been about 11 dB, although in some cases we have seen no change at all. We have extended this work now to include cracks which contain liquids and the results surprisingly indicate that ingress of liquid into a crack can have a much smaller effect on the reflection coefficient than we had feared—as little as 3 or 4 dB.

Chairman: Was this work done on samples with oxidised crack faces?

J. Whittle: Yes in some cases.

T. Currie: At the risk of being the last man on the stage playing my bass fiddle when not only the rest of the orchestra has gone but the audience has gone too, I would like to offer two comments. First, I would like to support Larry Chockie in echoing the words of the renowned Admiral—let's get it right first time. I believe that one contribution to this could be extensive use of triple shot radiography—one shot normal to the weld and two other shots parallel to the weld. Perhaps these will reduce the incidence or reduce the concern that exists about the continued existence of lack of fusion defects which I think by now is fairly well publicised as one of my concerns. I think a second concern I have is surface breaking defects and I have alluded earlier to the statistics both of Cowan and Nichols, of Phillips and Warwick and of Smith and Warwick, that show that on conventional vessels about 70 % of all the defects are detectable by visual examination. It does seem to me as not introducing an inordinate increase in the cost of the vessel if one requires that the clad surface be machined to give a better chance of seeing a surface defect. If one can see a surface defect that is a defect which has got a stress intensity about 1·2 times the stress intensity of an equivalent size body defect and moreover a fatigue crack growth rate, if it is on the inside surface 50 times greater approximately than the dry crack growth rate then again it offers a possibility for removing failure precursions of that kind or at least identifying them early. I think once you have identified a failure precursor it is that much easier to use techniques which can be used for size with confidence. So I would suggest that there are these two probabilities—triple shot radiography in the early stages of manufacture and physical examination during the inservice inspection.

Chairman: Thank you very much. We have a written question from Mr Becher which says that in fracture mechanics research the need often exists to follow a crack in the specimen as it advances under load. This requirement may include cases where crack front shape is changing in the course of mechanical testing. Does the Panel consider any of the advanced ultrasonic techniques which have been mentioned earlier today actually or potentially capable of performing this task

Professor Frederick: We have made respective counter-plots of internal dimensions of cracks and this offers potential for dealing with such aspects as changes in direction of cracks so here is one possibility, the use of the synthetic aperture approach.

K. E. Stahlkopf: I was just going to say that some of the work that Amos Holt has done shows acoustic holography can also be used but I think that each of us here believes that we have a favourite method which can do it.

A. E. Holt: How one tackles it depends specifically on what one wants to do. For measurement during the test one could probably use several of the different techniques referred to at this meeting. The kind of things which have to be answered is whether one wants to measure during test or after failure.

P. Hernalsteen: I would like to change the subject by putting on record another problem. Given an internal planar flaw of constant size with varying reflectivity because of varying compressive stress, what is the corresponding expected variations of apparent size using conventional 6 bB drop techniques with pulse echo probes? If relevant what would be the influence of angle between scanning beam, failure phase, flaw plane and the ratio of the flaw size to beam size?

Chairman: Although he did not get a paper to this meeting I would like to draw your attention to work done by Forgli of Norsk Veritas which adds to our information on ultrasonics detection reliability.

L. J. Chockie: There will be another phase of the PISC/PVRC programme. We have already agreed that we will donate three US plates to Japan. Japan has agreed that they will make further plates and the Europeans are involved in getting in on the programme. Now that you have all seen the results we would like comments or any guidance that can be given for the fabrication of the next six plates, in the terms of the programme, its objectives and achievements.

K. E. Stahlkopf: Rather than talk about breakthroughs I think we need to talk about improvements. We have many things, many different types of techniques that are before you that are not properly evaluated, so I think rather than ask what breakthroughs should we look at next I think what we need to do is very seriously concentrate on understanding the new techniques that have been made available to us.

Chairman: At this stage we have not only overrun our programme but run the risk of running out of audience. The vigorous interchange between experts which has been so much a feature of today both in the hall and in the corridors around it has made this for me anyway a really worthwhile day. The attendance and continued participation to this late hour indicates your agreement and I hope that the organisers of SMIRT will allow us to have such a meeting again. Before I close the meeting, on behalf of you all I wish to thank the authors, participants, organisers and staff for all that they have done.

Index

Accumulation techniques, 96
Acoustic emission testing, 17–18
  choice of techniques, 17–18
  monitoring by, 268
  pressure vessels, 18, 19–39, 270–3
    background, 20–3
    brittle fracture condition, 36
    effectiveness of, 37
    experimental details, 23–9
    in-elastic fracture condition, 36–7
    MAESA system, 28–9
    material properties, 23
    NORTEC system, 28–9
    objectives, 20–3
    results, 29–37
    shell plates and weld metal
      properties, 27
    tensile test details, 23
  spectral analysis, 41–4
Acoustical holography, 71–3, 75,
      234–49
Adaptive learning techniques, 45–57,
      98, 110–11, 273–4
Alternative procedures, 202, 227, 231
Amplitude correlation, 215
Argon shielded gas tungsten arc
      spectrum, 13
ASME Code Section XI, 128–9, 200,
      201, 224–6, 229, 230, 231,
      247

Austenitic stainless steels
  carbide precipitates, 89–90
  ferrite content, 90
  grain size, 88
  grain to wave orientation, 88–9
  microcracks, 90
  microstructure, 86
  propagation mode, 90
  ultrasonic attenuation, 88–94
  ultrasonic beam profile, 92–4
  ultrasonic pulse effects, 94
  ultrasonic testing, 85–105, 274–5
    performances, 98–102
    techniques, 95–8
  ultrasonic velocities, 94–5
  ultrasonic wavelength and
      frequency effects, 91–2

Bandpass filtering, 45
Beam variation, 96
Beamforming, 48, 53
Brittle fracture, 36

Carbide precipitates, 89–90
Cooling rate control, 6
Correct Acceptance Probability
      (CAP), 212

291

Correct Rejection Probability (CRP), 212, 213, 222, 229, 232
Crack(s)
  acoustic emission from, 29–35
  depth
    determination, 77
    measurement, 50
  detection, 45, 99
  growth model, 21
  sizing
    acoustic holography, in, 237
    imaging methods, with, 75
    nozzle forgings, in, 48–50
    scattered waves, by, 76
    thermal shock, 235–42
  tip
    measurement, 97
    micrographs, 21, 32
  reflections, defect sizing with, 66
Cross correlation technique, 97
CSNI programme, 277–83
Curved surface correction, 242–6

Defect(s)
  characterisation, 247, 251–63
  clusters, 246–7
  definition, 202
  detection, 98, 148, 227
  Detection Probability (DDP), 205, 213–22, 223, 228, 229, 231, 232
  evaluation, 148
  identification, 102
  location, 100, 110, 125, 148, 223, 253–7
  map, 194–8
  non-planar, 253–7, 262
  planar, 257–60, 263
  sizing, 59–83, 102, 110, 125, 148, 215–23, 251–63, 283–4
Destructive examination, 223–32, 240–2, 253
  comparison procedure, 204–7
  PVRC plates, or, 170–200
  results of, 203

Evaluation Task Force, 137
Evaluation Task Force Sub-Group, 138

Feedwater Nozzle Geometry Program (FwN GP), 50–6
Flaws. *See* Defects
Focusing probes, 68–71
Fracture toughness, 29
Frequency analysis, 97

Hall effect current transductor, 8–9
Heat-affected zone
  microstructure, 6
  reflectors, 260
Heavy section steel technology (HSST) test vessels, 234–49
Holography. *See* Acoustical holography
Human factors, 228
Hydrostatic testing
  nuclear reactors, of, 17–18
  pressure vessels, of, 25, 33, 35

Incomplete fusion, 5
Industry Cooperative-Pressure Vessel Research Committee Non-destructive programs, 117–27

Kaiser effect, 35

MAESA system, 28–9
Martensitic transformation, 6
Match filtering, 47
Mean normalised energy spectral density, 43
Mechanical properties, process variables effect on, 116
Metallurgical features, 257–60, 263
Monitoring by acoustic emission testing, 268
Multi-frequency analysis, 97

Non-destructive examination, 223–32
  field welds, of, 266–8
  thick section materials, of, 233–49, 283
NORTEC system, 28–9
Nuclear reactors, hydrostatic testing, 17–18
Nugget area, 6–7, 10

Operator qualification, 228

Pattern recognition techniques, 77, 110–11
Planar defects, 67
Planar reflectors, 74
Plate Inspection Steering Committee (PISC), 133–232, 277–84
  background, 135
  composition, 136–7
  constitution, 153
  destructive examination, 146–8, 150, 170–200
  evaluation and analysis, 148–50
  evaluation of trials, 200–23
  funding, 151
  general conclusions, 152
  historical review, 134–58
  limitations on the project, 225–9
  meetings, 157
  non-destructive examination, 146, 150
  participants, 155–7
  presentation of results, 207–12
  programme implementation, 138–40
  sub-committees, 137–8
  terms of reference, 138
  test
    plates, 140–4
    procedures, 144–5
  ultrasonic testing, 159–70
Pressure Vessel Research Committee (PVRC), 115–32, 135
  comparison of methods, 131
  comparison of rating factors, 130
  destructive examination, 170–200

Pressure Vessel Research Committee (PVRC)—*contd.*
  industry-cooperative test blocks, 119
  plate weld samples, 120
  recent programs, 128–31
  Specimen 201, 121–3
  Specimen 251J, 123–7
  statistical evaluation, 127
  ultrasonic testing, 121, 159–70
Pressure vessels
  acoustic emission testing. *See* Acoustic emission testing
  advanced concepts in nondestructive testing in service, 117
  data analysis, 109–11
  first in-service inspection, 108
  hydrostatic testing, 25, 33, 35
  in-service inspection, 117
  inspection
    data reproducibility, 108
    problems, 106, 275–7
  nozzle inspection, 45–57, 273–4
  preservice inspections, 108
  second in-service inspection, 109
  subsequent in-service inspections, 109
Process variables, effect on mechanical properties, 116
Proximity rules for assembling defects, 226
Pulse
  compression, 96
  wobbling, 96

Reactor pressure vessels. *See* Pressure vessels
Real-time imaging, 110
Rejection criteria, 227
Residual stresses, 191–4

Shadow techniques, 75–7
Signal averaging, 47
Signal processing methods, 45

Signal-to-noise levels, 45
Slag inclusion, 5
Spectral analysis of acoustic emission, 41–4
Steels
  austenitic stainless. *See* Austenitic stainless steels
  $2\frac{1}{4}$Cr–1 Mo, 19–39, 270–3
Stress intensity factor, 21, 29
Synthetic aperture focusing technique (SAFT), 73–5, 110
  ultrasonic testing (SAFT–UT), for, 95–6
Synthetic beam forming techniques, 95–6

Technical Working Group (Destructive Testing), 137
Thermal shock cracks, acoustic holography imaging of, 235–42
Thick section materials, non-destructive examination of, 233–49, 283

Ultrasonic probes, 95
Ultrasonic techniques
  amplitude evaluation methods, 63–4
  austenitic stainless steels. *See* Austenitic stainless steels
  calibration and characterisation of equipment, 163–6
  combined evaluation, 66–8
  defect sizing, for, 59–83
  echodynamic evaluation methods, 64–5
  evaluation and analysis, 148–50
  features to be evaluated, 203
  flaw imaging methods, 68–75
  focusing probes, 68–71
  pressure vessels in service, 117
  PVRC plates, 159–70

Ultrasonic techniques—*contd.*
  quality criteria for, 64
  sources of information, 61–3
  weld defects, 251, 283–4
  weldments, 116
Ultrasonic transducers, characterisation of, 165
Undercut weld, 5

Volumic defects, 67

Weld
  defects, 5, 251, 283–4
  discontinuities, 29
  evaluation, optoelectronic, 11–14
  mechanical properties, 4–7
  metal microstructure, 5–6
  porosity, 5
  quality monitor (real time), 3–15
    background, 3
    circuit description, 7
    design approach, 4
    field testing, 9–11
    laboratory test(s), 7–9
      results, 8–9
    large scale integration, 14
    modified prototype, 8–9
    optional electronic transduction methods, 13–14
    optoelectronic weld evaluation, 11–14
    requirements, 4
    voltage sensing lead, 9
Weld zone characteristics, 260
Welding arc physics, 12–13
Welding electrode composition effects, 260
Weldments, ultrasonic testing of, 116

Zircaloy, acoustic emission, 42